QUALITY ASSURANCE, UTILIZATION REVIEW & RISK MANAGEMENT: A CURRENT AND SELECTED BIBLIOGRAPHY

James T. Ziegenfuss, Jr., Ph.D.

Graduate Program in Public Administration
Pennsylvania State University at Harrisburg

AMERICAN BOARD OF QUALITY ASSURANCE AND
UTILIZATION REVIEW PHYSICIANS

Sarasota, Florida

Library of Congress Card No. 87-700 34

Copyright 1987 American Board of Quality Assurance
and Utilization Review Physicians
Sarasota, Florida

Printed in the United States of America

TABLE OF CONTENTS

—

DEDICATION

To J. Shue Hamman and his colleagues who have long recognized the need
for further knowledge and training in these fields.

Preface

The rapid expansion of information in all the areas related to
quality assurance, utilization review and risk management is increasingly
difficult to manage. Academicians and practitioners are hard-pressed to
keep up with the developments in each of these respective fields. The
information explosion requires an organized response in the form of
assistance in identifying key and current research and professional
developments. The American Board of Quality Assurance and Utilization
Review Physicians is contributing one response by sponsoring this
bibliography.

Formal bibliographies and personal collections of references to the
significant work in a field are certainly not new. They have a long and
well appreciated history. But their contribution to the development of
various areas of work is often not well recognized--except by those who
have had to begin practice or research without one. The contribution of
an integrating bibliography is often only fully appreciated when the
practice and research efficiencies generated by a large collection are
recognized (a parallel to the acceptance of efficiencies the health care
field itself is now struggling with).

As my colleague and I noted in a previous bibliography there is a
second purpose to these collections. Bibliographical work "supports
movement toward the integration of applied and theoretical work.
Theoreticians need to relate their new insights to others and build on
contributions made elsewhere. To do so they must be able to identify the
work. Practitioners need most of all to avoid 'reinventing the wheel.'
An ability to see what others have done is the shortest route to insuring
that the work required is truly new."

Finally those working in quality assurance, utilization review and
risk management need to have a sense of the field, particularly as to the
purposes and concepts, techniques and programs and the related management
issues. This set of references is designed to provide both an overview

of these three linked fields and to introduce readers to the scope and
depth of these rapidly developing areas. The collection does not provide
an exhaustive compilation for readers who want "all" the citations.
The collection does include a wide variety of philosophies, approaches
and programs which constitute these three areas of work.

I am grateful to those persons who have helped to gather this
information and compile this collection. I actually first became
interested in quality and evaluation work in the early 1970's when I was
working in the field of public health, particularly mental health and
addictions. We were then interested in how we would be able to assess
the quality of organizations that were funded to offer services to those
patients and clients. My focus then as it is now was on how do
organizations develop a structure and function that allows them to
achieve their desired purposes--delivering quality care that is both
effective and efficient. When I expanded my work to include mainstream
medical care in the mid 1970's I continued this interest in the
organizational level of health and medical care systems. This
bibliography thus represents both long standing work and continuing
interest in evaluation. It also stems from a specific and recent
involvement in the development of training programs for professionals
interested in these areas. The training need is fast growing but
programs are absent.

The bibliography is labelled "current and selected" for two reasons.
First, the references are primarily from the 1980's. Quality assurance
cites include the late 1970's. Second, I have tried to select from among
many published works. This was purposeful in order to insure the
currency of the work and to make available that which is most recent.
The bibliography should not be regarded as absolutely exhaustive.
Without doubt there are missed articles that others will consider to be
essential to the field. This collection should be useful, as an
addition, to those professionals who already have their own personal
collections of works in the field.

There are four major chapters in the book:

Chapter 1 Introduction offers some suggestions for reading in the three fields and some related areas, e.g., information systems and organizational development.

Chapter 2 Quality Assurance References offers citations related to theory, practice and research in quality assurance.

Chapter 3 Utilization Review References offers citations related to theory, practice and research in utilization review.

Chapter 4 Risk Management References offers citations related to theory, practice and research in risk management.

Each reference chapter presents the citations in five subsections as follows:

> Theories and Concepts
> Programs, Techniques, Procedures
> Research: Studies and Data
> Management
> Overviews

Theories and Concepts are the purposes, principles and underlying assumptions of the work in each field. Programs, Techniques and Procedures includes references on how the work is done. Research presents studies and evaluations of quality assurance, utilization review and risk management work from single case studies to large data set research. Management includes the developing, organizing, planning and controlling of each of these activities. Overviews is a collection of articles which present broad discussions of the field.

Many persons have assisted in the development of this bibliography. I am grateful for the word processing work of Debra Varner and her staff at GANCOM. I would especially like to thank J. Shue Hamman, M.D., Medical Director of ABQAURP, and Jarlath Warren, Executive Director. They were most helpful and are strong supporters of training and information dissemination in these fields.

Dr. Hamman has been leading the push for formal education programs in quality assurance and utilization review. His work in the past 10 years alone has already moved the field. This book is intended to contribute to his career long efforts.

James T. Ziegenfuss, Jr.
Harrisburg, Pennsylvania

Chapter 1 Introduction

This introductory chapter is designed to provide a set of readings for two purposes: (1) to introduce beginning professionals to the significant current and recent readings in the fields of quality assurance, utilization review and risk management: and (2) to enable already established professionals in these fields to identify current and recent publications in the event that they may have missed some of the newer developments. It is expected that professionals in the fields of quality assurance, utilization review and risk management will be aware of the new writings within each of their areas. However, as quality assurance, utilization review and risk management experience greater linkage there is a need to know more about the field that is not your primary focus. Thus the "new and unknown" readings are more likely to be in the related fields (for the established professionals in each area).

In addition, there are developments in other disciplines and on related topics which should be of interest to the physicians, nurses and other health and medical care persons active in quality assurance, utilization review and risk management. These include, for example, the fields of organizational development, health systems management, information systems and medical informatics.

The underlying assumption to this perspective is a belief that the issues dealt with in quality assurance, utilization review and risk management are inter and transdisciplinary in nature. Persons working in these fields must bring to their work a broad exposure to not one but a set of backgrounds—medical care, finance, information and database management, interpersonal psychology and individual and organizational development. This means that continuing professional development must be interdisciplinary in nature. No one discipline will have all the answers to the developmental needs of theoreticians and practitioners working in these three fields.

This set of suggestions for initial and continuing reading begins with definitions of the fields.

Definitions

The definitions of the three fields covered by this bibliography will help to establish a starting base of common understanding. These are the definitions that were used as the guides for the categorization of citations in this book.

Quality Assurance is defined as "including all decisions and actions explicitly purporting the satisfactory attainment of quality in products and services. Form and degree of assurance, as well as its proven effectiveness, influences the confidence of customers and the quality of products and services. The level of quality assurance also depends on quality cost, as it must be cost effective...Total quality assurance is the composite of all decisions and activities involving the producer, suppliers, distributors, and customers, directed toward attainment of quality" (Sinha and Willborn, 1985, p.32).

Utilization Review is defined as "formal prospective, concurrent, or retrospective critical examination of appropriate use of segments of the health care system, such as hospital, nursing home, emergency department, clinic and home care" (Meisenheimer, 1985, p.338).

Risk Management is defined as "the science for the identification, evaluation, and treatment of the risk of financial [and patient] loss" (Monagle, 1985, p.75). "Risk management is control of those circumstances of hospital health care [and other health care systems] that pose a threat to the safety and comfort of patients" (Meisenheimer, 1985, p.338).

In summary the field of quality assurance is focused on the assessment of the level of quality provided by the medical and health care organization and the development of both corrective and preventive measures designed to maintain and increase quality. Utilization review is examination of appropriate use of various segments of the health and medical care system. Finally, risk management is the management and control of factors which could adversely affect the patient.

2

Those working in these areas are acutely aware that there is now a strong and growing intersection of the fields.

Convergence and Linkage of Fields

The fields, if not exactly converging, are linking around the issue and the hunt for the systems (both human and technological) that provide the optimum level of quality in health and medical care. The notion of quality encompasses both absolute technical positions and perceived views on the part of consumers--both individual and organizational consumers. Defining, measuring and planning for quality are challenging tasks indeed.

Some definitions now consider that quality involves the appropriateness of service and therapy utilization both as to the correct choice that matches patient needs and to the intensity and duration of service delivery. Utilization review thus becomes a part of the greater search for quality. The tools and techniques of utilization review are a part of the greater task of maintaining and developing quality.

Risk management is involved as we admit that there is not an ability to design systems that lead to and perfectly maintain optimum levels of quality. The question that arises when we admit to imperfection is what is the level of risk that we are able to accept. This level of risk is in part an individual provider question. It is also in part an organizational question for the hospital as a whole to address (or other health care organization). And it is in part a societal question bound up in values and limited resources. What are the risks that a provider, a hospital and a society are willing to take?

In short quality is an elusive never-ending search involving utilization and multiple views on the levels of risk.

Suggested Readings

The following readings are suggested for those persons who are now in the fields of quality assurance, utilization review and risk

management and for those just entering. The latter group will find that
these books do not constitute the full information required to become
either a working professional or an academic in these fields. However,
this material does represent a strong starting point. For those in one
of the fields it is believed that the recent publications will be news
and that particularly some of the publications from the fields of
business and informations systems will be inviting.

For those critical publications and authors not listed, I apologize.
Along with an inability to list all works it is inevitable that
perceptions of the critical works in the field will differ, particularly
with the rapid development both within the fields and between them.

The suggested readings are divided into the following sections:

--Quality
--Quality Assurance
--Quality Control
--Utilization Review
--Risk Management
--Information Systems
--Organizational Development

Quality

Since an underlying purpose in all the fields is the delivery of
quality care, quality is a good starting point. Suggested readings on
quality are as follows:

Quality

Donabedian, A. Explorations in Quality Assessment and Monitoring Vol. 1
The Definition of Quality and Approaches to its Assessment, Ann Arbor,
Michigan, Health Administration Press, (1980).

Donabedian, A. The Criteria and Standards of Quality Vol. II, Ann Arbor,
Michigan, Health Administration Press, (1980).

Miller, M.C.; Knapp, R.G. Evaluating Quality of Care, Germantown,
Maryland, Aspen, (1979).

4

Quality Assurance Readings

How does one set about assessing, maintaining and developing quality. The following are the quality assurance readings.

Egdahl, R.H.; Gertman, P.M. Quality Assurance in Health Care, Aspen Germantown, Maryland, Aspen, (1980).

Greene, R. Assuring Quality in Medical Care: The State of the Art, Cambridge, Massachusetts, Ballinger, (1976).

Greenspan, J. Accountability and Quality Assurance in Health Care, Bowie, Maryland, The Charles Press Publishers, (1980).

Joint Commission on Accreditation of Hospitals. Maintaining Quality under Pressure: The Dilemma of the Small Hospital, Chicago, Illinois, JCAH, (1986).

Kaplan, Karen Orloff. The QA Guide: A Resource for Hospital Quality Assurance, Chicago, Illinois, JCAH, (1980).

Luke, R.D.; Krueger, J. Organization and Change in Health Care Quality Assurance, Germantown, Maryland, Aspen, (1983).

Payne, B. & Associates. The Quality of Medical Care: Evaluation and Improvement, Chicago, Illinois, Hospital Research and Educational Trust, (1976).

Williamson, J.W. Assessing and Improving Health Care Outcomes: The Health Accounting Approach to Quality Assurance, Cambridge, Massachusetts, Ballinger, (1978).

Williamson, J.W. & Associates. Teaching Quality Assurance and Cost and Containment in Health Care, San Francisco, California, Jossey-Bass Publishers, (1982).

Williamson J. W. Principles of Quality Assurance and Cost Containment in Health Care, San Francisco, California, Jossey-Bass Publishers, (1982).

Quality Control Readings

Quality control has been the term of choice in business and industry. The following are selected readings from that section. While the cases and topics may differ, concepts strategies and programs may be quite transferable.

All, L.S. Fundamentals of Industrial Quality Control, Reading, MA, Addison-Wesley, (1986).

Basu, A.P. Reliability & Quality Control, New York: North-Holland, Elsevier, (1986).

Besterfield, Dale, H. Quality Control, 2nd ed. text ed: Englewood Cliffs, NJ, Prentice Hall, (1986).

Quality Control: A Practical Approach, Englewood Cliffs, NJ: Prentice Hall (1986).

Burr, Irving. Statistical Quality Control Methods. (Statistics: Textbooks & Monographs: Vol. 16). New York: Dekker, (1976).

Caplan, Frank. The Quality System. A Sourcebook for Managers & Engineers. Radnor, PA, Chilton, (1980).

Charbonneau, Harvey, C.; Webster, Gordon L. Industrial Quality Control Englewood Cliffs, NJ, Prentice Hall, (1978).

Crosby, Phillip, B. Quality Is Free: The Art of Making Quality Certain. New York: NAL, (1980).

Deming, W.E. Quality, Productivity, Competitive Position, (1982), text ed. 45.00, MIT CAES.

Feigenbaum, Armand V. Total Quality Control. New York: McGraw, (1984).

Grant, E.L.; Leavenworth, R. Statistical Quality Control, 5th ed. (Industrial Engineering & Management Science Ser.). New York: McGraw, (1979).

Griffith, Gary. Quality Technician's Handbook. New York: Wiley, (1986).

Halpern. S. The Assurance Sciences: An Introduction to Quality Control & Reliability. Englewood Cliffs, NJ, Prentice Hall, (1978).

Juran, J.M. Quality Control Handbook. New York: McGraw, (1974).

Juran, J.M. & Gryna, Frank M., Jr. Quality Planning & Analysis: From Product Development Through Use. 2nd ed., New York: McGraw, (1980).

Lester, et al. Quality Control for Profit. (Quality Control Ser.). New York: Dekkerm, (1985).

Ott, E.L. Process Quality Contol. New York: McGraw, (1975).

Wadsworth, H.M., et al. Modern Methods for Quality Control & Improvement. New York: Wiley, (1986).

Utilization Review

To date there is very limited book literature on utilization review. The following are suggested readings from a study perspective. The articles in Chapter 3 offer the significant works as a whole.

Goldstein, H.M.; Horowitz, M.A. Utilization of Health Personnel: A Five Hospital Study. Germantown, MD: Aspen, (1979).

Utilization of Short Stay Hospitals. (Nat. Health Survey Ser.) Gov. Printing Office, (1986).

Risk Management

As with quality control there is a well developed literature on risk management in the business and industrial section. Along with the new offerings for health care readers specifically, business books are also suggested.

Covello, V.T., et al. Risk Evaluation & Management. (Vol. 1) New York Plenum Press, (1986).

Cox, M.B. Risk Management for the Department Head. Dienstein, Dianne, H., ed. (Legal Aspects of Medical & Health Records). Cox Publications, (1986).

Hellerman, S.A. Sovereign Risk Analysis. Winchester, MA, Allen Unwin, (1986).

Jasanoff, Shelia. Risk Management & Political Culture. (Social Science Perspectives Ser.). New York: Russell Sage, (1986).

Kraus, G.P. Health Care Risk Management: Organization & Claims Administration. Natl Health Pub. Rynd Comm., (1986).

Lewis, John H., et all. Risk Management Issues. Risk Management, (1984).

Monagle, John F. Risk Management: A Guide for Health Care Professionals. Germantown, MD, Aspen Pub., (1985).

Information Systems Readings

The importance of information systems to these three fields is well recognized. The following readings are suggested.

Blum, B.I., ed. Information Systems for Patient Care. Springer-Verlag, (1984).

Blum, Bruce, ed. A Framework for Medical Information Science. Vol. 3, 4, & 9. Philadelphia, PA, Taylor & Francis, (1984).

De Land, E.C., ed. Information Technology in Health Science Education. New York: Plenum Pub., (1978).

Doyle, Owen, et al. Analysis Manual for Hospital Information Systems. Ann Arbor, MI, Health Admin. Press, (1980).

Eisenfeld, J. & Delsi. C., eds. Mathematics & Computers in Biomedical Applications. New York: Elsevier, (1985).

Fassett, W.E.; Christensen, D.B. Computer Applications in Pharmacy. Philadelphia, PA, Lea & Febiger, (1986).

Green, L.; Kansler, C., eds. Professional & Scientific Literature on Patient Education: A Guide to Information Sources. Detroit, MI, Gale, (1980).

Gremy, F., et all, eds. Medical Informatics Europe 1981. Proceedings (Lecture Notes in Medical Informatics Ser., Vol. 11). New York: Springer-Verlag, (1981).

Grobe, S.J. Computer Primer & Resource for Nurses. Philadelphia, PA, Lippincott Nursing, Lippincott, (1984).

Hodge, Melville H. Medical Information Systems: A Resource for Hospitals. Germantown, MD, Aspen, (1978).

Kupfer, David J., et al. Mental Health Information Systems Design & Implementation. (Library & Information Science Ser., Vol. 19). New York: Dekker, (1976).

Medical Information Technology & Training Limited., ed. The Role of Technology in Medical Information. Gower, England, Gower Pub. Co., (1986).

Nair, Streedhar, ed. Computers in Critical Care & Pulmonary Medicine. New York: Plenum Pub., (1980).

Pretschner, D.P. Personal Computing in Nuclear Medicine. (Lecture Notes in Medical Informatics: Vol. 18). New York, Springer-Verlag, (1982).

Rowland, Howard S.; Rowland, Beatrice L. Hospital Software Sourcebook. Germantown, MD, Aspen, (1985).

Schmitz, Homer. Hospital Information Systems. Germantown, MD, Aspen, (1979).

Scholes, M., et al, eds. The Impact of Computers on Nursing: An International Review: Proceedings of the IFIP-IMIA Workshop on the Impact of Computers on Nursing, Church House Westminster, London, 8-9 Sept., 1982, & Harrogate, England, 10-15 Sept., 1982, 1983. North Holland, Elsevier, (1983).

Strickland-Hodge, Barry. How to Search the Medical Sources. Gower Pub., Gower, England, (1987).

Ziegenfuss, D.G.; Ziegnefuss, J.T. Health Information Systems: A Bibliography. New York: Plenum, (1984).

Organizational Development and Management Readings

Quality assurance, utilization review and risk management all have significant linkages to management and to the organization as a whole. The following readings address management and control--particulary in the new reimbursement environment--and the concepts and approaches to organizational development (OD). Organizational development addresses the longer term question of how we use feedback on quality for long term development of the organization--development toward higher quality levels.

Beer, M. Organizational Change and Development: A Systems Approach, Santa Monica, California, Goodyear, (1980).

Broyles, R.W. Planning and Internal Control Under Prospective Payment, Germantown, Maryland, Aspen, (1986).

Schein, E. Process Consultation, Reading, Massachusetts, Addison Wesley, (1969).

Smith, H.L.; Fottler, M.D. Prospective Payment: Managing for Operational Effectiveness, Germantown, Maryland, Aspen, (1985).

Ziegnefuss, J.T. DRGs and Hospital Impact: An Organizational Systems Analysis, New York, McGraw Hill, (1985).

Ziegenfuss, J.T. Patient-Client-Employee Complaint Programs An Organizational Systems Model, Springfield, Illinois, Charles C. Thomas, (1985).

Benefits

This bibliography is developed to support education and training. The benefits of increased training and continued development of academics and practitioners in these three fields are several.

Consumers, medical and health care organizations and professionals
working in health care quality assurance, utilization review and risk
management fields will all benefit.

Consumers will receive the benefit of ongoing reviews of medical
care quality by persons trained in current state-of-the-art techniques
and thinking. In place of uncertain and too often informal reviews,
quality assurance, utilization review and risk management experts will
lead the increasingly formalized and more sophisticated work. Each of
these fields is being recognized as a special area of work,
necessitating specialists.

Medical and health care organizations will have access to
professionals with higher levels of training to lead their organization's
development in each of these work areas. The availability of more
resources for professionals to continue their development will increase
the numbers and sophistication of trained professionals for insurers for
government, for industry buyers of care and for hospitals. This means
that these organizations will have qualified experts involved in the key
decisions that impact quality. They will be contributing more to the
debate on delivery systems.

Finally, professionals in these three fields will benefit from
training and from support materials in several ways. First, they will
continue the development of formal training programs and materials for
physicians, nurses and management colleagues who will be responsible for
this work. Second they will increase the recognition of the significance
of the work--which is now large enough in effort to require collection
and integration of the new concepts and techniques in the fields. Third,
this bibliography will hopefully spur readers to explore work in related
fields--business and information systems for example--which is just now
beginning to be recognized as relevant to quality assurance,
utilization review and risk management. Fourth, this collection will be
useful in developing the state-of-the-art in the work in these respective
fields. There is always a lag time between innovative developments in

the field and diffusion of these innovations to the greater professional audience. To the extent that this volume helps to cut into this delay it will be a useful contribution indeed.

Finally, I have listed at the end of this chapter background references which may be useful to those entering the field or for somewhat of a near term history for those already in the work. The balance of the volume should provide ample reading for all.

REFERENCES

Anderson, O.W.; Shields, M.C. "Quality measurement and control in physician making: state of the art." Health Serv. Res., 17(2):p125-55, (Summer 1982).

Ballantine, H. "Peer Evaluation." In E. Carels, D. Neuhauser, and W. Stason (Eds.), The Physician and Cost Control, Cambridge, Massachusetts, Oelgeschlager, Gunn, and Hain, (1980).

Bennis, E.G. Organizational Development: Its Nature, Origins, and Prospects, Reading, Massachusetts, Addison-Wesley, (1969).

Bertram, D.A.; Brooks-Betram, P.A. "The Evaluation of Continuing Medical Education: A Literature Review." Health Education Monographs, (5):p330-362, (1977).

Brook, R. "Studies of Process-Outcome Correlations in Medical Care Evaluation." Medical Care, (17):p868-873, (1979).

Brook, R.; Davies-Avery, A.; Greenfield, S.; Harris, J.; Lelah, J.; Solomon, N.; Ware, J. "Assessing the Quality of Medical Care Using Outcome Measures: An Overview of the Method." Medical Care (Supplement), (15), (1977).

Brook, R.H.; Williams, K.N.; Avery, A.D. "Quality Assurance Today and Tomorrow: Forecast for the Future." Annals of Internal Medicine, (85):p809-817, (1976).

Carroll, J.; Becker, S. "The Paucity of Coursework in Medical Care Evaluation." Journal of Medical Education, (50):p31-37, (1975).

Couch, N.; Tilney, N.; Raynoer, A.; Moore, F. "The High Cost of Low-Frequency Events: The Anatomy and Economics of Surgical Mishaps." New England Journal of Medicine, (304):p634-637, (1981).

Delbecq, A.L.; Van de Ven, A.H.; Gustafson, D.H. Group Techniques for Program Planning. Glenview, Illinois, Scott, Foresman, (1975).

Donabedian, A. "The Quality of Medical Care: Methods for Assessing and Monitoring the Quality of care for Research and for Quality Assurance Programs." Science, (200):p856-864, (1978a).

Enthoven, A. "Shattuck Lecture--Cutting Cost without Cutting the Quality of Care." New England Journal of Medicine, (298):p1229-1238, (1978a).

Fessel, W.J.; Van Brunt, E.E. "Assessing Quality of Care from the Medical Record." New England Journal of Medicine, (286):p134-138, (1972).

Fetter, R.B.; Shin, Y.; Freeman,; J.L.; Averill, R.F.; Thompson, J.D. "Case Mix Definition of Diagnosis-Related Groups." Medical Care, (18)Supplement, (1980).

12

Fetter, R.B.; Thompson, J.D.; Mills, R.E. "A System for Cost and Reimbursement Control in Hospitals." Yale Biology Journal, (49):p123-126, (1976).

Fifer, W.R. "Risk management and quality assurance: integration for optimal effectiveness." QRB, 5(8):p15-9, (Aug. 1979).

Garg, M.L.; Gliebe, W.A.; Elkhatib, M.B. "The Extent of Defensive Medicine: Some Empirical Evidence.: Legal Aspects of Medical Practice, 6,(2):p25-29, (1978b)

Garg, M.L.; Glieve, W.A.; Kleinberg, W.M. "Quality in Medical Practice: A Student Program." Journal of Medical Education, (52):p514-516, (1977).

Garg, M.L.; Kleinberg, W.M.; Gliebe, W.A. "A Course on Cost and Quality." QRB, 4(3):p22-26, (1978).

Garg, M.L.; Mulligan, J.L.; McNamara, M; Skipper, J.K.; Parekh, R.R. "Teaching Students the Relationship Between Quality and Costs in Medical Care." Journal of Medical Education, (50):p1085-1091, (1975).

Garland, C.H. "The Problem of Observer Error." Bulletin of the New York Academy of Medicine, (36):p570-584, (1960).

Gonnella, J.S.; Goran, M.S. "Quality of Patient Care. The Measurement of Change: The Staging Concept." Medical Care, (13):p467-473, (1975).

Gonnella, J.S.; Louis, D.Z.; McCord, J.J. "The Staging Concept: An Approach to the Assessment of Outcomes of Ambulatory Care." Medical Care, (14):p13, (1976).

Goran, M.J. "The Evolution of the PSRO Hospital Review System." Medical Care, 17(5):Supplement, (1979).

Hoare, C.H.; Burns, M.A.; Akerlund, K. "The perceived training needs of quality assurance professionals in eight eastern states." QRB, 11(3):p87-92, (Mar. 1985).

Institute of Medicine. Assessing Quality of Health Care: An Evaluation, Washington, D.C.; National Academy of Sciences, (1976).

Jessee, W.F. "Quality Assurance Systems: Why Aren't There Any?" QRB, (3,11):p16-18, (1977a).

Joint Commission on Accreditation of Hospitals. The QA Guide: A Resource for Hospital Quality Assurance, Chicago, Illinois, Joint Commission on Accreditation of Hospitals, (1980).

Kane, R.L.; Hogven, M. "Teaching Quality of Care Evaluation to Medical Students." Journal of Medical Education, (49):p778-780, (1974).

Kaplan, S.H.; Greenfield, S. "Criteria Mapping: Using Logic in Evaluation of Processes of Care." Quality Review Bulletin, 4:p3-9, (1978).

Komaroff, A.L. "Quality assurance in 1984." Med Care, 23(5):p723-24, (May 1985).

Mushlin, A.I.; Appel, P.A. "Quality Assurance in Primary Care: A Strategy Based on Outcome Assessment." Journal of Community Health, (3):p292-305, (1978).

Mushlin, A.I.; Appel, P.A. "Testing an Outcome Based Quality Assurance Strategy in Primary Care." Medical Care, (Supplement, 18(5):part 2, (1980).

Rutstein, D.; Berenbert, W.; Chalmers, T.C. "Measuring the Quality of Medical Care." New England Journal of Medicine, (294):p582-588, (1976).

Sanzar. P.J.; Worth, R.M. "Concurrent Quality Assurance in Hospital Care: Report of a Study by Private Initiative in PSRO.: New England Journal of Medicine, (198):p1171-1177, (1978).

Sheber, J. "Quality Assurance Concurrent Review Assures Quick Response to Faculty Care. Hospital, Journal of the American Hospital Association, (54):p55-57, (1980).

Siebert, M.K. "Risk management: A Bibliography." J. A. Med. Rec. Assoc., 56(10):p38, (Oct. 1985).

Warner, A.M. Education for roles and responsibilities in quality assurance. QRB, 11(3):p78-80, (Mar. 1985).

Warner, A.M. "Education for roles and responsibilities in quality assurance: physician leadership." QRB, 11(4):p111-4, (Apr. 1985).

Weisbord, M.R. "Why Organization Development Hasn't Worked (So Far) in Medical Centers." Health Care Management Review, (1):p18-31, (1976).

Williams, K.N.; Brook, R.H. "Quality Measurement and Assurance: A Literature Review." Health and Medical Care Services Review, 1(3):p, (1978).

Williamson, J.W.; Alexander, M.; Miller, G.E. "Continuing Education in Patient Care Research: Physician Response to Screening Test Results." Journal of the American Medical Association, (201):p938-942, (1967).

Williamson, J.W.; Aronovitch, S.; Simonson, L.; Ramirez, D.; Kelley, D. "Health Accounting, an Outcome-Based System of Quality Assurance: Illustrative Application to Hypertension." Bulletin of the New York Academy of Medicine, (51):p727-738, (1975).

Ziegenfuss, J.T. "On the Need for A Physician Residency in Quality Assurance and Utilization Review." Quality Assurance and Utilization Review 1 (4), (1986).

CHAPTER 2:

QUALITY ASSURANCE REFERENCES

Theory and Concept

0001   Alaszewski, A.   Problems in measuring and evaluating the
       quality of care in mental handicap hospitals.
       Health Soc. Serv. J., 88(4581):pA9-15, (Mar. 10, 1978).

0002   Alexander, L.L.; Lewis, N.   Why quality assurance?
       J. Natl. Med. Assoc., 73(4):p347-51, (Apr. 1981).

0003   Andrew, R.R.   Quality assurance in private hospitals.
       Aust. Clin. Rev., (6):p11-5, (Sep. 1982).

0004   Bailit, H.L.   Quality assurance and development of
       criteria and standards.   Dent. Clin. North Am.,
       29(3):p457-63, (Jul. 1985).

0005   Bartlett, D.P.; Intagliata, J.   Integration of quality
       assurance and program evaluation activities in alcoholism
       treatment programs: Part I.   QRB, 5(11):p24-8, (Nov.
       1979).

0006   Beezley, D.; Tabel, C.; Kordick, M.   Support service
       evaluation: part II--defining the problems and its
       importance.   QRB, 6(4):p8-12, (Apr. 1980).

0007   Bergman, B.B.   Editorial: Let's stop looking over our
       shoulders.   Pediatrics, 56(3):p345-7, (Sep. 1975).

0008   Blake, B.L.   Quality assurance: an ethical
       responsibility.   Superv. Nurse, 12(2):p32-8, (Feb. 1981).

0009 Blanton, W.B. External factors will affect quality
     assurance in the '80s [interview]. Hosp. Peer Rev.,
     7(1):p3-4, (Jan. 1982).

0010 Blum, H.L. Evaluating health care. Med. Care,
     12(12):p999-1011, (Dec. 1974).

0011 Boehm, A.H. Medical audit by physicians.
     Dimens. Health Serv., 52(1):p10,13, (Jan. 1975).

0012 Bohnet, N.L. Quality assurance as an ongoing component
     of hospice care. QRB, 8(5):p7-11, (May 1982).

0013 Bouchard, R.E.; Tufo, H.M.; Beaty, H.N. The impact of a
     quality assurance program on post graduate training in
     internal medicine. JAMA, 253(8):p1146-50, (Feb. 22,
     1985).

0014 Brook, R.H.; Williams, K.N. Quality of health care for
     the disadvantaged. J. Community Health, 1(2):p132-56,
     (Winter 1975).

0015 Burakoff, R.P.; Demby, N.A. Quality Assurance.
     Historical perspective and critical issues.
     Dent. Clin. North Am., 29(3):p427-36, (Jul. 1985).

0016 Burck, K. The role of quality assurance in good
     laboratory practices. Clin. Toxicol., 15(5):p627-40,
     (Dec. 1979).

0017 Burkhart, R.L. Quality administration: the forgotten
     half of quality assurance. Radiol Manage, 3(4):p6-10,
     (Sep. 1981).

0018 Butler, R.J. Quality assurance in hospital dental
     practice. Aust. Dent. J., 29(4):p257-9, (Aug. 1984).

0019 Chism, S. Quality controls, quality patient service,
     and quality assurance. NLN Publ., (52-1598):p5-10,
     (1975).

0020 Christoffel, T. Medical care evaluation: an old new
     idea. Hosp. Med. Staff, 5(10):p11-16, (Oct. 1976).

0021 Cicatiello, J.; Zimmer, M.J.; Christman, L. NAQ Forum:
     quality assurance. Nurs. Adm. Q., 1(3):p77-84, (Spring
     1977).

0022 Cohn, S.S. Audit enhances patients' environment.
     Hospitals, 51(9):p61-2, (May 1, 1977).

0023 Crawford, J.B. In-house quality assurance. Purch. Adm.,
     5(3):p1,10, (Mar. 1981).

0024 De La Haye, W. Quality assurance in radiography. The
College's contribution. Report from the Quality
Assurance Working Party. Radiography, 51(597):p144,
(May-Jun. 1985).

0025 de Verdier, C-H; Haabrekke, O.; Leskinen, E.; Uldall, A.
Quality assurance in clinical chemistry--time to go from
theory to action. Scand. J. Clin. Lab. Invest.,
46(5):p393-6, (Sep. 1986).

0026 Decker, C.M. Quality assurance: accent on monitoring.
Nurs. Manage., 16(11):p20-4, (Nov. 1985).

0027 Dennis, B.W.; Pierpaoli, P.G. Quality assurance--a
hospital pharmacy management perspective.
Curr. Concepts Hosp. Pharm. Manage., 3(2):p18-21, (Summer
1981).

0028 Dennis, D.A. Quality assurance in the health care
curriculum [letter]. QRB, 7(3):p4-6, (Mar. 1981).

0029 Diamond, I. An old look at quality assurance.
Ann. Clin. Lab. Sci., 16(3):p255-8, (May-Jun. 1986).

0030 DiAngelis, A.J. Comprehensive dental care. Quality
assurance: definitions and directions for the 1980s.
J. Dent. Educ., 48(6Suppl):p27-33, (Jun. 1984).

0031 Dieter Haussmann, R.K.; Hegyvary, S.T.; Newman, J.F.;
Bishop, A.C. Monitoring quality of nursing care.
Health Serv. Res., 9(2):p135-48, (Summer 1974).

0032 Dodosh, M.N. Quality of mercy carries a guarantee at an
Ohio hospital. Wall St. J. [Midwest Ed.], 58(73):p1,18,
(Jan. 27, 1978).

0033 Does infection rate measure quality of care?
Hosp. Infect. Control, 5(7):p111-2, (Jul. 1978).

0034 Donabedian, A. Measuring and evaluating hospital and
medical care. Bull NY Acad. Med., 52(1):p51-9, (Jan.
1976).

0035 Doughty, E.O. Quality assurance: who? where? why?
Hosp. Equip. Supplies, 21(6):p7, (Jun. 1975).

0036 Duncan, A. Quality assurance: what now and where next?
Br. Med. J., 280(6210):p300-2, (Feb. 2, 1980).

0037 Eddy, D.M. Clinical policies and the quality of clinical
practice. N. Engl. J. Med., 307(6):p343-7, (Aug. 5,
1982).

0038 Editorial: Quality not negotiable. Hospitals,
     48(20):p43, (Oct. 16, 1974).

0039 Editorial: The courage to complain. Nurs. Mirror,
     142(15):p33, (Apr. 8, 1976).

0040 Egdahl, R.H.; Taft, C.H. Editorial: On measuring
     "quality" health care: beyond the hospital.
     N. Engl. J. Med., 294(3):p161-2, (Jan. 15, 1976).

0041 Eisenberg, J.M.; Sussman, E.J. Harder data for the soft
     science of quality assurance [editorial].
     Med. Decis. Making, 2(1):p7-11, (1982).

0042 Evolution of quality assurance reflected in new
     standard. Staff, Joint Commission on Accreditation
     Hospitals. QRB, 5(6):p2-3, (Jun. 1979).

0043 Farrington, J.F.; Felch, W.C.; Hare, R.L. Sounding
     board. Quality assessment and quality assurance: the
     Performance-review alternative. N. Engl. J. Med.,
     303(3):p154-6, (Jul. 17, 1980).

0044 Ferguson, J.W. Risk management and quality assurance:
     partners in liability reduction. Hospitals,
     53(4):p42,46,201, (Feb. 16, 1979).

0045 Fifer, W.R. Risk management and quality assurance;
     integration for optimal effectiveness. QRB, 5(8):p15-9,
     (Aug. 1979).

0046 Fifer, W.R.; Aldrich, S.Y. The tyranny of standards.
     JAMA, 231(7):p709-10, (Feb. 17, 1975).

0047 Filiatrault, L.J.; Larsen, P.J. Quality assurance
     activities as a part of a residency training program: an
     examination of the potentials. Med. Rec. News,
     58(5):p6,8,10-1 passim, (Oct. 1977).

0048 Flint, L.S.; Hammett, W.H.; Martens, K. Quality
     assurance in the emergency department. Ann. Emerg. Med.,
     14(2):p134-8, (Feb. 1985).

0049 Funkhouser, G.R. Quality of care. Part one. Nursing,
     6(12):p22-31, (Dec. 1976).

0050 Gatere, G. Quality assurance: a look at the concept.
     Kenya Nurs. J., 13(2):p27-32, (Dec. 1985).

0051 Gibson, R.W. Quality assurance.
     J. Natl. Assoc. Priv. Psychiatr. Hosp., 8(3):p15-6, (Fall
     1976).

0052 Gilbert, B. Relating quality assurance to credentials and privileges. QRB, 10(5):p130-5, (May 1984).

0053 Goldberg, B.A. The duty of hospitals and hospital medical staffs to regulate the quality of patient care. West. J. Med., 129(5):p443-51, (Nov. 1978).

0054 Greeley, H. Credentialing ER physicians; priority for QA in hospitals [interview]. Hosp. Peer Rev., 6(4):p40-2, (Apr. 1981).

0055 Greenspan, J. Medical audit: an effective arm of quality assurance. Hosp. Community Psychiatry, 28(12):p901-3, (Dec. 1977).

0056 Gregg, T.E.; Hahn, J.A. Demystifying quality assurance. Trustee, 33(2):p16-8, (Feb. 1980).

0057 Griffith, J.R. A proposal for new hospital performance measures. Hosp. Heath Serv. Adm., 23(2):p60-84, (Spring 1978).

0058 Grogan, J. Perspectives on pharmacy and quality assurance--a talk with Jim Grogan [interview]. Top. Hosp. Pharm. Manage., 1(3):p91-9, (Nov. 1981).

0059 Gurevich, I. I.V. quality assurance theory and practice. NITA, 6(6):p409-12, (Nov.-Dec. 1983).

0060 Gustafson, C.I.; Walden, R.T. The smaller hospital in the health care system. First step in QAP (Quality Assurance Program). Hospitals, 48(19):p143-4,146, (Oct. 1, 1974).

0061 Hadley, R.D. At Lourdes Hospital: Quality assurance program shows useful results. Am. Nurse, 9(2):p6,8, (Feb. 15, 1977).

0062 Harbo, J.N.; Heaney, K.M. Quality assurance. A reviewer's perspective. Dent. Clin. North Am., 29(3):p589-93, (Jul. 1985).

0063 Honovich, D. Quality assurance--perspective. Tex. Hosp., 37(10):p19, (Mar. 1982).

0064 How do you "assure" quality without promising the impossible? Second Opin. Health Care Issues, 1(2):p3-6, (Apr. 1980).

0065 Howell, J.N. Quality assurance: the growth of a concept and evolvement of change. Milit. Med., 147(10):p856-60, (Oct. 1982).

0066 Hughes, S.L. Home health monitoring: ensuring quality in home care services. Hospitals, 56(21):p74-80, (Nov. 1, 1982).

0067 Hurwitz, L.S.; Kohler, E. The benefits of evaluating care provided to children hospitalized with insulin dependent diabetes mellitus. QRB, 7(6):p13-21, (Jun. 1981).

0068 Hutton, B.F.; Smart, R.C. Practicality of National Electrical Manufacturers Association performance specification measurements for user-based acceptance testing and routine quality assurance [letter]. J. Nucl. Med., 26(4):p430-3, (Apr. 1985).

0069 Hyden, J.P. What the Hospital Corporation of America has learned in its quality assurance program. QRB, 3(1):p8-10, (Jan. 1977).

0070 Issues in quality assurance. QRB editorial advisory board. QRB, 5(2):p11-6, (Feb. 1979).

0071 Jarvis, B.M. Quality assurance--towards a workable definition. NZ Nurs. J., 76(6):p12-5, (Jun. 1983).

0072 Jessee, W.F. Quality assurance systems: why aren't there any? QRB, 3(11):p16-8,26, (Nov. 1977).

0073 Kane, R.A. Assuring quality of care and quality of life in long term care. QRB, 7(10):p3-10, (Oct. 1981).

0074 Katz, P.S. Integrating quality assurance, utilization review, and risk management activities for the small hospital. QRB, 12(3):p114-5, (Mar. 1986).

0075 Kearns, P.M. Utilization review expanded into quality assurance program. Hospitals, 54(17):p62-3, (Sep. 1, 1980).

0076 Kerr, I.L. Quality assurance and the dentist-patient relationship. North Am, 29(3):p581-8, (Jul. 1985).

0077 Kiikuni, K. Quality assurance in Japanese hospitals. World Hosp., 18(2):p29, (May 1982).

0078 Kohles, M.T. The smaller hospital in the health care system. Education and training support quality assurance. Hospitals, 48(19):p149-50,152-3, (Oct. 1, 1974).

0079 Kresky, B.; Cohen, A. Considerations for evaluation of patient care in emergency departments. QRB, 6(12):p8-15, (Dec. 1980).

0080 Krinsky, L@W.; Carone, P.A. The assessment of quality care: is it patient progress or the amount of paper work? <u>J. Asthma Res.</u>, 16(4):p121-4, (Jul. 1979).

0081 Laessig, R.H.; Ehrmeyer, S.S.; Hassemer, D.J. Quality control and quality assurance. <u>Clin. Lab. Med.</u>, 6(2):p317-27, (Jun. 1986).

0082 Larson, E. Combining nursing quality assurance and research programs. <u>J. Nurs. Adm.</u>, 13(11):p32-5, (Nov. 1983).

0083 Lawson, N.S.; Haven, G.T.; Ross, J.W. Regional quality assurance for the 1980's, current status and future directions. <u>Am. J. Clin. Pathol.</u>, 74(4Suppl):p552-9, (Oct. 1980).

0084 Leach, J.; Nagy, S.; Cercone, R. Adopting a quality assurance program. <u>Dimens. Health Serv.</u>, 58(4):p30,32, (Apr. 1981).

0085 Lee, B.A.; Lee, W.A. Patient care audit, not medical audit: a proposal. <u>Med. Rec. News</u>, 46(4):p15-23, (Aug. 1975).

0086 Legge, D. General issues in quality assurance. <u>Aust. Clin. Rev.</u>, (14):p14-20, (Sep. 1984).

0087 Legge, D.G.; Hutton, P.A. Quality assurance in hospital medicine: a report. <u>Aust. NZ J. Med.</u>, 11(6):p687-96, (Dec. 1981).

0088 Lewis, C.E. The state of the art of quality assessment--1973. <u>Med. Care</u>, 12(10):p799-806, (Oct. 1974).

0089 Linn, M.W.; Gurel, L.; Linn, B.S. Patient outcome as a measure of quality of nursing home care. <u>Am. J. Public Health</u>, 67(4):p337-44, (Apr. 1977).

0090 Linn, M.W.; Linn, B.S. Qualities of institutional care that affect outcome. <u>Aged Care Serv. Rev.</u>, 2(3):p1,3-14, (1980).

0091 Liptzin, B. Quality assurance and psychiatric practice: a review. <u>Am. J. Psychiatry</u>, 131(12):p1374-7, (Dec. 1974).

0092 Longest, B.B., Jr. Design and behavioral strategies for cost containment and quality assurance. <u>J. Med. Syst.</u>, 5(1-2):p97-110, (1981).

0093 Lynch, T. Monitoring Ontario's health services. <u>Dimens. Health Serv.</u>, 54(11):p36-8, (Nov. 1977).

0094 Markus, A.C. Quality assurance--panacea or Trojan
      horse? Comments from a British physician. QRB,
      7(2):p21-2, (Feb. 1981).

0095 Mass, D.; Galen, R.S. The predictive value theory
      redefines quality assurance. Am. J. Med. Technol.,
      47(12):p965-70, (Dec. 1981).

0096 Matoth, Y. Quality assurance--an Israeli point of view.
      QRB, 7(2):p7-9, (Feb. 1981).

0097 McIntyre, K.J. Iowa hospitals spend $1 million, dissect
      incidents. Bus. Insur., 12(13):p37-8, (Jun. 26, 1978).

0098 McKillop, W. Is high-quality care assessable?
      Hospitals, 49(2):p43-7, (Jan. 16, 1975).

0099 McClure, M.L. Quality assurance and nursing education:
      a nursing service director's view. Nurs. Outlook,
      24(6):p367-9, (Jun. 1976).

0100 McMahon, J.A. Editorial: The assurance of quality
      care: A shared responsibility. J. Am. Podiatry Assoc.,
      65(3):p199-201, (Mar. 1975).

0101 McSherry, C.K. Quality assurance and surgical practice.
      Surg. Clin. North Am., 62(4):p751-9, (Aug. 1982).

0102 Migliozzi, A.A. Quality assurance in occupational health
      nursing. Occup. Health Nurs., 33(2):p63-5, (Feb. 1985).

0103 Mikeal, R.L.; Brown, T.R.; Lazarus, H.L.; Vinson, M.C.
      Quality of pharmaceutical care in hospitals.
      Am. J. Hosp. Pharm., 32(6):p567-74, (Jun. 1975).

0104 Miller, T.W.; Jay, L.L. These requirements will improve
      the quality of health care. Pharm. Times, 47(6):p34-5,
      (Jun. 1981).

0105 Mills, D.H. Quality assurance: whose responsibility?
      Trustee, 29(3):p8,12-3, (Mar. 1976).

0106 Moeller, D. What's so different about quality assurance
      in small, rural hospitals? Hospitals,
      55(11):p77,79-80,82, (Jun. 1, 1981).

0107 Monagle, J.F. Risk management is linked with quality of
      care. Hospitals, 54(17):p57-9, (Sep. 1980).

0108 Moore, B. Quality assurance. Quality that counts.
      Nurs. Times, 80(50:p20, (Dec. 12-18, 1984).

0109 Mulholland, J.H.; Bittle, L. Quality assurance & risk management in Maryland hospitals in the 1980s. Md. State Med. J., 31(4):p60-2, (Apr. 1982).

0110 Nafziger, J. Quality assurance: doing it my way. HPN Hosp. Purch. News, 6(4):p11, (Apr. 1982).

0111 Nelson, A.R. Relation between quality assessment and utilization review in a functioning PSRO. N. Engl. J. Med., 292(13):p671-5, (Mar. 27, 1975).

0112 Orlikoff, J.E.; Lanham, G.B. Why risk management and quality assurance should be integrated. Hospitals, 55(11):p54-5, (Jun. 1, 1981).

0113 Orth-Gomer, K.; Britton, M.; Rehnqvist, N. Quality of care in an outpatient department: the patient's view. Soc. Sci. Med., 13A(3):p347-50, (May 1979).

0114 Ostrow, P.C. The historical precedents for quality assurance in health care. Am. J. Occup. Ther., 37(1):p23-6, (Jan. 1983).

0115 Peele, R.; Palmer, R.R. Standards and quality control: problems and pitfalls. Adm. Ment. Health, 3(2):p146-55, (Spring 1976).

0116 Pelley, G. One step toward quality assurance. Hospitals, 49(8):p77-8,82, (Apr. 16, 1975).

0117 Porterfield, J.D. Evaluation of the care of patients: Codman revisited. Bull NY Acad. Med., 52(1):p30-8, (Jan. 1976).

0118 Porterfield, J.D. A farewell look at JCAH standard audit requirements. Hosp. Med. Staff, 6(7):p29, (Jul. 1977).

0119 Price, S.B. Quality assurance monitoring in children@s residential care: changing paradigms. QRB, 11(8): p242-5, (Aug. 1985).

0120 Purinton, L.W. Accountability through corporate responsibility in community hospitals. AHME, 8(1):p6-9, (Spring 1975).

0121 Quality assurance in nursing: an interpretation definitions, beliefs, assumptions. AARN News Lett., 42(5):p13-4, (May 1986).

0122 Quality assurance v. cost containment in peer review. Med. J. Aust., 1(3Suppl):p40-4,45-8,49, (Apr. 9, 1977).

0123 Questions on quality assurance. Perspect Accredit., (5):p10, (Sep.-Oct. 1979).

0124 Ransdell, L.A. Quality assurance--coming of age. Times, 21(5):p11-23, (May-Jun. 1980)

0125 Recommended guidelines for quality assurance in hospital centralized intravenous admixture services. Am. J. Hosp. Pharm., 37(5):p645-55, (May 1980).

0126 Restuccia, J.D.; Holloway, D.C. Methods of control for hospital quality assurance systems. Health Serv. Res., 17(3):p241-51, (Fall 1982).

0127 Rinaldi, L.A. Quality assurance '81--satisfying JCAH. Nurs. Manage., 12(9):p23-4, (Sep. 1981).

0128 Roberts, R.F. Preventing poor-quality medical care: knowledge/action disconsonance. Med. J. Aust., 2(13):p710-2, (Dec. 1979).

0129 Rosen, P. Editorial: Defining quality of ED care-a complex problem. JACEP, 5(4):p273-4, (Apr. 1976).

0130 Rudd, T.N. Improving the quality of life in hospital. Nurs. Mirror, 139(23):p53-4, (Dec. 5, 1974).

0131 Runnells, G. Quality assurance a must for central service, expert says [interview]. Hospitals, 55(23):p49, (Dec. 1, 1981).

0132 Ryan, P.J. Central service: outline of recommendations for a quality assurance program. Hosp. Top., 60(3):p44-5, (May-Jun. 1982).

0133 Ryder, R. [Quality assurance of nursing and philosophy of nursing]. Kango. Tenbo., 8(8):p56-62, (Aug. 1983).

0134 Sanazaro, P.J. Quality assessment and quality assurance in medical care. Annu. Rev. Public Health, 1:p37-68, (1980).

0135 Sandlow, L.J. Ambulatory care: the center of the system. Quality for walking patients. Hospitals, 49(5):p95-9, (Mar. 1, 1975).

0136 Schron, S.R. Quality assurance vs. cost containment: "Damned if you do, damned if you don't." AANNT, 9(2):p13-23, (Apr. 1982).

0137 Shaffer, K.L.; Lindenstein, J.; Jennings, T.A. Successful QA program incorporates new JCAH standard. Hospitals, 55(16):p117-20, (Aug. 16, 1981).

0138 Shanahan, M. Patient care evaluation: coming of age in the 80s. QRB, 7(4):p10-1, (Apr. 1981).

0139 Skillicorn, S.A. A conversation with Dr. Stanley A. Skillicorn: a leading proponent of integrated, problem-oriented quality assurance is interviewed by the QRB [by Cheryl Tabatabai]. QRB, 7(4):p20-3, (Apr. 1981).

0140 Skillicorn, S.A. Improved quality controls in hospitals: a necessity. J. Leg. Med. (Chicago), 2(4):p471-89, (Dec. 1981).

0141 Slack, P. Quality assurance. What's best for the patient? Nurs. Times, 81(2):p20, (Jan. 9-15, 1985).

0142 Small, E.W. Quality assurance in the hospital environment. J. Hosp. Dent. Pract., 14(3):p105-10, (3rd Quarter 1980)

0143 Smart, G.A. Monitoring in medicine. J. R. Coll. Physicians Lond., 9(4):p355-70, (Jul. 1975).

0144 Smith, D. Quality control should be hospital-wide. Dimens. Health Serv., 53(7):p37-9, (Jul. 1976).

0145 Sniff, D. The evolution of a quality assurance program. QRB, 6(1):p26-9, (Jan. 1980).

0146 Spivak, H.R.; Levy, J.C.; Bonanno, R.A.; Cracknell, M. Patient and provider factors associated with selected measures of quality of care. Pediatrics, 65(2):p307-12, (Feb. 1980).

0147 Spotts, S.J. A nursing diagnosis taxonomy for quality assurance and reimbursement. Part I. Pa. Nurse, 36(1): p5,12, (Jan. 1981).

0148 Stern, S.K. Quality assurance: ADA perspective. J. Hosp. Dent. Pract., 14(2):p76-9, (2nd Qrt. 1980).

0149 Stolar, M.H. Quality assurance for hospital pharmacy. Part I: Basic concepts. Am. J. Hosp. Pharm., 32(3):p276-80, (Mar. 1975).

0150 Survey of hospital quality assurance activities in internal medicine. Report to Board of Continuing Education, 1984. Aust. Clin. Rev., (17):p72-7, (Jun. 1985).

0151 Sushkevich, G.N.; Rakovianu, N. [Significance and organizational principles of a quality assurance program in nuclear medicine]. Med. Radiol. (Mosk) (USSR), 30(1):p23-8, (Jan. 1985).

0152 Swanson, A.L. New guides provide a framework for quality
      care. Hosp. Trustee, 1(1):p25, (May 1977).

0153 Symposia supports philosophy of QA standard.
      Perspect. Accredit., (3):p9-10, (May-Jun. 1981).

0154 Symposium on quality assurance. Dent. Clin. North Am.,
      29(3):p425-617, (Jul. 1985).

0155 Thompson, R. Medical care in the '80s. Quality
      assurance. J. Tenn. Med. Assoc., 74(11):p801-6, (Nov.
      1981).

0156 Thompson, R.E. How quality assurance minimizes risk.
      Hospitals, 53(16):p52, (Aug. 16, 1979).

0157 Thompson, R.E. The perils, legal and otherwise, if
      hospitals do not implement quality appraisal/action
      plans. Second Opin. Health Care Issues, 1(5):p1-7, (Jul.
      1980).

0158 Tupa, B.M. Monitoring OR quality assurance.
      Todays OR Nurse, 8(9)p27-31, (Sep. 1986).

0159 Vanagunas, A.; Egelston, E.M.; Hopkins, J.; Walczak,
      R.M. Principles of quality assurance. QRB, 5(2):p3-6,
      (Feb. 1979).

0160 Vogel, D.P.; Gurwich, E.; Hutchinson, R.A. The quality
      assurance of professional staff.
      Curr. Concepts Hosp. Pharm. Manage., 3(2):p8-11,14-7,
      (Summer 1981).

0161 Washington memo: Quality assurance programs.
      Hosp. Med. Staff, 5(4):p18-9, (Apr. 1976).

0162 Wendorf, B. Ethical Decision-Making in quality
      assurance. QRB, 8(1):p4-6, (Jan. 1982).

0163 Westerman, J.H.; Spano, R.M.; Keyes, M.A. Public
      accountability, quality assurance and social work.
      Soc. Work Health Care, 2(1):p33-42, (Fall 1976).

0164 Wide scope of hospital's quality assurance told.
      Hosp. Peer Rev., 3(3):p33-6, (Mar. 1978).

0165 Williamson, J.W. Formulating priorities for quality
      assurance activity. Description of a method and its
      application. JAMA, 239(7):p631-7, (Feb. 13, 1978).

0166 Wilson, L.L. Hospital medicine and quality assurance:
      The Australian experience. World Hosp., 18(1):p26-7,
      (Feb. 1982).

0167 Yoder, D.L. Patient care quality assurance.
      Hosp. Trustee, 3(3):p25-7, (May-Jun. 1979).

0168 Youell, L. Benefits of quality assurance to patients.
      AARN News Lett., 38(11):p23-4, (Dec. 1982).

0169 Zintel, H.A. Gathering of data helps improve the quality
      of hospital patient care. Bull Am. Coll. Surg.,
      63(5):p26-8, (May 1978).

Techniques Programs Procedures

0170 A methodology for preparing "ideal" treatment outlines
      in psychiatry. The Quality Assurance Project. Aust.
      NZ J. Psychiatry, 16(3):p153-8, (Sept. 1982).

0171 Ackerman, D.; Vicha, D. A quality assurance program
      based on a financial model. QRB, 6(9):p2-4, (Sept.
      1980).

0172 Ackerman, V.P.; Pritchard, R.C. External quality
      assurance in microbiology. The programme of the Royal
      College of Pathologists of Australasia. Pathology,
      16(3):p235-9, (Jul. 1984).

0173 Adamow, C.L. Self-assessment: a quality assurance tool.
      J. Am. Diet. Assoc., 81(1):p62-3, (Jul. 1982).

0174 Adams, H.G.; Campbell, A.F. TRIRAD as quality assurance
      tool. Milit. Med., 150(11):p622-4, (Nov. 1985).

0175 Affeldt, J.E. Long-term care baseline survey fosters
      quality assurance. Hospitals, 56(12):p56, (Jun. 16,
      1982).

0176 Affeldt, J.E. Antibiotic review is part of integrated
      quality assurance activities. Hosp. Med. Staff, 8(12):
      p12-4, (Dec. 1979).

0177 Ahuja, S.D. Physical and technological aspects of
      quality assurance in radiation oncology. Radiol.
      Technol., 51(6):p759-74, (May-Jun. 1980).

0178 Akhter, M.N. Quality assurance under the Missouri PRO
      program. Mo. Med., 82(6):p297-9, (Jun. 1985).

0179 Allison, S.; Kinloch, K. Four steps to quality
      assurance. Can. Nurse, 77(11):p36-8, (Dec. 1981).

0180 Anderson, K.; Mattsson, O. Quality assurance in radiographic imaging included in the film marking procedure. Acta. Radiol. [Diagn.], 24(1):p63-5, (1983).

0181 Anderson, R.E.; Hill, R.B. The autopsy: instrument of quality assessment. Pathologist, 33(11):p629-30, (Nov. 1979).

0182 Anderson, T.B.; Forquer, S.L. Use of a concerns-based technical assistance model for quality assurance implementation. QRB, 8(12)p4-11, (Dec. 1982).

0183 Anderson T.P.; Baldridge, M.; Ettinger, M.G. Quality of care for completed stroke without rehabilitation: evaluation by assessing patient outcomes. Arch. Phys. Med. Rehabil. 60(3):p103-7, (Mar. 1979).

0184 Appendix F to hospital resources document. Quality assurance and education in the emergency department-- American College of Surgeons Committee on Trauma. Bull. Am. Coll. Surg., 65(2):p34-5, (Feb. 1980).

0185 Armenian, H.K. Developing a quality assurance program in the State of Bahrain. QRB, 4(8):p9-11, (Aug. 1978).

0186 Aydelotte, M.K. Quality assurance programs in health care agencies. No. 52-1572. NLN Publ., (52-1572):p1-11, (1975).

0187 Bailit, H.L. Quality assurance in general dentistry (part I.). Compend. Contin. Educ. Dent., 1(1):p49-55, (Jan.-Feb. 1980).

0188 Baker, B.M. How to develop a CSR quality assurance program. Hosp. Top., 59(5):p42-5, (Sep.-Oct. 1981).

0189 Bailit, H.L. Quality assurance in general dentistry (part II). Compend. Contin. Educ. Dent., 1(3):p177-84. (May-Jun. 1980).

0190 Barney, M. Measuring quality of patient care: a computerized approach. Superv. Nurs, 12(5):p40-4, (May 1981).

0191 Barr, D.M.; Woolstadt, L.J.; Goodrich, L.L.; Pittman, J.G.; Booher, C.E.; Evans, R.L. The Rockford School of Medicine undergraduate quality assurance program. J. Med. Educ., 51(5):p370-7, (May 1976).

0192 Barr, W.T.; Williams, F.D. Technical quality assurance in histopathology. Med. Lab. Sci., 40(3):p257-61, (Jul. 1983).

28

0193 Bartilotta, K.; Rzasa, C.B. Quality assurance utilizing a computerized patient information system. QRB, 8(3):p17-22, (Mar. 1982).

0194 Bartlett, D.P.; Intagliata, J. Integration of quality assurance and program evaluation activities in alcoholism treatment programs: Part II. QRB, 6(1):p17-22, (Jan. 1980).

0195 Bartlett, R.C.; Tetreault, J.; Evers, J.; Officer, J.; Derench, J. Quality assurance of gram-stained direct smears. Am. J. Clin. Pathol., 72(6):p984-9, (Dec. 1979).

0196 Bates, B.A.; Alexander, S.A.; Gale, C.; Roberts, R.F.; Pearson, I.Y. Quality assurance in a multidisciplinary group. Priority setting in an intensive care unit. Aust. Clin. Rev., (16):p12-8, (Mar. 1985).

0197 Batsakis, J.G.; Lawson, N.S.; Gilbert, R.K. Introduction to the Report on the Quality Assurance Programs of the College of American Pathologists, 1981. Am. J. Clin. Pathol., 76(4 Suppl.):p512-3, (Oct. 1981).

0198 Beautyman, W.; Rawnsley, H.M. A proposal for a department of pathology improvement program. Pathologist, 35(2):p 92-6, (Feb. 1981).

0199 Beck, B.; Hardwick, K. Inpatient audit simplified. Hospitals, 52(19):p75-8, (Oct. 1, 1978).

0200 Beck, B.; Hardwick, K. A concurrent surgical miniaudit procedure: use of generic outcome screening criteria to detect anesthesia and other perioperative problems. QRB, 7(3):p21-4, (Mar. 1981).

0201 Benson, D.; Wilder, B.; Gartner, C. The QIP form: the one-page quality assurance tool. QRB, 12(3):p87-9, (Mar. 1986).

0202 Berg, J.K.; Kelly, J.T. Evaluation of psychosocial health care in quality assurance activities. Med. Care, 19(1):p24-9, (Jan. 1981).

0203 Berkman, B.; Rehr, H. Social work undertakes its own audit. Soc. Work. Health Care, 3(3):p273-86, (Spring 1978).

0204 Berkman, B.; Rehr, H. Seven steps to audit. Soc. Work Health Care, 2(3):p295-303, (Spring 1977).

0205 Black, A.; Emerton, E. Quality assurance measures in th@ Purchasing Department. Dimens. Health Serv., 62(9):p22-24, (Oct.-Nov.1985).

0206 Blalock, W.R. Quality assurance in a university teaching
     hospital. Case Stud. Health Adm., 2:p174-8, (1980).

0207 Bradham, R.R.; Buxton, J.T.; Clark, J.S. Quality
     assurance in the surgery department of a community
     hospital. J. S.C. Med. Assoc., 79(5):p286-7, (May 1983).

0208 Brashear, J. Alternate review systems assure good care.
     Hosp. Peer. Rev., 3(7):88-90, (Jul. 1978).

0209 Broekemeier, R.L.; Brewer, P.E.; Johnson, M.K. Audit
     mechanism for hospital drug distribution. Am. J. Hosp.
     Pharm., 37(1):p85-8, (Jan. 1980).

0210 Brown, D.E.; Levy, J.D.; Sarmiento, M. Patient-oriented
     QA activities. Greater Southeast Community Hospital,
     Washington, DC. QRB, 10(1):p19-22, (Jan. 1984).

0211 Brown, D.E.; Levy, J.D.; Sarmiento, M. Patient-oriented
     QA activities. QRB. 10(1):p19-22, (Jan. 1984).

0212 Brown, E.M. Quality assurance in anesthesiology---the
     problem-oriented audit. Anesth. Analog., 63(6):p611-5,
     (Jun. 1984).

0213 Bruce, G.L.; Hinds, P.; Hudak, J.; Mucha, A.; Taylor,
     M.C.; Thompson, C.R. Implementation of ANA's quality
     assurance program for clients with end-stage rental
     disease. ANS, 2(2):p79-95, (Jan. 1980).

0214 Buddi, J. Quality assurance in a home health agency.
     NLN Publ., (52-1843):p61-71, (1980).

0215 Bullen, M.A.; Bye, R.T. Raycheck--a new radiological test
     instrument for quality assurance. Radiography, 45(540):p
     278-83, (Dec. 1979).

0216 Bulman, T. Ambulatory care: a practical way to quality
     assurance. Nurs. Manage., 16(12):p19-24, (Dec. 1985).

0217 Burger, M.C. A quality assurance program. OH,
     25(6):p15-7, (Jun. 1981).

0218 Burkle, W.S. Developing a quality assurance program for
     clinical services. Hosp. Pharm.,
     17(3):p125-7,131-2,135-8passim, (Mar. 1982).

0219 Bush, R.S. Quality assurance in radiation therapy:
     clinical and physical aspects. Future plans: clinical.
     Int. J. Radiat. Oncol. Biol. Phys., 10(Suppl. 1):p39-4,
     (Jun. 1984).

0220 Bush, R.S. Quality assurance in radiation therapy: clinical and physical aspects. Quality assurance: past and present in Canada. Int. J. Radiat. Oncol. Biol. Phys., 10(Suppl. 1):p19-2.

0221 Buske, S.M. Quality assurance in the ambulatory care setting. Times, 22(5):p3-5, (Jun. 1981).

0222 Byalin, K.; Jed, J.; Bender, P. Initiating a quality assurance program in a public psychiatric outpatient service. QRB, 10(5):p136-42, (May 1984).

0223 Cada, R.L.; West, D.K. Quality assurance practice in rural and urban hospital clinical laboratories Health Lab. Sci., 15(2):p112-20, (Apr. 1978).

0224 Caldwell, G.B. Use of employee surveys in quality assurance programs. QRB, 7(7):p19-22, (Jul. 1981).

0225 Cameron, J.C. Using a computer profile to assess quality of care in a psychiatric hospital. Hosp. Community Psychiatry, 27(9):p623, (Sep. 1976).

0226 Cardellino, H. Quality assurance from a process audit approach. Nurs. Manage., 17(9):p55-8, (Sept. 1986).

0227 Carey, D.L. Institutional cleaning and maintenance: program at Rhode Island hospital unites quality assurance, training. Laund. News, 7(4):p11,13, (Apr. 1981.

0228 Carlton, R. Establishing a total quality assurance program in diagnostic radiology. Radiol. Technol., 52(1):p23-38, (Jul.-Aug. 1980).

0229 Carver, A.M. Development and implementation of a hospital -wide quality assurance program at the King Khaled Eye Specialist Hospital in Kingdom of Saudi Arabia. Aust. Clin. Rev., 5(19):p188-90, (Dec. 1985).

0230 Catlin, D. Quality of assurance at Memorial Hospital. An active program in review. Clin. Bull., 6(3):p91-2, (1976).

0231 Celeste, S.M.; Folick, M.A.; Dumas, K.M. Identifying a standard for pin site care using the quality assurance approach. Orthop. Nurs., 3(4):p17-24, (Jul.-Aug. 1984).

0232 Chae, Y.M. Computer-based quality assurance system. Yonsei. Med. J., 26(1):p49-58, (1985).

0233 Chaffey, J.T. Quality assurance in radiation therapy: clinical considerations. Int. J. Radiat. Oncol. Biol. Phys., 10(Suppl. 1):p15-, (Jun. 1984).

0234 Chernesky, R.H.; Lurie, A. The functional analysis study: a first step in quality assurance. Soc. Work Health Care, 1(2):p213-23, (Winter 1975-1976).

0235 Cimprich, B. Quality assurance: a program of nursing care for patients with lung cancer. Cancer Nurs., 4(5):p409-18, (Oct. 1981).

0236 Clark, M.R.; MacIntyre, K.A. Patient care appraisal as a guide for the design of continuing medical education: 10 years' experience in the maritime provinces. Can. Med. Assoc. J., 118(2):p131-8, (Jan. 21, 1978).

0237 Clemence, E. Assuring quality in dietetic services. Dimens. Health Serv., 55(6):14,16, (Jun. 1978).

0238 Cohen, A.G.; Tucker, E. Department of nursing implementation of JCAH standards: a quality assurance program applied. Hosp. Top., 58(2):p38-40, (Mar.-Apr. 1980).

0239 Colchamiro, E.K.; Herbst, E.; Carr, N.; Kourre, N. Quality assurance in prison health care: the New York City experience. QRB, 8(3):p23-4, (Mar. 1982).

0240 Cole, L.; Cayten, C.G.; Staroscik, R. Auditing the quality of care in emergency departments. JACEP, 5(1):p32-5, (Jan. 1976).

0241 College of American Pathologists Quality Assurance Programs. Am. J. Clin. Pathol., 80(4 Suppl.):p551-647, (Oct. 1983).

0242 Coulthard, S.W. PSRO: a new direction for quality assessment in Otolaryngology. Trans. Am. Acad. Ophthalmol. Otolaryngol., 84(4):pORL413-6, (Jul.-Aug. 1976).

0243 Cradduck, T.D.; Busemann-Sokole, E. Use of NEMA protocols for routine quality assurance [letter]. J. Nucl. Med., 26(1):p95-7, (Jan. 1985).

0244 Crandell, C.E. Diagnostic quality control: the missing link in dental radiology quality assurance. Oral Surg. Oral Med. Oral Pathol., 62(2):p212-, (Aug. 1986).

0245 Crane, V.S.; Louviere, M.L. I.V. therapy problem-solving with quality assurance. NITA, 6(6):p430-2, (Nov.-Dec. 1983).

0246 Crawford, N.; Smith, S,; Myer, N. Design for a coordinated, problem-focused quality assurance program. QRB, 6(7):p9-14, (Jul. 1980).

0247 Cunningham, J.R. Quality assurance in radiation therapy: clinical and physical aspects. Int. J. Radat. Oncol. Biol. Phys., 10(Suppl. 1):p105-, (Jun. 1984).

0248 Curtis, D.J.; Jones, R.L. Quality assurance in repeat films. CRC Crit. Rev. Diagn. Imaging., 14(4):p281-320, (1981).

0249 Danielson, N.E. Quality assurance in the central service department. Med. Instrum., 15(4):p277-8, (Jul.-Aug. 1981).

0250 Darnell, R.E.; Fitch, D.H. External review in quality assurance. Phys. Ther., 60(5):p559-63, (May 1980).

0252 Davis, A.; Nagelhout, M.J.; Hoban, M.; Barnard, B. Bowel management: a quality assurance approach to up grading programs. J. Gerontol. Nurs., 12(5):p13-7, (May 1986).

0253 Davis, S.; Bryant, J. Quality assurance for the small hospital. Times, 21(8):p4-5,16, (Nov. 1980).

0254 Davitt, P.A. A service-based quality-assurance program. Nurs. Adm. Q., 6(1):p22-5, (Fall 1981).

0255 De Armond, M.M. A quality assurance program for a Mental Health Service. J Am. Coll. Health Assoc., 30(3):p139-40, (Dec. 1981).

0256 Debski-Himberger, A. A quality assurance program for psychiatric nursing. Superv. Nurse, 11(11):p25-6, (Nov. 1980).

0257 Dehn, T.G. Quality assurance methods for radiology departments. QRB, 6(6):p11-4, (Jun. 1980).

0258 Deiker, T.; Osborn, S.M.; Distefano, M.K., Jr.; Payer, N.W. Consumer accreditation developing a quality assurance patient evaluation scale. Hosp. Coummunity Psyshiatry, 32(8)p565-7, (Aug. 1981).

0259 Delaney, M.C.; Trachtenberg, J. Discharge planning: a quality assurance program in a cancer research hospital. Cancer Nurs., 3(2):p138-44, (Apr. 1980).

0260 Demby, N.A.; Rosenthal, M.; Angello, M.; Calhoun, W.F. A comprehensive quality assurance system for practicing dentists. Dent. Clin. North Am., 29(3):p545-56, (Jul. 1985).

0261 DeVries, R.A. New approaches to U.S. medical care assessment. World Hosp., 17(1):p40-3, (Feb. 1981).

0262 Dinel, B. Quality assurance in hospital pharmacy practice. Can. J. Hosp. Pharm., 32(4):p101-5, (Jul.-Aug. 1979).

0263 Distel, L. More than chart review: a new problem-oriented.nursing quality assurance program. QRB, 7(1): p26-9, (Jan. 1981).

0264 Donahue, J.J. Clinical quality assurance in the pharmaceutical industry. Cancer Tret. Rep., 69(10):p1195 -7, (Oct. 1985).

0265 Donald, K.J.; Collie, J.P. The autopsy in quality assurance. Clinical practice in a teaching hospital. Aust. Clin. Rev., (2):p16-21, (Aug. 1981).

0266 Doss, H.L.; James, J.D.; Killough, D.M.; Snodgrass, G.L. Microbiologic quality assurance for intravenous admixtures in a small hospital. Am. J. Hosp. Pharm., 39(5):p832-5, (May 1982).

0267 Doust, K.M. Quality assurance in a third party payments system. A model plan. Aust. Clin. Rev., (3):p12-5, (Nov. 1981).

0268 Drew, R.J. Quality' assurance of electrosurgical devices: a manufacturer s view. Med. Instrum., 14(5):p255-6, (Sept.-Oct. 1980).

0269 Drexler, L.; Caliendo, M.A. Developing and implementing a nutritional care audit. J. Am. Diet. Assoc., 76(4): p374-7, (Apr. 1980).

0270 Drogege, R.T. A quality assurance protocol for CT scanners. Radiology, 146(1):p244-6, (Jan. 1983).

0271 Duckett, S.J.; Kristofferson, S.M. An index of hospital performance. Med. Care, 16(5):p400-7, (May 1978).

0272 Dyer, E.D.; Monson, M.A.; Cope, M.J. Increasing the quality of patient care through performance counseling and written goal setting. Nurs. Res., 24(2):p138-44, (Mar.-Apr. 1975).

0273 Edmunds, L. A computer assisted assurance model. J. Nurs. Adm., 13(3):p36-43, (Mar. 1983).

0274 el-Guebaly, N.; Papineau, D. Economic constraints and quality assurance in mental health services: Can. J. Psychiatry, 29(2):p115-20, (Mar. 1984).

0275 Ellingham, C.T.; Fleischaker, K. Competencies in physical therapy: a resource for written self-assessment and clinical performance evaluation and a component of a department's quality assurance program. Phys. Ther. 62(6):p845-9, (Jun. 1982).

0276 Esser, P.D.; Fawwaz, R.A. A spatially calibrated display and associated quality assurance. Med. Phys., 7(2):p168, (Mar.-Apr. 1980).

0277 Eusana, P.L. Effective scheduling - the foundation for quality care. J. Nurs. Adm., 8(1):p12-7, (Jan. 1978).

0278 Felber, W. [Quality assurance in materials preparation]. Dent. Echo., 55(7):p10-2,14-6, (Nov. 1985).

0279 Felton, G.; Frevert, E.; Galligan, K.; Neill, M.K.; Williams, L. Pathway to accountability: implementation of a quality assurance program. J. Nurs. Adm., 6(1):p20-4, (Jan. 1976).

0280 Ferguson, K.; Bowden, L.; Halman, M.; Huff, A.; Langlie, J.; Morgan, G. Social work quality assurance based on medical diagnosis and task: a second-stage report. Soc. Work Health Care, 6(1):p63-71, (Fall 1980).

0281 Ferguson, K.; Bowden, M.L.; Lachiniet, D.; Malcolm, A.; Morgan, G. Initiation of a quality assurance program for social work practice in a teaching hospital. Soc. Work Health Care, 2(2):p205-17, (Winter 1976-1977).

0282 Fifer, W.R. Infection control as a quality control in an integrated hospital quality assurance program. Am. J. Infect. Control, 9(4):p120-2, (Nov. 1981).

0283 Finkle, B.S. Quality assurance in analytical toxicology. J. Anal. Toxicol., 7(3):p158-60, (May-Jun. 1983).

0284 Finley-Cottone, D.; Link, M.K. Quality assurance in critical care. Crit. Care Nurse, 5(2):p46-9, (Mar.-Apr. 1985).

0285 Finnegan, R. Components and requirements of a QA program for the medical record service. Med. Rec. News, 50(2): p12,14-22, (Apr. 1979).

0286 Fleisher, D.S.; Brown, C.R., Jr.; Zeleznik, C.; Escovitz, G.H.; Omdal, C. The mandate project: institutionalizing a system of patient care quality assurance. Pediatrics, 57(5):p775-82, (May 1976).

0287 Forquer, S.L.; Anderson, T.B. A concerns-based approach to the implementation of quality assurance systems. QRB, 8(4):p14-9, (Apr. 1982).

0288 Fredenburg, A.M. The quality assurance issue: one hospital library's approach. Bull. Med. Libr. Assoc., 72(3):p311-4, (Jul. 1984).

0289 Freeberg, M.L. Participation in a Department of Health, Education, and Welfare project. Monitoring patient care. No. 52-1572. NLN Publ., (52-1572):p21-3, (1975).

0290 Fries, R.C.; Heide, P.W. Establishing a software quality assurance program for microprocessor-based medical equipment. Med. Instrum., 20(3):p156-61, (May-Jun. 1986).

0291 Gallina, J.N. Pharmacy department quality control assurance program. Hosp. Pharm., 14(1):p44, (Jan. 1979).

0292 Ganti, A.R.; Piper, N.J.; Nagy, E.J. Quality control program: an aid to quality care. Phys. Ther., 54(3):p233-8, (Mar. 1974).

0293 Gardner, K. Quality assurance at St. Joseph Hospital. QRB, 9(6)p160-2, (Jun. 1983).

0294 Gardner, R.M.; Clausen, J.L.; Crapo, R.O.; Epler, G.R.; Hankinson, J.L.; Johnson, J.L, Jr.; Plummer, A.L. Quality assurance in pulmonary function laboratories. Am. Rev. Respir. Dis., 134(3):p625-7, (S@pt. 1986).

0295 Garrell, M. Quality assurance monitoring and quality assurance programs: a system for improving patient care. Conn. Med., 43(9):p579-80, (Sept. 1979).

0296 Gaskill, A., Jr.; Jayanty, R.K. A quality assurance program for determination of herbicides in estuarine waters. J. Environ. Sci. Health [B], 16(4):p453-63, (1981).

0297 George, A.J. A rapid-return regional quality assurance scheme for coagulation. Med. Lab. Sci., 41(3):p219-25, (Jul. 1984).

0298 Georgopoulos, B.S. An open-system approach to evaluating the effectiveness of hospital emergency departments. Emerg. Med. Serv., 7(6):p118-29, (Nov.-Dec. 1978).

0299 Geyman, J.P. Cost-containment teaching with concurrent quality assurance: a model for family practice [editorial]. J. Fam. Pract., 18(6):p833-4, (Jun. 1984).

0300 Giddings, J.C. Quality assurance in haematology and blood coagulation testing [editorial]. Med. Lab. Sci., 41(3):p207-8, (Jul. 1984).

0301 Glaze, S.; Schneiders, N.; Archer, B.; Bushong, S.
      Computer-assisted quality assurance for radiographic
      equipment. Med. Phys., 7(4):p386-8, (Jul.-Aug. 1980).

0302 Glendinning, M. Quality assurance in physiotherapy.
      Aust. Clin. Rev., (3):p22, (Nov. 1981).

0303 Glicksman, A.S.; Reinstein, L.E.; Brotman, R.; McShan, D.
      Quality assurance programs in clinical trials. Cancer
      Treat. Rep., 64(2-3)p:425-33, (Feb.-Mar. 1980).

0304 Glicksman, A.S.; Reinstein, L.E.; McShan, D.; Laurie, F.
      Radiotherapy Quality Assurance Program in a cooperative
      group. Int. J. Radiat. Oncol. Biol. Phys., 7(11):p156-,
      (Nov. 1981).

0305 Glor, B.A.; Barko, W.F. Sociotechnical systems using an
      industrial tested technology to design quality assurance
      standards in health care systems. Milit. Med., 147(4):
      p313-7, (Apr. 1982).

0306 Goldson, A.L.; Nibhanupudy, J.R. Guidelines for
      comprehensive quality assurance in brachytherapy. Int.
      J. Radiat. Oncol. Biol. Phys., 10(Suppl. 1):p111, (Jun.
      1984).

0307 Gonzalez, R.O. Activities in connection with quality
      assurance in radiation therapy performed in Argentina:
      physical aspects. Int. J. Radiat. Oncol. Biol. Phys.,
      10(Suppl. 1):p73-, (Jun. 1984).

0308 Gonnella, J.S.; Goran, M.J. Quality of patient care-a
      measurement of change: the staging concept. Med. Care,
      12(6):p467-73, (Jun. 1975).

0309 Gonnella, J.S.; Louis, D.Z.; McCord, J.J. The staging
      concept--an approach to the assessment of outcome of
      ambulatory care. Med. Care, 14(1):p13-21, (Jan. 1976).

0310 Goplerud, E.N.; Finger, J. Quality assurance in a CMHC:
      a program to use underutilized resources. QRB, 10(5):
      p150-2, (May 1984).

0311 Goran, M.J. The evolution of the PSRO hospital review
      system. Med. Care, 17(5 Suppl.):p1-47, (May 1979).

0312 Gothlin, J.H.; Alders, B. Analysis of an image quality
      assurance program. Eur. J. Radiol., 5(3):p228-30, (Aug.
      1985).

0313 Gotowka, T.; Bailit, H.L. Quality assurance systems for
      hospital outpatient dental programs: background. Spec.
      Care Dentist, 1(5):p211-217, (Sept.-Oct. 1981).

0314   Gotowka, T.D.; Bailit, H.L.; Ellis, C.D. Quality
       assurance systems for hospital outpatient dental
       programs: Spec. Care Dentist, 2(3):p125-34, (May-Jun.
       1982).

0315   Gottlieb, T.W.   Quality assurance in a long term care
       facility.   QRB, 10(2):p51-4, (Feb. 1984).

0316   Gould, E.J.   Standardized home health nursing care plans:
       a quality assurance tool.   QRB, 11(11):p334-8, (Nov.
       1985).

0317   Grant, A.K.   Quality assurance, medical audit and
       continuing medical education.   Ann. Acad. Med.Singapore,
       10(4):p566-9, (Oct. 1981).

0318   Grant, R.L.   Quality assurance in community mental health
       centers: why it may not be working.   QRB, 8(9):p3-7,
       (Sept. 1982).

0319   Greenfield, S.; Cretin, S.; Worthman, L.G.; Dorey, F.J.;
       Soloman, N.E., Goldberg, G.A.   Comparison of a criteria
       map to a criteria list in quality-of-care assessment for
       patients with chest pain: the relation of each to out-
       come.   Med. Care, 19(3):p255-72, (Mar. 1981).

0320   Griffith, N.L.; Megel, M.E.   Quality assurance and
       educational approach.   Nurs. Outlook, 29(11):p670-3,
       (Nov. 1981).

0321   Gurwich, E.L.; Hanold, L.; Schaeffer, P.   A first-phase
       quality assurance program for intravenous admixtrure
       aseptic technique.   Hosp. Pharm., 17(3):p119-21, (Mar.
       1982).

0322   Guy, M.E.; Moore, L.S.   The goal attainment scale for
       psychiatric inpatients: development and use of a quality
       assurance tool.   QRB, 8(6):p19-29, (Jun. 1982).

0323   Hamilton, J.C.   Quality assurance: an approach.
       Physiother. Can., 31(1):p11-4, (Jan.-Feb. 1979).

0324   Hanks, G.E.   Future plans for quality assurance in
       radiation oncology in the United States.   Int. J.
       Radiat. Oncol. Biol. Phys., 10(Suppl. 1):p35-, (Jun.
       1984).

0325   Hansen, P.J.   A new approach for quality assurance.
       Aviat. Space Environ. Med., 52(10):p627-8, (Oct. 1981).

0326   Hansen, P.J.   A look at quality assurance through the
       audit process.   Aviat. Space Environ. Med., 51(9 Pt. 1):
       p937-8, (Sept. 1980).

0327 Harris, R.L. Quality assurance in industrial hygiene
      education with assessment of student performance. Am.
      Ind. Hyg. Assoc. J., 44(5):pA6-12, (May 1983).

0328 Hart, G.C.; Davis, K.M. Quality assurance for multi-
      crystal gamma counters. Med. Lab. Sci., 40(3):p223-8,
      (Jul. 1983).

0329 Harty, M.K. A program to evaluate intensive psychiatric
      hospital treatment. J. Natl. Assoc. Priv. Psychiatr
      Hosp., 8(3):p21-5, (Fall 1976).

0330 Hattner, J.A.; Wood, P. Assuring quality nutritional
      care in an acute-care setting. J. Am. Diet. Assoc.
      77(2):p165-7, (Aug. 1980).

0331 Haussmann, R.K.; Hegyvary, S.T. Monitoring the quality
      of nursing care. No. 52-1572. NLN Publ.,
      (52-1572):p12-20, (1975).

0332 Hayami, A. [Quality assurance programs in dental radio-
      graphy]. Nippon Shika Ishikai Zasshi, 38(9):p921-5,
      (Dec. 1985).

0333 Hegedus, K.S.; Bourdon, S.M. On the scene: Beth Israel
      Hospital. Evaluation research: a quality assurance
      program. Nurs. Adm. Q., 5(3):p26-30, (Spring 1981).

0334 Heggie, J.C.; Petty, R.J. Quality assurance protocols
      for diagnostic X-ray equipment. Part II: Fluoroscopic
      X-ray equipment. Australas. Phys. Eng. Sci. Med.,
      8(3):p116-25, (Jul.-Sept. 1985).

0335 Heggie, J.C.; Petty, R.J. Quality assurance protocols
      for diagnostic X-ray equipment. Part 1: General radio-
      graphic units. Australas. Phys. Eng. Sci. Med., 8(1):
      p32-41, (Jan.-Mar. 1985).

0336 Heintz, D.H. Arbitration of malpractice claims: a
      hospital-based pilot project. Inquiry, 13(2):p177-86,
      (Jun. 1976).

0337 Henry R.L.; Johnson, C.R. Pathology data quality
      assurance and data retrieval at the National Center for
      Toxicological Research. J. Environ. Pathol. Toxicol.,
      3(3 Spec. No.):p169-78, (1980).

0338 Hill, B.S. The missing ingredient in quality assurance
      programs. Superv. Nurse, 10(11):p19,22, (Nov. 1979).

0339 Hill, R.K. Quality assurance in ambulatory care.
      Primary Care, 7(4):p713-21, (Dec. 1980).

0340 Hines, J. Quality assurance in community nursing workshop papers. The nursing audit. Lamp, 36(11):p9-10, (Dec. 1979).

0341 Hoffman, R.P.; Ellerbrock, M.C.; Lovett, J.E. A multihospital medication allergy audit: a means to quality assurance. Hosp. Pharm., 17(4):p202-4,209-11, (Apr. 1982).

0342 Hoffmann, R.P.; Ravin, R.; Colaluca, D.M.; Gifford, R.; Grimes, D.; Grzegorczyk, R.; Keown, F.; Kuhr, F.; McKay, R.; Peyser, J.; Ryan, R.; Zalewski, C. Development of a multihospital quality assurance program. Hosp. Pharm. 15(7):p365-8,379-1,373-4 passim, (Jul. 1980).

0343 Hogan, N.S. Expert urges expanded functions for patient reps. Hosp. Peer. Rev., 5(5):p56-7, (May 1980).

0344 Holmes, T.W.; McCullough, E.C. Acceptance testing and quality assurance of automated scanning film densitometers used in the dosimetry of electron and photon therapy beams. Med. Phys., 10(5):p698-700, (Sept.-Oct. 1983).

0345 Hoory, S.; Levy, L.M.; Schiff, R.; Moskowitz, G.; Bandyopadhyay, D. Quality assurance in nuclear medicine: a computerized approach. Health Phys., 47(3):p468-71, (Sep. 1984).

0346 Horowitz, K.N.; Lamnin M. Design and implementation of a quality-assurance program for pharmaceutical services. Am. J. Hosp. Pharm., 37(1):p82-4, (Jan. 1980).

0347 Horwitz, W.; Kamps, L.R.; Boyer, K.W. Quality assurance in the analysis of foods and trace constituents. J. Assoc. Off. Anal. Chem., 63(6):p1344-54, (Nov. 1980).

0348 Hunt, R.S.; Redmond, J.M. Emergency services: basic assessment model proves effective, adaptable, economical. Hospitals, 52(6):165-6,168,170passim, (Mar. 16, 1978).

0349 Hunter, S.A.; Dunlop, C.R. Developing a quality assurance plan in a medical center. QRB, 6(9):p11-5, (Sept. 1980).

0350 Jackson, J.M.; Hughes, W. External quality in hematology. The programme of the Royal College of Pathologists of Australia. Pathology, 17(4):p573-8, (Oct. 1985).

0351 Jackson, M.M.; Lynch, P. Applying an epidemiological structure to risk management and quality assurance activities. QRB, 11(10):p306-12, (Oct. 1985).

0352 Jeffrey, L.P.; Temkin, L.A.; Krugman, M.E. Assuring the quality of medications stored in patient care areas. Am. J. Hosp. Pharm., 32(3):p283-5, (Mar. 1975).

0353 Jerge, C.R.; Orlowski, R.M. Quality assurance and the dental record. Dent. Clin. North Am., 29(3):p483-96, (Jul. 1985).

0354 Jessee, W.F. Quality assurance: evaluating services of small, swing-bed hospitals. Hospitals, 56(22):p74-7, (Nov. 16, 1982).

0355 Johnson, L.; MacLellan, L.; Richardson, E.; Sandel, J. Development of a quality assurance program: Colonel Belcher Hospital. AARN News Lett., 41(10):p17, (Nov. 1985).

0356 Joseph, E. Data tracking, management system produces better QA/RM activities. Hosp. Peer Rev., 7(1):p10-2, (Jan. 1982).

0357 Kaistha, K.K.; Tadrus, R. Improved cost effective thin-layer detection techniques for routine surveillance of commonly abused drugs in drug abuse urine screening and proficiency testing programs with built-in quality assurance. J. Chromatogr., 267(1):109-16, (Sept. 2, 1983).

0358 Kammerer, J. Quality assurance for ESRD: a successful program. ANNA J., 11(6):p25-7, (Oct. 1984).

0359 Kasprisin, C.A.; Kasprisin, D.O.; Marks, D.; Yogore, M.G; Williams, H.L. Quality assurance beyond the bloodbank. Superv. Nurse, 12(5):P45-8, (May 1981).

0360 Kaufman, M.; Vermeersch, J.A. Quality assurance in ambulatory nutritional care. I. Past, present, and future. J. Am. Diet Assoc., 78(6)p577-82, (Jun. 1981).

0361 Kearns, P.M. Utilization review expanded into quality assurance program. Hospitals, 54(17):p62-3, (Sept. 1, 1980).

0362 Keblusek, J. Discharge planning for continuity of care. Quality assurance. NLN Publ., (20-1977):p55-60, (Jun. 1985).

0363 Kekki, P. Quality assurance in primary medical care. Scand. J. Prim. Health Care, 1(3-4):p132-8, (1983).

0364 Keys, P.W.; Narduzzi, J.V. Drug audit: a component of quality assurance. QRB, 5(1):p17-23, (Jan. 1979).

0365 King, B. Quality assurance programmes for nurses. Aust. Health Rev., 4(1):p14-5, (Jan. 1981).

0366 Kirkpatrick, D.L.; Shotwell, A.J. Optometric quality assurance. J. Am. Optom. Assoc., 56(5): P390-4, (May 1985).

0367 Kirkpatrick, K.W.; Flasck, E.D. How to implement a quality assurance program. Todays OR Nurse, 3(12): p26-30,59, (Feb. 1982).

0368 Klerman, L.V. Evaluating service programs for school-age parents: design problems. Eval. Health Prof., 2(1):p55 -70, (Mar. 1979).

0369 Klopfer, A.H. Improving quality assurance in hospitals. Conn. Med., 45(7):p443-4, (Jul. 1981).

0370 Knickerbocker, G.G. The evaluation of resuscitation and critical care equipment: a user's quality assurance service. Crit. Care Med., 9(5):p401-2, (May 1981).

0371 Knittig, M.J. Quality assurance in ambulatory care. J. Arkansas. Med. Soc., 82(5):p228-9, (Oct. 1985).

0372 Kokuyama, T. [Quality assurance program--American nurses' approach to the "nursing quality"]. Kango Tenbo 7(2):p122-6, (Feb. 1982).

0373 Kordick, M.F. A quality assurance system based on management by objectives. QRB, 9(3):p83-5, (Mar. 1983).

0374 Korsak, A.J. How to use malpractice data in quality assessment. Hosp. Med. Staff, 9(2):p28-36, (1980).

0375 Krejci, C.B. Quality assurance audit. J. Am. Diet Assoc., 76(4):p378, (Apr. 1980).

0376 Kuehl, D.W.; Butterworth, B.C.; Johnson, K.L. Supplemental quality assurance criteria for high-resolution gas chromatography/high-resolution mass spectrometric determination of 2,3,7,8-tetrachlorodibenzo-p-dioxin in biological tissue. Anal. Chem., 58(7):p1598-9, (Jun. 1986).

0377 Kunin, C.M.; Sabatino, F.G. Antibiotic usage surveillance: an overview of the issues. QRB, 5(1):p4-8, (Jan. 1979).

0378 Ladwig, J.P. A quality assurance program in action. Med. Rec. News, 50(2):p13,22-7,30-4, (Apr. 1979).

0379 Laing, M; Nish, M. Eight steps to quality assurance: Part one. Can. Nurse, 77(10)p22-5, (Nov. 1981).

0380 Land, M.J.; Gaska, J.; Shull, J.C.; Jones, D.R. A comprehensive quality assurance program for hospital pharmacy departments. Top Hosp. Pharm. Manage., 1(3):p81-9, (Nov. 1981).

0381 Langenfeld, M.L.; Rzasa, C.B. A model for integrating the quality assurance activities of two small hospitals. QRB, 7(10):p32-6, (Oct. 1981).

0382 LaViolette, S. Quality assurance pressures may spur use of epidemiology systems. Mod. Health Care, 10(12):p78, 80, (Dec. 1980).

0383 Lawson, L.A.; Blouin, R.A.; Parker, P.F. Quality assurance program for a clinical pharmacokinetic service. Am. J. Hosp. Pharm., 39(4):p607-9, (Apr. 1982).

0384 Lebow, J. Evaluation of an outpatient pediatric practice through the use of consumer questionnaires. Med. Care, 13(3):p250-5, (Mar. 1975).

0385 Lillensand, K.M.; Koroff, S. Nursing process evaluation: a quality assurance tool. Nurs. Adm. Q., 7(3):p9-14, (Spring 1983).

0386 Lindstrom, R. Designing a shared radiology quality assurance program. Dimens. Health Serv., 56(1):p16-7, (Jan. 1979).

0387 Lindy, C.N. A three-part approach to quality assurance in nursing. QRB, 6(3):p12-6, (Mar. 1980).

0388 Lohff, M.R. Preliminary observations on the Quality Assurance Service Therapeutic Drug Monitoring Program. Am. J. Clin. Pathol., 74(4 Suppl.):p542-5, (Oct. 1980).

0389 Lomando, K.; Faulconer, D.R. A workable plan for OR quality assurance. AORN J., 35(7):p1291-5, (Jun. 1982).

0390 Longabaugh, R.; Fowler, D.R.; Hostetler, M.; McMahon, L.; Sullivan, C. Focus on patient problems: use or the problem-oriented record in a proposed evaluation study of social isolation. QRB, 4(4):p4-7, (Apr. 1978).

0391 Longest, B.B., Jr. Design and behavioral strategies for cost containment and quality assurance. J. Med. Syst., 5(1-2)p97-110, (1981).

0392 Looney, D.H.; Gibson, C. Standards of practice: nutritional quality assurance in acute-care hospitals. J. Am. Diet. Assoc., 79(1):p64-5, (Jul. 1981).

43

0393 Luff, C.A.; Walker, P.C., 2nd. Computer code for the recording of patients' problems. Comput. Biomed. Res., 8(3):p267-78, (Jun. 1975).

0394 Lurie, A. The impact of quality assurance on social work. An overview of current peer review mechanisms. QRB, 3(7):p25-6,32, (Jul. 1977).

0395 Lurie, A. Social service conducts two quality assurance programs. Hospitals, 53(3):p67-9, (Feb. 1, 1978).

0396 Macaluso, D.; Stein, B.; Polster, L.R. CHAMP: a comparative study approach. QRB, 6(7):p19-24, (Jul. 1980).

0397 Macartney, J.C.; Henson, D.E.; Codling, B.W. Quality assurance in anatomic pathology. Am. J. Clin. Pathol., 75(3 Suppl.):p467-75, (Mar. 1981).

0398 Mackie, L.C.; Welch, J.W. Quality assurance audit for the nursing process. Nurs. Times, 78(42):p1757-8, (Oct. 20-26, 1982).

0399 Mackie, R.J.; Peddie, R.; Pendleton, R. Quality assurance. A design for perioperative nurses. AORN J., 42(1):p58-61,64-9,72-6, (Jul. 1985).

0400 Management of nursing care: quality assurance program uses objective standards to measure performance. Health Serv. Manager, 10(6):p6-7, (Jun. 1977).

0401 Mansfield, M. The occupation of therapists: role of psychiatric occupational therapists and preparation of generic audit criteria. QRB, 4(4):p8-12, (Apr. 1978).

0402 Manson-Hing, L.R.; Bloxom, R.M. A stepwedge quality assurance test for machine and processor in dental radiography. J. Am. Dent. Assoc., 110(6):p910-3, (Jun. 1985).

0403 Mapa, J.; Turner, G. Quality assurance: a new approach. Dimens. Health Serv., 61(3):p12-4, (Mar. 1984).

0404 Marcin, J.; Forrest, J.L. Quality assurance: a model for dental hygiene. Dent. Hyg., 56(4):p16-8,22-4,26-34, (Apr. 1982).

0405 Marsh, L.A. Quality assurance activities in a small community hospital. QRB, 9(3):p77-80, (Mar. 1983).

0406 Martin, R.D. A method for documenting and displaying problem-focused activities. QRB, 7(4):p24-7, (Apr. 1981).

0407 McAninch, M. Quality assurance in the residential and outpatient mental health setting. QRB, 10(6):p181-5, (Jun. 1984).

0408 McAuliffe, W.E. Measuring the quality of medical care: process versus outcome. Milbank Mem. Fund Q, 57(1):118-52, (Winter 1979).

0409 McColl, M.A.; Quinn, B. A quality assurance method for community occupational therapy. Am. J. Occup. Ther., 39(9):p570-7, (Sept. 1985).

0410 McCollum, W.E. Hospital system works to ensure risk management, quality of care. Hospitals, 52(19):p86-8, (Oct. 1, 1978).

0411 McGowan, P. Quality Assurance Program: QAP know-how sparks zest. RNABC News, 14(3):p8-9, (Apr. 1982).

0412 McInerny, K.F.; Archer, S.E. Quality assurance in NSW public hospitals. Aust. Nurses J., 12(8):p46-9, (Mar. 1983).

0413 McKeever, D.A. Ministry to staff aids quality control. Hospitals, 49(14):p181,184, (Jul. 16, 1975).

0414 McKenzie, R.; Hines, J. Implementation of a quality assurance programme in community nursing. Aust. Nurses J., 10(2):p34-7, (Aug. 1980).

0415 McManus, C.D.; Smalley, D.L.; Sanders, D.E. Monitoring laboratory services through concurrent review. QRB, 8(2):p5-9, (Feb. 1982).

0416 McMartin, C. One way to measure quality of patient care. Mich. Hosp., 15(9):p18-9, (Sept. 1979).

0417 McNamara, J.J.; Gourji, A.; Green, M. Assessing the quality of care by house staff in a municipal hospital emergency department. JACEP, 5(4):p257-61, (Apr. 1976).

0418 Medical records program improves, QA, RM, UR and cash flow. Hosp. Peer Rev., 7(4):p41-3, (Apr. 1982).

0419 Mehnert, T. The reassessment process: key to a meaningful quality assurance program. QRB, 11(4):p127-31, (Apr. 1985).

0420 Meisel, S. A pharmacy-based quality assurance program. QRB, 9(5):p147-8, (May 1983).

0421 Menzel, F.S.; Teegarden, K. Quality assurance: a Tri-Level model. Am. J. Occup. Ther., 36(3)p163-9, (Mar. 1982).

0422 Meudt, R.; Buser, C.; Bosch, A. [The concept of sono-
graphic organ diagnosis--a contribution to quality
assurance]. Ultraschall. Med., 7(2):p54-8, (Apr. 1986).

0423 Miler, R.; Drake, M. Standards of nursing performance.
Tools for assuring quality care. QRB, 6(5);p16-9, (May
1980).

0424 Miller, S.I. A multidimensional problem-oriented review
and evaluation system for psychiatric patient care.
Med. Rec. News, 48(1):p9-12, (Feb. 1977).

0425 Miller, S.I.; Schlachter, R.H. A multidimensional
problem-oriented review and evaluation system.
Am. J. Psychiatry, 132(3):p232-5, (Mar. 1975).

0426 Mills, W. Quality assurance and nursing diagnosis. AARN
News Lett., 42(4):p23-4, (Apr. 1986).

0427 Minniear, W.A. On the scene: the Duke University
Hospital experience in QA. Nurs. Adm., 1(3):p7-9,
(Spring 1977).

0428 Moore, L.; Damewood, D.M.; Floyd, C.; Jewell, K. A
method for achieving quality assurances in nursing
education. Nurs. Health Care, 5(5):p269-74, (May 1984).

0429 Morgenstein, S.; Simpkins, S.; Maring, J. Development of
a quality assurance program as an integral part of the
physical therapy system. Phys. Ther., 62(4):p464-9,
(Apr. 1982).

0430 Morris, C.R. A blueprint for hospitalwide quality
assurance. Hosp. Med. Staff, 9(12):p11-6, (Dec. 1980).

0431 Morrison, B.J.; Rehr, H.; Rosenberg, G.; Davis, S.
Consumer opinion surveys: a hospital quality assurance
measurement. QRB, 8(2):p19-24, (Feb. 1982).

0432 Moyer, R.F. Quality assurance of electron-beam energy
using an aluminum wedge. Radiology, 140(1):p237-9, (Jul.
1981).

0433 Mulholland, J.H.; Bittle, L. Quality assurance & risk
management in Maryland hospitals in the 1980s. Md.
State Med. J., 31(4):p60-2, (Apr. 1982).

0434 Murthy, M.S.; Derman, H. Quality assurance in surgical
pathology--personal and peer assessment. Am. J. Clin.
Pathol., 75(3 Suppl.):p462-6, (Mar. 1981).

0435 Mushlin, A.I.; Appel, F.A. Testing an outcome-based
quality assurance strategy in primary care. Med.Care,
18(5 Suppl.):p1-100, (May 1980).

0436 Nadolny, M.D. The patient care audit. Hosp. Top., 57(6)
:30-3, (Nov.-Dec. 1979).

0437 National standards and review criteria for diabetes
patient education programs: quality assurance for
diabetes patient education. Diabetes. Educ., 12(3):p286
-91, (Summer 1986).

0438 Needham, L.L.; Burse, V.W.; Korver, M.P.; Lapeza, C.R.;
Liddle, J.A.: Bayse, D.D.; Price, H.A. Design and
demonstration of a quality assurance program for
labor-intensive analytical systems. J. Anal. Toxicol.,
7(6):p279-82, (Nov.-Dec. 1983).

0439 Newman, F.L. Outcome evaluation and quality assurance
in mental health. QRB, 8(4):p27-31, (Apr. 1982).

0440 Nichols, A.C.; Wirginis, M.B. Linking standards of care
with nursing quality assurance--the SCORE method. QRB,
11(2):p57-63, (Feb. 1985).

0441 Nobles, C. The new quality assurance program. Times,
20(6):p10,15, (Sept.-Oct. 1979).

0442 Noel, P.R. Toxicity testing, hazard assessment and data
quality assurance for chemical regulatory purposes.
Dev. Toxicol. Environ. Sci., 8:p453-63, (1980).

0443 Novick. L.F.; Dickinson, K.; Asnes, R.; Lan, S.M.;
Lowenstein, R. Assessment of ambulatory care:
application of the tracer methodology. Med. Care,
14(1):p1-12, (Jan. 1976).

0444 Nusslin, F. [Methods of quality assurance in computed
tomography using test measurements on a CT/T-8800 as a
example]. Rontgenpraxis, 37(8):p293-6, (Aug. 1984).

0445 Oberfell, M.S.; Ometer, J.L. Quality assurance. II.
Application of oncology standards against a levels of
caremodel. J. Am. Diet Assoc., 81(2):p129-35, (Aug.
1982).

0446 Oller, W.L.; Gough, B.; Littlefield, N.A. Chemical
surveillance and quality assurance for preparation of
dosed (2-AAF) animal feed (ED01 study). J. Environ.
Pathol. Toxicol., 3(3 Spec. No.):p203-10, (1980).

0447 Ometer, J.L. An intradepartmental process audit to
measure quality of care. J. Am. Diet. Assoc., 75(5):
566-8, (Nov. 1979).

0448 Ometer, J.L.; Oberfell, M.S. Quality assurance. I.
A levels of care model. J. Am. Diet. Assoc., 81(2):p
129-32, (Aug. 1982).

0449 Orlikoff, J.E.; Lanham, G.B. Integrated approach improves quality assurance, risk management activities. Hospitals, 54(17):p59-61, (Sept. 1, 1980).

0450 Oulton, R. Use of incidence report data in a system-wide quality assurance/risk management program. QRB, 7(6):p2-7, (Jun. 1981).

0451 Padilla, G.V.; Grant, M.M. Quality assurance programme for nursing. J. Adv. Nurs., 7(2):p135-45, (Mar. 1982).

0452 Palmer, R.H.; Strain, R.; Maurer, J.V.; Rothrock, J.K.; Thompson, M.S. Quality assurance in eight adult medicine group practices. Med. Care, 22(7):p632-43, (Jul. 1984).

0453 Paras, P. Quality assurance of nuclear medicine instrumentation. Ric. Clin. Lab., 11(4):p357-77, (Oct.-Dec. 1981).

0454 Park, B.A.; Benderev, K.P. Quality assurance program for a drug information center. Am. J. Hosp. Pharm., 42(10): p2180-4, (Oct. 1985).

0455 Patient interviews aid quality control. Profiles Hosp. Mark., (1):p30-1, (1st Quarter 1981).

0456 Patterson, D. Quality assurance in the clinical area. Jamaican Nurse, 22(2):p21-2, (1982).

0457 Peter, M.A. Duke Hospital's Quality Assurance Program in nursing: background, organization and evolvement. Nurs. Adm. Q., 1(3):p9-25, (Spring 1977).

0458 Pien, F.D.; Bruce, A. Infection control quality assurance programs in a community hospital. APIC, 6(2):p14-5, (Jun. 1978).

0459 Pilat, J.M. Considerations in evaluation of hospitals social work services for alcoholic patients. QRB, 5(11) :p20-3, (Nov. 1979).

0460 Pinkerton, P.H.; Wood, D.E. Quality assurance in the blood bank [letter]. Lancet, 1(8283):p1246, (May 29, 1982).

0461 Ponce, A.Z.; Ponce, M.L. The X-ray checker. Basic radiographic quality assurance. Clin. Prevent. Dent., 6(2):p27-9, (Mar.-Apr. 1984).

0462 Posey, L.M. Establishing quality-assurance systems for admixture services [editorial]. Am. J. Hosp. Pharm., 40(11):p1902, (Nov. 1983).

0463 Pray, S. Quality assurance of manufacturer-supplied
unit dose packages. Hosp. Pharm., 14(2):p66,68,70-1,
(Feb. 1979).

0464 Price, M. Quality assurance: implementing a management
information system for nursing. Tex. Hosp., 37(2):p8-9,
(Jul. 1981).

0465 Private initiative in quality assurance. Colo. Med.,
77(1):p17-8, (Jan. 1980).

0466 Privileges and quality assurance mechanisms for
nonphysicians. Hosp. Med. Staff, 9(4):p34-6, (Apr.
1980).

0467 "Problem-focused" vs. "program-focused"--the light dawns!
Second Opin. Health Care Issues, 2(1):p2-6, (Jan. 1981).

0468 Problem-oriented recording: a significant component of a
quality assurance program. Can. Nurse, 77(11):p39-40,
(Dec. 1981).

0469 Quality assessment and patient care. No. 52-1572.
NLN Publ., (52-1572):p1-56, (1975).

0470 Quality assessment: programs and process. Presentations
from the March 1974 and March 1975 Forums for Nursing
Service Administrators in the West; sponsored by the
Western Regional Assembly of Constituent Leagues.
NLN Publ., (52-1598):p1-47, (1975).

0471 Quality assurance in nutritional care. Ontario Hospital
Association/Ontario Dietetic Association Quality
Assurance of Nutritional Care Committee. Dimens.
Health Serv., 59(7):p16-7, (Jul. 1982).

0472 Quality assurance for office laboratories [letter].
JAMA, 256(2):p211-2, (Jul. 11, 1986).

0473 Quality assurance programs for diagnostic radiology
facilities: Food and Drug Administration. Final
recommendation. Fed. Regist., 44(239):p71728-40, (Dec.
11, 1979).

0474 Quality assurance systems within central service department. Infect. Control Rounds, 2(2):p7, (Mar.-Apr. 1978).

0475 Quality assurance: the Lima Memorial Hospital experience.
Nurs. Adm. Q., 7(3):p59-74, (Spring 1983).

0476 Quality of care: selected influences and methodological
dilemmas. Commun. Nurs. Res., 11:p81-9, (1978).

0477 Quality-of-care index shows board how hospitals rate. Hosp. Peer. Rev., 5(3):p32-3, (Mar. 1980).

0478 Recommendations for quality assurance in dental radiography. Oral Surg. Oral Med. Oral Pathol., 55(4): p421-26, (Apr. 1983).

0479 Reichert, K. Quality assurance in social work in hospitals: a systems perspective [editorial]. Am. J. Public Health, 69(4):329-31, (Apr. 1979).

0480 Reinhoff, O.; Machleidt, W. Feedback of therapeutic skills for quality assessment within ward sessions in psychiatry. Methods Inf. Med., 20(1):p23-7, (Jan. 1981).

0481 Reinstein, L.E.; McShan, D.; Glicksman, A.S. A dosimetry review system for cooperative group research. Med. Phys., 9(2):p240-9, (Mar.-Apr. 1982).

0482 Richman, A. Quality assurance, PSRO and the medical record for psychiatric patients. Med. Rec. News, 49(2):p38-41,44-8,50, (Apr. 1978).

0483 Rifkin, M.; Lynne, C.; Williams, R.; Hilsenbeck, C. Tracking quality assurance problems in a large teaching hospital. Jackson Memorial Hospital, Miami. 7(9):p25 -9, (Sept. 1981).

0484 Robertson, S.C.; Martin, E.D., Jr. Continuing education: a quality assurance approach. Am. J. Occup. Ther., 35(5):p312-6, (May 1981).

0485 Rodger, C. A quality assurance program that is hospital-wide. Mich. Hosp., 16(5):p16-7, (May 1980).

0486 Roedler, H.D. [Quality assurance in nuclear medicine]. Strahlenschutz Forsch Prax, 27:p130-9, (1986).

0487 Roemer, M.I.; Hopkins, C.E. Comment on "evaluating the quality of hospital care through severity-adjusted death rates: some pitfalls." Med. Care, 12(10):p882-4, (Oct. 1974).

0488 Rotwein, S. The word processor--a transcription quality assurance mechanism. J. Am. Med. Rec. Assoc., 52(3):p70-4, (Jun. 1981).

0489 Rouse, S.; Cowen, A.R. Quality assurance of fluorographic camera systems. Radiography, 49(587):p251-5, (Nov. 1983).

0490 Rozenfeld, M.; Jette, D. Quality assurance of radiation dosage: usefulness of redundancy. Radiology, 150(1): p241-4, (Jan. 1984).

0491 Ruark, T. Quality assurance in the business office.
J. Patient Acc. Manage., p6-8, (Oct. 1981).

0492 Rubenstein, L.; Mates, S.; Sidel, V.W. Quality-of-care
assessment by process and outcome scoring. Use of
weighted algorithmic assessment criteria for evaluation
of emergency room care of women with urinary tract
infection. Ann. Intern. Med., 86(5):p617-25, (May 1977).

0493 Russell, Z. A comprehensive radiology quality assurance
program. QRB, 6(6):p15-8, (Jun. 1980).

0494 Rutstein, D.D.; Berenberg, W.; Chalmers, T.C.; Child,
C.G, 3rd; Fishman, A.P.; Perrin, E.B. Measuring the
quality of medical care. A clinical method.
N. Engl. J. Med., 294(11):p528-8, (Mar. 11, 1976).

0495 Sadin, R.R. Professional Standards Review
Organizations. Another quality assurance program.
Phys. Ther., 55(12):p1315-9, (Dec. 1975).

0496 Saladino, A.J. The efficacy of the autopsy in medical
quality assurance. Clin. Lab. Med., 4(1)p165-84, (Mar.
1984).

0497 Satzger, R.D.; Bonnin, E.; Fricke, F.L. Development of a
quality assurance program for determination of ultratrace
background levels of lead and cadmium in raw agricultural
crops by differential pulse anodic stripping voltammetry.
J. Assoc. Off. Anal. Chem., 67(6):p1138-40, (Nov.-Dec.
1984).

0498 Savander, G.R. Development of an outcome assessment and
informational system for physical therapy. A
multi-institutional project. Phys. Ther., 57(8):p891-6,
(Aug. 1977).

0499 Schenck, J.M. Quality assurance experiences within a
physical therapy curriculum. Phys. Ther., 60(7):p882 u,
(Jul. 1980).

0500 Schiller, R.; Behm, V. Auditing dietetic services:
first of a series. Hospitals, 53(8):p122-7, (Apr. 1979).

0501 Shimeld, A. A clinical demonstration program in quality
assurance. Am. J. Occup. Ther., 37(1):p32-5, (Jan.
1983).

0502 Schneiders, N.J.; Bushong, S.C. CT quality assurance:
computer assisted slice thickness determination. Med.
Phys., 7(1):p61-3, (Jan.-Feb. 1980).

0503 Schroeder, P.S.; Maibusch, R.M.; Anderson C.A.; Formella, N.M. A unit-based approach to nursing quality assurance. QRB, 8(3):p10-2, (Mar. 1982).

0504 Scott, W.R.; Flood, A.B.; Ewy, W. Organizational determinants of services, quality and cost of care in hospitals. Milbank Mem. Fund Q., 57(2):p234-64, (Spring 1979).

0505 Seijo, C.A. A CT scanning protocol for a quality assurance program. Radiol. Technol., 52(5): p497-509, (Mar.-Apr. 1981).

0506 Selbmann, H.K. [Role of medical information processing for quality assurance in obstetrics]. Geburtshilfe Fraunheilkd, 43(Suppl. 1):p82-6, (Jun. 1983).

0507 Self, P.C.; Gebhart, K.A. A quality assurance process in health sciences libraries. Bull. Med. Libr. Assoc., 68(3):p288-92, (Jul. 1980).

0508 Shamansky, S.L.; Young, K.L. Quality assurance in the community health nursing setting: getting started. Wash. State J. Nurs., 53:p33-7, (1981).

0509 Shannon, M. A measure of the fulfillment of health needs. Int. J. Aging Hum. Dev., 7(4):p353-77, (1976).

0510 Shaughnessy, P.W.; Kurowski, B. Quality assurance through reimbursement. Health Serv. Res., 17(2):p157 -83, (Summer 1982).

0511 Shaw, C.D. The quality assurance project at the King's Fund Centre in London. QRB, 12(4):p150-1, (Apr. 1986).

0512 Shaw, M.A.; Russell, W.L.; Bradham, D.D. Quality assurance in a clinical pharmacy program. QRB, 10(3): p87-9, (Mar. 1984).

0513 Shephard, M.D.; Penberthy, L.A.; Fraser, C.G. Evolution of a national urine quality assurance programme: the Australasian experience, 1981-1983. J. Clin. Pathol., 37(4):p415-23, (Apr. 1984).

0514 Shephard, M.D.; Penberthy, L.A.; Fraser, C.G. A quality assurance programme for quantitative urine analyses. Pathology, 14(3):p327-31, (Jul. 1982).

0515 Sherber, J. Review ensures quick response to faulty care. Hospitals, 54(15);p55-7, (Aug. 1980).

0516 Sherman, P.S.; Gomez, M. Quality assurance uses of levels of functioning ratings: applications in a community mental health center. QRB, 8(7):p22-30, (Jul. 1982).

0517 Shimeld, A. A clinical demonstration program in quality assurance. Am. J. Occup. Ther., 37(1):p32-5, (Jan. 1983).

0518 Skillicorn, S.A. Practice traits of physicians: a neglected quality assurance issue. QRB, 11(4):p108-10, (Apr. 1985).

0519 Skreenock, J.J. Electrosurgical quality assurance: the view from the OR table. Med. Instrum., 14(5):p261-3, (Sept.-Oct. 1980).

0520 Small, E.W. Quality assurance in the hospital environment. J. Hosp. Dent. Pract., 14(3):p105-10 (1980).

0521 Smeltzer, C.H.; Feltman, B.; Rajki, K. Nursing quality assurance: a process, not a tool. J. Nurs. Adm., 13(1): p5-9, (Jan. 1983).

0522 Smith, N.G. A systemwide quality assurance/risk management program. Hosp. Med. Staff, 8(8):p40-4, (Aug. 1979).

0523 Souhami, L. Quality assurance in radiation therapy: clinical aspects. Int. J. Radiat. Oncol. Biol. Phys., 10(Suppl. 1):p69-7, (Jun. 1984).

0524 Spano, R.M.; Lund, S.H. Accountability, evaluation, and quality assurance in a hospital social service department. QRB, 6(10):p14-9, (Oct. 1980).

0525 Stearns, G.; Fox, L.A. A three-phase plan for integrating quality assurance activities. QRB, 6(1):p13 -6, (Jan. 1980).

0526 Stender, H.S. [Practical quality assurance in x-ray diagnosis (author's transl)]. Zur praktischen Qualitatssicherung in der Rontgendiagnostik. Rontgenblatter, 33(12):p618-25, (Dec. 1980).

0527 Stephany, T.M. Quality assurance for hospice programs. Oncol. Nurs. Forum, 12(3):p33-40, (May-Jun. 1985).

0528 Stevens, J.E. Quality assurance in long term care. QRB, 9(8):p229-30, (Aug. 1983).

0529 Stewart, R.D.; Burgman, J.; Cannon, G.M.; Paris, P.M. A computer-assisted quality assurance system for an emergency medical service. Ann. Emerg. Med. (UNITED STATES), 14(1):p25-9, (Jan. 1985).

0530 Stieve, F.E. [Quality assurance in radiology; development, requirements, conclusions]. Strahlenschutz Forsch Prax, 27:p1-22, (1986).

0531 Stolar, M.H. Quality assurance of pharmaceutical services: an objective-based planning strategy. Am. J. Hosp. Pharm., 38(2):p209-12, (Feb. 1981).

0532 Stolar, M.H. Quality assurance of pharmaceutical services. Can. J. Hosp. Pharm., 30(2):p45-7, (Mar.-Apr. 1977).

0533 Suntharalingam, N. Quality assurance in radiation therapy: future plans in physics. Int. J. Radiat. Oncol. Biol. Phys., 10(Suppl. 1):p43-, (Jun. 1984).

0534 Svensson, G.K. Quality assurance in radiation therapy: physics efforts. Int. J. Radiat. Oncol. Biol. Phys., 10(Suppl. 1):p23-, (Jun. 1984).

0535 Svensson, H. Quality assurance in radiation therapy: physical aspects. Int. J. Radiat. Oncol. Biol. Phys., 10(Suppl. 1):p59-6, (Jun. 1984).

0536 Sveska, K.J.; Roffe, B.D.; Solomon, D.K. Evaluation of quality assurance technique for a pharmockinetic dosing service. Drug Intell. Clin. Pharm., 20(4):p302-6, (Apr. 1986).

0537 Swamidoss, P. Quality assurance through in-house hospital inspections. J. Natl. Med. Assoc., 77(7):p581-4, (Jul. 1985).

0538 Swope, M.B. Rehabilitation can use joint approach to quality assurance. Hospitals, 55(19)p69-71, (Oct. 1, 1981).

0539 Symposium on methodology and quality assurance in cancer clinical trials. Washington, DC, October 24-26, 1984. Cancer Treat. Rep., 69(10):p1039-229, (Oct. 1985).

0540 Taylor, H. An overall approach to quality assurance at Moorabbin Hospital. The role of the medical record administrator. Aust. Clin. Rev., (4):p31-3, (Mar. 1982).

0541 Thompson, A.B.; Wilson, A.M. Quantity first, then quality: a hospital looks at cost-effective staff utilization. Can. Nurse, 77(5):p22-6, (May 1981).

0542 Thompson, J.S. Diagnosis related groups and quality assurance. Top Health Care Financ., 8(4):p43-9, (Summer 1982).

0543 Thompson, R.E. A patient care review model to suit both
      hospitals and PSROs. Hospitals, 54(16):61-3, (Aug. 16,
      1980).

0544 Thompson, R.E.; Rodrick, A.B. Integrating patient
      concerns into quality assurance activities: the focus
      group method. QRB, 8(2):p16-8, (Feb. 1982).

0545 Thur, M.P. OR/pharmacy drug quality assurance. AORN J.,
      23(4):p624,626,628, (Mar. 1976).

0546 Tucker, F., II. Using a patient information system in
      social work quality assurance activities. QRB, 8(3):
      p25-7, (Mar. 1982).

0547 Tucker, J. Evaluating medical records provides effective
      QA [interview]. Hosp. Peer. Rev., 6(5):p58-9, (May
      1981).

0548 Turco, S.J. Quality assurance in I.V. admixture programs.
      Hosp. Pharm., 14(6):p307, 311-3, (Jun. 1979).

0549 Ungethum, M. [Quality assurance in implants for bone
      surgery]. Biomed. Tech., 28(12):p282-91, (Dec. 1983).

0550 Ungethum, M. Quality assurance for implants in bone
      surgery. J. Med. Eng. Technol., 8(3):p108-14, (May-Jun.
      1984).

0551 Valachovic, R.W.; Reiskin, A.B.; Kirchhof, S.T. A
      quality assurance program in dental radiology. Pediatr.
      Dent., 3(1):p26-32, (Mar. 1981).

0552 Valentine, J. Peer review, quality of care, and
      problem-oriented records: three aspects of
      accountability. Hosp. Community Psychiatry,
      25(10):p678-9, (Oct. 1974).

0553 Van Herten, J.H. [The FONA-Commission. Quality assurance
      with reference to Errors Accidents and Near-accidents].
      Tijdschr Ziekenverpl, 38(22):p671-5, (Oct. 29, 1985).

0554 Vanzetti, G. Quality assurance in radiommunoassay: a
      goal for the eighties. J. Nucl. Med. Allied Sci., 26(4)
      P201-4, (Oct.-Dec. 1982).

0555 Vermeersch, J.A.; Kaufman, M. Quality assurance in
      ambulatory nutritional care. II. Field testing of
      criteria. J. Am. Diet Assoc., 78(6):p582-6, (Jun. 1981).

0556 Vogel, D.P. Bringing quality assurance to the pharmacy.
      Health Serv. Manager, 14(10):p11-3, (Oct. 1981).

0557 Vogel, D.P.; Gurwich, E.; Campagna, K.; Sula, J.; Eck, T.A.; Hutchinson, R.A. Pharmacy unit devises quality assurance plan. Hospitals, 54(11):p83-5, (Jun. 1, 1980).

0558 Walczak, R.M. JCAH perspective: quality assurance in anesthesia services. AANA J., 50(5):p462-4, (Oct. 1982).

0559 Walkley, P.H., Jr. University hospital develops model quality assurance program. Hospitals, 50(18):p73-5, (Sep. 16, 1976).

0560 Walter Reed quality assurance activities described. Hosp. Peer. Rev., 3(5):p70-3, (May 1978).

0561 Walts, L.; Blair, F. Making quality assurance work in the emergency department. JEN, 9(1):p59-60, (Jan.-Feb. 1983).

0562 Wambersie, A. The role of the ICRU in quality assurance in radiation therapy. Int. J. Radiat. Oncol. Biol. Phys., 10(Suppl. 1):p81-, (Jun. 1984).

0563 Wascom, K.R.; Keiser, M.F. Quality assessment of emergency department activities. Emerg. Med. Serv. 10(1):p21-6, (Jan.-Feb. 1981).

0564 Watkinson, S.; Moores, B.M.; Hill, S.J. Reject analysis: its role quality assurance. Radiography, 50(593):p189-94, (Sept.-Oct. 1984).

0565 Watkinson, S.; Shaw, M.; Moores, B.M.; Eddleston, E. Quality assurance: a practical programme. Radiography, 49(578):p27-32, (Feb. 1983).

0566 Webster, H.J. Quality assurance in the central service department. Hosp. Adm. Can., 18(1):p16-8, (Jan. 1976).

0567 Weiner, J.P.; Gibson, G.; Munster, A.M. Use of prophylactic antibiotics in surgical procedures: peer review guidelines as a method for quality assurance. Am. J. Surg. , 139(3):p348-51, (Mar. 1980).

0568 Wenz, B.; Dugan, E.P. The quality assurance of antiglobulin reactions with Fab-sensitized reagent red blood cells. Transfusion, 21(1):p50-4, (Jan.-Feb. 1981).

0569 West, J.G. An autopsy method for evaluating trauma care. J. Trauma, 21(1):p32-4, (Jan. 1981).

0570 West, W.G.; Freudenstein, C.S. A quality assurance program for central supply. Hosp. Top., 59(1):p33-8, (Jan.-Feb. 1981).

0571 Westfall, U.E. Nursing diagnosis: its use in quality assurance. Top Clin. Nurs., 5(4):p78-88, (Jan. 1984).

0572 Wheeler, P.S. Risk prevention, quality assurance, and the missed diagnosis conference. Radiology, 145(1): p227-8, (Oct. 1982).

0573 Whitcomb, J.E.; Stueven, H.; Tonsfeldt, D.; Kastenson, G. Quality assurance in the emergency department. Ann. Emerg. Med., 14(12):p1199-204, (Dec. 1985).

0574 White, S.J.; Godwin, H.N. A unit dose quality assurance program. Hosp. Pharm., 12(2):p90-6, (Feb. 1977).

0575 Williamson, J.W.; Greenfield, S.; Van Andel, H.; Torr, S. Are portable analysers incompatible with quality assurance? Quality assurance in The Netherlands: Part 2. An evaluation of the CBO peer review experience in hospital care. Aust. Clin. Rev., 6(20):p4-8, (Mar. 1986).

0576 Willis, R. Setting up quality assurance in a private hospital. Aust. Clin. Rev., (9):p29-34, (Jun. 1983).

0577 Wolfe, P.C.; Haveliwala, Y. A model for program evaluation in a unitized setting. Hosp. Community Psychiatry, 27(9):p647-9, (Sep. 1976).

0578 Wolter, J.M. Quality assurance in a cooperative group. Cancer Treat. Rep., 69(10):p1189-93, (Oct. 1985).

0579 Wong, W.T. Quality assurance in surgical practice through auditing. Am. J. Surg., 139(5):p669-72, (May 1980).

0580 Yaffe, R. Analyzing hospital discharge data to support utilization review and quality assurance activities. Top. Health Rec. Manage., 2(3):p31-44, (Mar. 1982).

0581 Zalar, R.W.; Houston-Screnzel, D. A quality assurance plan for an ambulatory care department. J. Ambulatory Care Manage., 5(3):p64-9, (Aug. 1982).

0582 Zambito, R.F. Quality assurance of hospital dental care: the hospital and quality of care. J. Hosp. Dent. Pract., 14(2):p80-4, (2nd Qrt. 1980).

0583 Zelonis, A.; Fleischer, N.; Walling, R. A pharmacy quality assurance program. Hosp. Formul., 14(2):p205, 208-9,211, (Feb. 1979).

0584 Zimble, J.A. Credentialing within the quality assurance structure. The approach implemented at the Naval Regional Medical Center, Orlando (interview by Barbara Wendorf). QRB, 6(5):p10-5, (May 1980).

0585 Zimmer, J.G. Areawide quality assurance studies in long term care facilities. QRB, 8(7):p2-6, (Jul. 1982).

Research: Studies and Data

0586 Alaszewski, A. The situation of nursing administrators in hospitals for the mentally handicapped: problems in measuring and evaluating the quality of care. Soc. Sci. Med., 12(2A):p91-7, (Mar. 1978).

0587 Aldhizer, T.G.; Solle, M.M.; Bohrer, R.O. A multidisciplinary audit of diabetes mellitus. J. Fam. Pract., 8(5):p947-51, (May 1979).

0588 Allanach, E.J.; Allanach, B.C. Diabetes teaching follow up compliance: a quality assurance evaluation. Milit. Med., 149(2):p73-5, (Feb. 1984).

0589 Anderson, D.; Legator, M.S. Practical issues in the evaluation of monitoring techniques: need for validation, quality assurance and establishment of baseline levels. IARC Sci. Publ., (59):p431-3, (1984).

0590 Armenian, H.K.; Dajani, A.W.; Fakhro, A.M. Impact of peer review and itemized records on care in a health center in Bahrain. QRB, 7(9):p6-11, (Sep. 1981).

0591 Bailey, P.E. Hematology quality assurance: the RCPA survey compared with a survey using fresh blood [letter]. Pathology, 17(4):p659-60, (Oct. 1985).

0592 Bailit, H.L. Quality assurance: the research perspective. J. Conn. State Dent. Assoc., 54(1):p4-6, (Winter 1980).

0593 Baughman, B.B.; Knutson, C.O.; Ahmad, W.; Jones, C.E.; Polk, H.C., Jr. The surgical treatment of carcinoma of the colon and rectum: an index of quality care and sociologic and geographic distribution. Ann. Surg., 183(5):p550-5, (May 1976).

0594 Bays, C.W. Case-mix differences between nonprofit and for-profit hospitals. Inquiry, 14(1):p17-21, (Mar. 1977).

0595 Becker-Gaab, C.; Borcke, E.; Bunde, E.; Hagemann, G.;
Kutterer, G.; Lang, G.R.; Schofer, H.; Stender, H.S.;
Stieve, I..E.; von Volkmann, T.; et al. [Image quality
assurance in x-ray diagnostic units. Information on DIN
6868 standard series]. Radiologe., 25(11):p529-33, (Nov.
1985).

0596 Beghi, E.; Sasanelli, F.; Spagnoli, A.; Tognoni, G.
Quality of care of epilepsy in Italy: multi-hospital
survey of diagnosis and treatment of 1104 epileptic
patients. Epilepsia, 23(2):p133-48, (Apr. 1982).

0597 Berbatis, C.G.; Eckert, G.M.; Neale, F.G.; Rothwell,
J.P. Quality assurance of drug therapy in hospitals:
patient serum creatinine values used by ward pharmacists
in checking dosage regimens. Med. J. Aust., 1(2):p46-7,
(Jan. 27, 1979).

0598 Bernard-Stevens, J.; Gust, W.F.; Moore, G.; Zetterman,
R. Monitoring quality of care in urban and rural medical
centers in Nebraska. Nebr. Med. J., 67(5):p124-6, (May
1982).

0599 Blumberg, M.S.; Gentry, D.W. Routine hospital charges
and intensity of care: a cross-section analysis of fifty
states. Inquiry, 15(1):p58-73, (Mar. 1978).

0600 Brazil, A. Quality assurance anecdotes: it's a great
life, if you don't weaken. Tex. Hosp., 35(11):p36, (Apr.
1980).

0601 Brenner, L.H.; Jessee, W.F. Delays in diagnosis: a
problem for quality assurance. QRB, 9(11):p337-44, (Nov.
1983).

0602 Brook, R.H.; Williams, K.N.; Rolph, J.E. Use, costs, and
quality of medical services: impact of the New Mexico
peer review system. A 1971-1975 study. Ann. Intern.
Med., 89(2):p256-63, (Aug. 1978).

0603 Brunner, M.A. Op-Site: research or quality assurance
study? Orthop. Nurs., 2(5):p37,56, (Sep-Oct. 1983).

0604 Buchner, H. [Quality assurance in roentgen tomography.
Initial report on a sectional phantom assembly for all
parameters]. ROFO. 141(4):p453-9, (Oct. 1984).

0605 Burkle, W.S.; Matzke, G.R.; Lucarotti, R.L. Development
of competency standards for quality assurance in clinical
pharmacokinetics. Hosp. Pharm., 15(10):p494-6, (Oct.
1980).

0606 Chambers, L.W.; Bruce-Lockhart, P.; Black, D.P.; Sampson, E.; Burke, M. A controlled trial of the impact of the family practice nurse on volume, quality, and cost of rural health services. Med. Care, 15(12):p971-81, (Dec. 1977).

0607 Chase, R.S.; Burg, F.D. Reexamination/recertification: measurement of professional competence and relation to quality of medical care. Arch. Surg., 112(1k0):p19-25, (Jan. 1977).

0608 Chassin, M.R.; McCue, S.M. A randomized trial of medical quality assurance. Improving physicians' use of pelvimetry. JAMA, 256(8):p1012-6, (Aug. 22-29, 1986).

0609 Cohen, M.R. Discrepancies in unit dose cart fills. Hosp. Pharm., 15(1):p17-9, (Jan. 1980).

0610 Comparison of hospitals with regard to outcomes of surgery. Health Serv. Res., 11(2):p112-27, (Summer 1976).

0611 Compton, P.J.; Stuart, M.C.; Lazarus, L. Error in laboratory reference limits as shown in a collaborative quality-assurance program. Clin. Chem., 32(5):p845-9, (May 1986).

0612 de Almeida, C.E.; Cecatti, E.R. Quality assurance in radiation therapy: clinical and physical aspects. Teletherapy equipment and simulators. Int. J. Radiat. Oncol. Biol. Phys., 10 Suppl. 1:p99-103, (Jun. 1984).

0613 Detmer, D.E.; Moylan, J.A.; Rose, J.; Schulz, R.; Wallace, R.; Daly, R. Regional categorization and quality of care in major trauma. J. Trauma, 17(8):p592-9, (Aug. 1977).

0614 Didonato, K. Quality assurance. High-dose, short-term steroid therapy (40 days). Cancer Nurs., 7(3):p251-5, (Jun. 1984).

0615 DiSilvio, T.V.; Lawson, N.S.; Haven, G.T.; Gilmore, B.F. Stability of mean assay values of magnesium and iron in lyophilized quality control serum: a study based on data from the quality assurance service (QAS) of the College of American Pathologists. Am. J. Clin. Pathol., 80(4 Suppl.):p563-9, (Oct. 1983).

0616 Distel, L. A nursing quality assurance investigation of orthopedic patient care. QRB, 8(10):p20-2, (Oct. 1982).

0617 Donofrio, N.M., Jr.; Hanson, J.A.; Hirsch, J.H.; Moore, W.E. Investigating the efficacy of current quality assurance performance tests in diagnostic ultrasound. JCO, 12(5):p251-60, (Jun. 1984).

0618 Doss, H.L.; James, J.D.; Killough, D.M.; Snodgrass, G.L. Microbiologic quality assurance for intravenous admixtures in a small hospital. Am. J. Hosp. Pharm., 39(5):p832-5, (May 1982).

0619 Duff, R.S.; Cook, C.D.; Margolis, C.Z.; Lattanzi, W.E.; Landwirth, J. A review of pediatric inpatient care. Am. J. Dis. Child, 129(12):p1422-4, (Dec. 1975).

0620 Dwyer, J.; Fitch, F.R.; Doolan, P.T.; Dwyer, V.M.; Halls, N.A.; Tallentire, A. Towards microbiological quality assurance in radiation sterilization processing: the limiting case model appli@d to a microbial population having a distribution of radiation responses. J. Appl. Bacteriol., 59(2):p189-94, (Aug. 1985).

0621 Eastaugh, S.R. Limitations on quality assurance effectiveness: Improving psychiatric inpatient drug prescribing habits of physicians. J. Med. Syst., 4(1):p27-43, (1980).

0622 Eckelman, W.C.; Herrara, N.E.; Hauser, W. Radiopharmaceutical quality assurance--pilot study [letter]. J. Nucl. Med., 22(1):p94, (Jan. 1981).

0623 Eder, H.; Schofer, H. [A constancy test for quality assurance of x-ray film including film processing]. Ein Konstanztest zur Qualitatssicherung in der Rontgen-Aufnahmetechnik einschliesslich der Filmverarbeitung. Rontgenpraxis, 38(1):p22-9, (Jan@ 1985).

0624 Eichhorn, M.L.; Frevert, E.I. Evaluation of a primary nursing system using the quality patient care scale. J. Nurs. Adm., 9(10):p11-5, (Oct. 1979).

0625 Escovitz, G.H.; Burkett, G.L.; Kuhn, J.C.; Zeleznik, C.; Gonnella, J.S. The effects of mandatory quality assurance: a review of hospital medical audit processes. Med. Care, 16(11):p941-9, (Nov. 1978).

0626 Farman, A.G.; Hines, V.G. Radiation safety and quality assurance in North American dental schools. J. Dent. Educ., 50(6):p304-8, (Jun. 1986).

0627 Feigenson, J.S.: Feigenson, W.D.; Gitlow, H.S.; McCarthy, M.L.; Greenberg, S.D. Outcome and cost for stroke patients in academic and community hospitals. Comparison of two groups referred to a regional rehabilitation center. JAMA. 240(17):p1878-80, (Oct. 20, 1978).

0628 Feller, I.; Tholen, D.; Cornell, R.G. Improvements in burn care, 1965 to 1979. JAMA, 244(18):p2074-8, (Nov. 7, 1980).

0629 Fernow, L.C.; Mackie, C.; McColl, I.; Rendall, M. The effect of problem-oriented medical records on clinical management controlled for patient risks. Med. Care, 16(6):p476-87, (Jun. 1978).

0630 Fernow, L.C.; McColl, I.; Thurlow, S.C. Measuring the quality of clinical performance with hernia and myocardial infarction patients, controlling for patient risks. Med. Care, 19(3):p273-80, (Mar. 1981).

0631 Finkelstein, S.M.; Budd, J.R.; Ewing, L.B.; Wielinski, C.L.; Warwick, W.J.; Kujawa, S.J. Data quality assurance for a health monitoring program. Methods Inf. Med., 24(4):p192-6, (Oct. 1985).

0632 Forehand, J.M. Nursing quality assurance study of code blue drills. QRB, 10(4):p117-9, (Apr. 1984).

0633 Garb, J.L.; Brown, R.B.; Garb, J.R.; Tuthill, R.W. Differences in etiology of pneumonias in nursing home and community patients. JAMA, 240(20):p2169-72, (Nov. 10, 1978).

0634 Garrell, M.; Jekel, J.F. A comparison of quality of care on a teaching and non-teaching service in a university affiliated community hospital. Conn. Med., 43(10):p659-63, (Oct. 1979).

0635 Gerstein, J. Refining a study design to assess delays in reporting radiologic test results. QRB, 6(12):p16-20, (Dec. 1980).

0636 Glaser, S.M.; Dehn, T.G. Reject film study. Cost and quality considerations in a radiology department. QRB, 6(6):p19-22, (Jun. 1980).

0637 Glicksman, A.S.; Reinstein, L.E.; Laurie, F. Quality assurance of radiotherapy in clinical trials. Cancer Treat. Rep., 69(10):p1199-205, (Oct. 1985).

0638 Greenstein, M. First-hand account. Quality assurance experiences in a State psychiatric facility. QRB, 3(7):p28,31, (Jul. 1977).

0639 Grundmann, R.; Salamon, C.; Weber, F. [Quality assurance in general surgery by prospective patient documentation. A comparison over 5 years]. Zentralbl. Chir., 111(5):p252-60, (1986).

0640 Hagemann, G. [Technical controls with test objects for quality assurance of x-ray diagnostic equipment]. Technische Kontrollen mit Prufkorpern zur Qualitatssicherung von Rontgendiagnostikanlagen. Fortschr. Geb. Rontgenstr. Nuklearmed. Erganzungsband., 123:p138-55, (1985).

0641 Hanks, G.E.; Kramer, S. Quality assurance in radiation therapy: clinical and physical aspects. Consensus of best current management: The starting point of clinical quality assessment. Int. J. Radiat. Oncol. Biol. Phys., 10 Suppl. 1:p87-97, (Jun. 1984).

0642 Hardy, M.E. Implementation of unit management and clinical nurse specialists: patients' perception of the quality of general hospital care and nursing care. Commun. Nurs. Res., 8:p325-35, (Mar. 1977).

0643 Hart, G.C. Moire interference in gamma camera quality assurance images. J. Nucl. Med., 27(6):p820-3, (Jun. 1986).

0644 Hassenstein, E.; Nusslin, F. [Medical and physical aspects of quality assurance in radio-oncology]. Strahlentherapie, 161(11):p685-93, (Nov. 1985).

0645 Hayes, D.M. Perceptions of cancer care by professionals and nonprofessionals. Eval. Health Prof., 1(3):p29-56, (Oct. 1978).

0646 Hegedus, K.S.; Bourdon, S.M. On the scene: Beth Israel Hospital. Evaluation research: a quality assurance program. Nurs. Adm. Q., 5(3):p26-30, (Spring 1981).

0647 Hein, M.A. The quality of perinatal care in small rural hospitals. JAMA, 240(19):p2070-2, (Nov. 3, 1978).

0648 Herrmann, F.; Heuerburg-Heusler, D.; Nissen, P. [Statistical principles for the validation of diagnostic procEdures. A contribution to quality assurance exemplified by Doppler sonography]. Ultraschall. Med., 7(2):p52-69, (Apr. 1986).

0649 Heuwer, K.: Laurinat, H. [Quality assurance of medical and nursing functions in the health service. 1. International training course in Barcelona]. Krankenpflege, 39(7-8):p238-4, (Jul-Aug. 1985).

0650 Hokanson, J.A.; Guernsey, B.G.; Bryant, S.G.; Doutre, W.H.; Ingrim, N.B.; Grant, J.A.; Galvan, E. The feasibility of barcode-based dispensing quality assurance programs. Drug Intell. Clin. Pharm., 18(1):p76-8, (Jan. 1984).

0651 Horder, M. Selection and quality assurance of tests in multicenter trials. Scand. J. Clin. Lab. Invest. [Suppl.], 179:p51-6, (1985).

0652 Horn, S.D.; Pozen, M.W. An interpretation of implicit judgments in chart review. J. Community Health, 2(4):p251-8, (Summer 1977).

0653 Howanitz, P.J.; McBride, J.H.; Kliewer, K.E.; Rodgerson, D.O. Prevalence of antibodies to HTLV-III in quality-assurance sera. Clin. Chem., 32(5):p773-7, (May 1986).

0654 Inui, T.S.; Hill, T.A.; Leiby, G.M. Hospital screening for tuberculosis: a quality assurance trial. Med. Care, 17(4):p347-54, (Apr. 1979).

0655 Julien, J.Y.; Barbeau, G. Pharmacological analysis of patient's charts in a long-term care hospital. Can. J. Hosp. Pharm., 34(2):p42-6, (Mar-Apr. 1981).

0656 Keywood, D. The effects of an integrated service on standards of health care. Nurs. Mirror, 143(15):p63-6 contd, (Oct. 7, 1976).

0657 Kirchman, M.M. The quality of care in occupational therapy: an assessment of selected Michigan hospitals. AJOT, 33(7):p425-31, (Jul. 1979).

0658 Kirkegaard, L.H.; Fout, R.E. Reactivity per unit weight: an important parameter in the quality assurance of antibody reagents for vaccine analysis. Dev. Biol. Stand., 59:p185-8, (1985).

0659 Knowles, R.C.; Gilmore, B. Quality control of agar diffusion susceptibility tests: data from the Quality Assurance Service Microbiology program of the College of American Pathologists. Am. J. Clin. Pathol., 80(4 Suppl.):p603-8, (Oct. 1983).

0660 Knowles, R.C.; Gilmore, B.F. Quality control of agar diffusion susceptibility tests. Data from the Quality Assurance Service Microbiology Program of the College of American Pathologists. Am. J. Clin. Pathol., 76(4 Suppl):p590-6, (Oct. 1981).

0661 Knowles, R.C.; Moore, T.D. Quality control of agar diffusion susceptibility tests. Data from the Quality Assurance Service Microbiology Program of the College of American Pathologist. Am. J. Clin. Pathol., 74(4 Suppl):p581-5, (Oct. 1980).

0662 Koepke, J.A.; Protextor, T.J. Quality assurance for multichannel hematology instruments. Four years' experience with patient mean erythrocyte indices. Am. J. Clin. Pathol., 75(1):p28-33, (Jan. 1981).

0663 Kresky, B.; Mangano, L. Study of drug overdose patients in an emergency department. QRB, 6(7):p15-8, (Jul. 1980.

0664 Landsberg, G. Quality assurance activities in community mental health centers: changes over time. Community Ment. Health J., 21(3):p189-97, (Fall 1985).

0665 Lasky, L.C.; Lin, A.; Kahn, R.A.; McCullough, J. Donor platelet response and product quality assurance in plateletpheresis. Transfusion, 21(3):p247-60, (May-Jun. 1981).

0666 Lawson, N.S.; Haven, G.T.; DiSilvio, T.V.; Gilmore, B.F. Glucose stability in lyophilized chemistry quality control serum. A study of data from the quality assurance service (QAS) program of the College of American Pathologists. Am. J. Clin. Pathol., 78(4 Suppl):p597-606, (Oct. 1982).

0667 Lawson, N.S.; Haven, G.T.; DiSilvio, T.V.; Gilmore, B.F. Stability of sodium and potassium in lyophilized quality control serum. A study of data from the Quality Assurance Service Program of the College of American Pathologists. Am. J. Clin. Pathol., 76(4 Suppl):p581-9, (Oct. 1981).

0668 Levy, R.; Goldstein, B.; Trott, A. Approach to quality assurance in an emergency department: one-year review. 13(3):p166-9, (Mar. 1984).

0669 Lindsay, M.I., Jr.; Nobrega, F.T.; Offord, K.P.; Carter, E.T.; Rutherford, B.D.; Kennel, A.J.; Mankin, H.T. Quality-of-care assessment. II. Outpatient medical care following hospital dismissal after myocardial infarction. Mayo. Clin. Proc., 52(4):p220-7, (Apr. 1977).

0670 Linn, B.S. Burn patients' evaluation of emergency department care. Ann. Emerg. Med., 11(5):p255-9, (May 1982).

0671 Littbrand, B. Quality assurance in radiation therapy: multidisciplinary considerations--European experience. Int. J. Radiat. Uncol. Biol. Phys., 10 Suppl. 1:p67-, (Jun. 1984).

0672 Locker, D.; Dunt, D. Theoretical and methodological issues in sociological studies of consumer satisfaction with medical care. Soc. Sci. Med., 12(4A):p283-92, (Jul. 1978).

0673 Lohr, K.N.; Brook, R.H. Quality assurance and clinical pharmacy: lessons from medicine. Drug Intell. Clin. Pharm., 15(10):p758-65, (Oct. 1981).

0674 Longest, B.B., Jr. An empirical analysis of the quality/ cost relationship. Hosp. Health Serv. Adm., 23(4):p20-35, (Fall 1978).

0675 Lutz, W.R.; Maddox, B.J.; Kase, K.R. Daily check instrument for photon and electron beam quality assurance of medical linacs. Med. Phys., 12(4):p462-5, (Jul-Aug. 1985).

0676 Lyons, T.F.; Payne, B.C. Interdiagnosis relationships of physician performance measures in hospitals. Med. Care, 15(6):p475-81, (Jun. 1977).

0677 Mannisto, M. An assessment of productivity in health care. Hospitals, 54(18):p71-6, (Sep. 16, 1980).

0678 Marks, S.D.; Greenlick, M.R.; Hurtado, A.V.; Johnson, J.D.; Henderson, J. Ambulatory surgery in an HMO. A study of costs, quality of care and satisfaction. Med. Care, 18(2):p127-46, (Feb. 1980).

0679 Marriner, A. The research process in quality assurance. Am. J. Nurs., 79(12):p2158-61, (Dec. 1979).

0680 Martini, C.J.; Allan, G.H.; Davison, J.; Backett, E.M. Health indexes sensitive to medical care variation. Int. J. Health Serv., 7(2):p293-309, (1977).

0681 McAuliffe, W.E. On the statistical validity of standards used in profile monitoring of health care. Am. J. Public Health, 68(7):p645-51, (Ju 1978).

0682 McMillin, B.A.; Jasmund, J.M. A quality assurance study of height and weight measurements. QRB, 11(2):p53-7, (Feb. 1985).

0683 Miller, M.B.; Elliott, D.F. Errors and omissions in diagnostic records on admission of patients to a nursing home. J. Am. Geriatr. Soc., 24(3):p108-16, (Mar. 1976).

0684 Miller, P.L.; Berry, T.J. Use of computers in studying quality of care. QRB, 6(5):p25-9, (May 1980).

0685 Miller, T.W.; Lee, L.T. Quality assurance: focus on environmental perceptions of psychiatric patients and nursing staff. J. Psychiatr. Nurs., 18(12):p9-14, (Dec. 1980).

0686 Molzahn-Yanitski, A.E. Reliability and validity of a quality assurance instrument for a renal dialysis unit. Nephrol. nurse, 5(6):p8-12, (Nov-Dec. 1983).

0687 Moore, K. Quality assurance & nursing audit: are they effective? Nurs. Manage., 13(2):p18-22, (Feb. 1982).

0688 Mossel, D.A.; Bonants-Van Laarhoven, T.M.; Ligtenberg-Merkus, A.M.; Werdler, M.E. Quality assurance of selective culture media for bacteria, moulds and yeasts: an attempt at standardization at the international level. J. Appl. Bacteriol., 54(3):p313-27, (Jun. 1983).

0689 Munyworki, S.; Shimoni, M.; Hyndman, G. Satisfaction among outpatients visiting four health units in Kiambu District, Kenya. East Afr. Med. J., 52(6):p306-18, (Jun. 1975).

0690 Nakamura, R.M.; Rippey, J.H. Quality assurance and proficiency testing for autoantibodies to nuclear antigen. Arch. Pathol. Lab. Med., 109(2):p109-14, (Feb. 1985).

0691 Nelson-Wernick, E.; Currey, H.S.; Taylor, P.W.; Woodbury, M.; Cantor, A. Patient perception of medical care. Health Care Manage. Rev., 6(1):p65-72, (Winter 1981).

0692 Nelson, E.C.; Kirk, J.W.; Bise, B.W.; Chapman, R.J.; Hale, F.A.; Stamps, P.L.; Wasson, J.H. The cooperative information project: Part 2: some initial clinical, quality assurance, and practice management studies. J. Fam. Pract., 13(6):p867-76, (Nov. 1981).

0693 Nowotny, R.; Rechtberger, W. A linear X-ray sensor for quality assurance measurements. Health Phys., 44(6):p682-4, (Jun. 1983).

0694 Oakley, R.S.; Bradham, D.D. Review of quality assurance in hospital pharmacy. Am. J. Hosp. Pharm., 40(1):p53-63, (Jan. 1983).

0695 Olin, P.; Bolme, P.; Ewert, G.; Lagerkvist, B.; Sterky, G.; Tengvald, K.; Zetterstrom, R. Quality of care: a tracer diagnosis study of acute otitis media, comparing a district paediatric service with paediatric and otolaryngology emergency departments. Acta Paediatr. Scand., 68(3):p305-13, (May 1979).

0696 Orden, S.R.; Collette, P.; Souchek, J.; Masover, L.; Stamler, J. Physician and patient assessment of ambulatory care in a University facility. J. Community Health, 4(1):p23-32, (Fall 1978).

0697 Ostrow, P.C.; Kuntavanish, A.A. Improving the utilization of occupational therapy: a quality assurance study. Am. J. Occup. Ther., 37(6):p388-91, (Jun. 1983).

0698 Oxley, D.K. Critical decisions in the clinical laboratory. Pathologist, 34(9):p458-60, (Sep. 1980).

0699 Palmer, R.H.; Louis, T.A.; Hsu, L.N.; Peterson, H.F.; Rothrock, J.K.; Strain, R.; Thompson, M.S.; Wright, E.A. Med. Care, 23(6):p751-70, (Jun. 1985).

0700 Palmer, R.H.; Reilly, M.C. Individual and institutional variables which may serve as indicators of quality of medical care. Med. Care, 17(7):p693-717, (Jul. 1979).

0701 Parente, R.; Anderson-Parente, J. Alternative research strategies for occupational therapy, Part 2: Ideographic and quality assurance research. Am. J. Occup. Ther., 40(6):p428-31, (Jun. 1986).

0702 Pascoe, D.W.; Wilson, A.; Worsfold, J.B. Patients' attitudes to health care: a literature review. World Hosp., 14(3):p165-70, (Aug. 1978).

0703 Perez, C.A.; Gardner, P.; Glasgow, G.P. Radiotherapy quality assurance in clinical trials. Int. J. Radiat. Oncol. Biol. Phys., 10 Suppl.:p119-25, (Jun. 1984).

0704 Ponto, J.A.; Ponto, L.L. Cost-effectiveness of routine radiochemical quality assurance testing of technitium Tc 99m radiopharmaceuticals. Am. J. Hosp. Pharm., 43(5):p1218-22, (May 1986).

0705 Potsaid, M.S.; Rhea, J.T.; Llewellyn, H.J.; Pfister, R.C.; Newhouse, J.H; Yoder, I.C. Quality assessment and assurance in diagnostic imaging. Theoretical and practical considerations and a quality audit of the excretory urogram. Radiology, 127(3):p583-8, (Jun. 1978).

0706 Presly, A.S.; Ballinger, B.R.; Fraser, D.; Lindsay, B.
An evaluation of the reduction in patient numbers in
psychogeriatric wards. Health Bull., 38(1):p32-6, (Jan.
1980).

0707 [Quality assurance in x-ray diagnosis. Criteria--
procedure--results]. Qualitatssicherung in der
Roetgendiagnostik. Kriterien--Verfahren--Ergebnisse.
Fortschr. Geb. Rontgenstr. Nuklearmed. Erganzungsband.,
123:p1-190, (1985).

0708 Racoveanu, N.T. [International survey of the status of
dosimetry for controlling quality assurance in
radiotherapy (WHO)]. Med. Radiol., 30(9):p71-4, (Sep.
1985).

0709 Raff, U.; Spitzer, V.M.; Hendee, W.R. Practicality of
NEMA performance specification measurements for
user-based acceptance testing and routine quality
assurance. J. Nucl. Med., 25(6):p679-87, (Jun. 1984).

0710 Raynes, N.V.; Pratt, M.W.; Roses, S. Aides' involvement
in decision-making and the quality of care in
institutional settings. Am. J. Ment. D@fic.,
81(6):p570-7, (May 1977).

0711 Reiners, C.; Moll, E. [Quality assurance in vitro
diagnosis in nuclear medicine]. Strahlenschutz
Forsch Prax, 27:p140-54, (1986).

0712 Rhee, S.O. Relative importance of physicans' personal
and situational characteristics for the quality of
patient care. J. Health Soc. Behav., 18(1):p10-5, (Mar.
1978).

0713 Rhee, S.O. Factors determining the quality of physician
performance in patient care. Med. Care, 14(9):p733-50,
(Sep. 1976).

0714 Rhee, S.O. U.S. medical graduates versus foreign medical
graduates. Are there performance differences in
practice? Med. Care, 15(7):p568-77, (Jul. 1977).

0715 Rhee, S.O.; Lyons, T.; Payne, B. Interrelationships of
physician performances: technical quality and
utilization and implications for quality and utilization
controls. Med. Care, 16(6):p496-501, (Jun. 1978).

0716 Rhee, S.O.; Lyons, T.F.; Payne, B.C. Patient race and
physician performances: quality of medical care,
hospital admissions and hospital stays. Med. Care,
17(7):p737-47, (Jul. 1979).

69

0717 Rifkin, M.; Lynne, C.; Williams, R.; Hilsenbeck, C. Managing quality assurance activities in a large teaching hospital. QRB. 7(8):27-32, (Aug. 1981).

0718 Roake, J.A.; Morton, J. Acute appendicitis: a quality assurance analysis. NZ Med. J., 96(742):p788-90, (Oct. 26, 1983).

0719 Rosenberg, thw. Professional productivity and quality assurance phases II-V. JACEP, 6(7):p286-95, (Jul. 1977).

0720 Roy, A.; Looney, G.L.; Anderson, G.V. Prospective vs. retrospective data for evaluating emergency care: a research methodology. JACEP, 8(4):p142-6, (Apr. 1979).

0721 Sanazaro, P.J.; Worth, R.M. Concurrent quality assurance in hospital care. Report of a study by Private Initiative in PSRO. N. Engl. J. Med., 298(21):p1171-7, (May 25, 1978).

0722 Schmall, B.; Conti, P.S.; Bigler, R.E.; Zanzonico, P.B.; Dahl, J.R.; Sundoro-Wu, B.M.; Jacobsen, J.K.; Lee, R. Synthesis and quality assurance of [11C] alpha-aminoisobutyric acid (ATB), a potential radiotracer for imaging and amino acid transport studies in normal and malignant tissues. Int. J. Nucl. Med. Biol., 11(3-4):p209-14, (1984).

0723 Schwing, C. [Diagnostic error using ultrasound. Potential risks caused by deficient quality assurance by the manufacturer]. Fehldiagnose per Ultraschall. Potentielle Risiken durch mangelhafte Qualitatssicherung der Hersteller. Fortschr. Med., 103(14):p82-3, (Apr. 11, 1985).

0724 Segovia, J. Institutional outpatient clinics: a case study in unmet needs. Med. Care, 17(3):p255-66, (Mar. 1979).

0725 Selbmann, H.B.; Warncke, W.; Eissner, H.J. Comparison of hospitals supporting quality assurance. Methods Inf. Med., 21(2):p75-80, (Apr. 1982).

0726 Shaughnessy, P.W.; Breed, L.D.; Landes, D.P. Assessing the quality of care provided in rural swing bed hospitals. QRB, 8(5):p12-20, (May 1982).

0727 Shortell, S.M.; LoGerfo, J.P. Hospital medical staff organization and quality of care: results for myocardial infarction and appendectomy. Med. Care, 19(10):p1041-55, (Oct. 1981).

0728 Sinclair, C.; Frankel, M. The effect of quality assurance activities on the quality of mental health services. QRB, 8(7):p7-15, (Jul. 1982).

0729 Smith, M.K.; Fullen, D. Quality assurance audit: sodium-restricted menus. J. Am. Diet. Assoc., 85(10):p1320-1, (Oct. 1985).

0730 Soroker, E.P. An analysis of pediatric outpatient care. Health Soc. Work, 2(2):p89-103, (May 1977).

0731 Spector, R.; McGrath, P.; Alpert, J.; Cohen, P.; Aikins, H. Medical care by nurses in an internal medicine clinic. Analysis of quality and its cost. JAMA, 232(12):p1234-7, (Jun. 23, 1975).

0732 Spivak, H.R.; Levy, J.C.; Bonanno, R.A.; Cracknell, M. Patient and provider factors associated with selected measures of quality of care. Pediatrics, 62(2):p307-13, (Feb. 1980).

0733 Stewart, J.E. The effect of quality assurance efforts on patient care. Top Hosp. Pharm. Manage., 1(3):p11-21, (Nov. 1981).

0734 Strain, R.; Palmer, R.H.; Maurer, J.V.; Lyons, L.A.; Thompson, M.S. Implementing quality assurance studies in ambulatory care. QRB, 10(6):p168-73, (Jun. 1984).

0735 Thomas, T. Quality assurance anecdotes: quality accountability at Flow Memorial Hospital. Tex. Hosp., 36(4):p12-3, (Sep. 1980).

0736 Tracy, R.P.; Currie, R.M.; Young, D.S. Reproducibility and quality assurance of two-dimensional gel electrophoresis of serum specimens. Clin. Chem., 28 (4 Pt 2):p908-14, (Apr. 1982).

0737 Treatment outlines for the management of schizophrenia. The Quality Assurance Project. Aust. NZ J. Psychiatry, 18(1):p19-38, (Mar. 1984).

0738 Treatment outlines for the management of the somatoform disorders. The Quality Assurance Project. Aust. NZ J. Psychiatry, 19(4):p397-407, (Dec. 1985).

0739 Treatment outlines for the management of anxiety states. The Quality Assurance Project. Aust. NZ J. Psychiatry, 19(2):p138-51, (Jun. 1985).

0740 Truscott, B.L.; Kretschmann, C.M.; Toole, J.F.; Pajak, T.F. Early rehabilitative care in community hospitals: effect on quality of survivorship following a stroke. Stroke, 5(5):p623-9, (Sep-Oct. 1974).

0741 VA launches study of 'multi-level' care. US Med.,
      14(9):p1-7, (May 1, 1978).

0742 van der Voorde, F.; van der Snoek, J.A.; Reerink, E. A
      quality assurance study of the barium enema: report from
      a hospital in The Netherlands. QRB, 7(2):p10-3, (Feb.
      1981).

0743 Vanloh, S.W.; Stanges, M.T.; Cohen, R. Assessing the
      performance of hospital support services. Hospitals,
      52(15):p163-4,166, (Aug. 1, 1978).

0744 Vasey, E.K. Evaluation of care in the emergency
      department. A comparison of process and outcome
      criteria. QRB, 2(9):p12,27, (Sep. 1976).

0745 Vik, A.G.; MacKay, R.C. How does the 12-hour shift
      affect patient care? J. Nurs. Adm., 12(1):p11-4, (Jan.
      1982).

0746 Votava, K.M.; Cleveland, T.; Hiltunen, K. Home care of
      the patient dependent on mechanical ventilation: home
      care policy development and goal setting using outcome
      criteria for quality assurance. Home Healthc. Nurse,
      3(2):p18-25, (Mar-Apr. 1985).

0747 Wagner, P.L.; Stapleton, J.A.; Stein, R.; Wadina, C.
      Care of the child with fever: a quality assurance study.
      QRB, 10(10):p325-30, (Oct. 1984).

0748 Wasserman, B.S. Auditing oral health care in a teaching
      hospital. J. Hosp. Dent. Pract., 13(1):p17-23, (1979).

0749 Watkinson, L.R.; Fraser, C.G. An inter-laboratory
      quality-assurance survey of emergency clinical
      biochemistry tests. Ann. Clin. Biochem., 21(Pt
      6):p494-7, (Nov. 1984).

0750 Welker, K. [Quality assurance in dosage calculations
      with computers]. Zu Fragen der Qualitatssicherung bei
      der Dosisberechung mit Computern.
      Radiobiol. Radiother. (Berl), 25(6):p839-45, (1984).

0751 Wendorf, B. In the forefront: analysis of problems
      chosen for review by support services. QRB, 6(4):p13-4,
      (Apr. 1980).

0752 Werman, D.S.; Agle, D.; McDaniel, E.; Schoof, K.G.
      Survey of psychiatric treatment effectiveness in a
      medical student clinic. Am. J. Psychother.,
      30(2):p294-302, (Apr. 1976).

0753 Westermeyer, J.; Doheny, S.; Stone, B. An assessment of
      hospital care for the alcoholic patient. Alcoholism,
      2(1):p53-7, (Jan. 1978).

0754 Whitehead, M.E.; Fitzwater, J.E.; Lindley, S.K.; Kern,
      S.B.; Ulirsch, R.C.; Winecoff, W.F. III. Three thousand
      cases. Am. J. Clin. Pathol., 81(4):p487-91, (Apr. 1984).

0755 Whitehead, M.E.; Grieve, J.H.; Payne, M.J.; Ross, M.S.
      Quality assurance of histopathologic diagnosis in the
      British Army: role of the Army Histopathology Registry
      in completed case review. J. R. Army Med. Corps,
      132(2):p71-5, (Jun. 1986).

0756 Williamson, J.W.; Braswell, H.R.; Horn, S.D. Validity of
      medical staff judgments in establishing quality assurance
      priorities. Med. Care, 17(4):p331-46, (Apr. 1979).

0757 Williamson, J.W.; Greenfield, S.; van Andel, H.; Torr,
      S. Quality assurance in The Netherlands: Part 1. An
      evaluation of the CBO peer review experience in hospital
      care. Aust. Clin. Rev., 5(19):p160-7, (Dec. 1985).

0758 Willis, R.W. A quality assurance study of one hospital's
      approach to bereavement management. Bull. Am. Protestant
      Hosp. Assoc., 41(2):p50-5, (1977).

0759 Wilner, S.; Schoenbaum, S.C.; Monson, R.R.; Winickoff,
      R.N. A comparison of the quality of maternity care
      between a health-maintenance organization and
      fee-for-service practices. N. Engl. J. Med.,
      304(13):p784-7, (Mar. 26, 1981).

0760 Wilson, J.F.; Marshall, R.W.; Williams, J.; Richens, A.
      Accuracy and precision of gas-liquid chromatographic,
      high-pressure liquid chromatographic and enzyme
      immunoassay techniques for the measurement of
      theophylline concentrations in serum: a comparison based
      on external quality assurance measurements.
      Ther. Drug Monit., 6(2):p243-50, (1984).

0761 Windsor, R.A. Improving patient-education assessment
      skills of hospital staff: a case study in diabetes.
      Patient Couns. Health Educ., 3(10):p26-9, (1st Quarter
      1981).

0762 Winialski, N. Multidisciplinary alcoholism audit covers
      acute, O.P. care. Hosp. Peer Rev., 3(10):p135-7, (Oct.
      1978).

0763 Wolinsky, H. Trouble at Eagle Butte. Am. Med. News,
      23(37):p3,5-6 Suppl., (Sep. 1980).

0764 Zimmer, J.G. Areawide quality assurance studies in long
      term care facilities. QRB, 8(7):p2-6, (Jul. 1982).

0765 Zoebelein, E.; Levy, M.; Greenwald, R.A. The effect of
      quality assurance review on implementation of an
      automatic stop-order policy. QRB, 8(8):p12-7, (Aug.
      1982).

Management

0766 A management-information system can assure a successful
      QA program. Hosp. Peer Rev., 6(9):p103-5, (Sep. 1981).

0767 Aduddell, P.A.; Weeks, L.C. A cost-effective approach to
      quality assurance. Nurs. Econ. 2(4):p279-82, (Jul-Aug.
      1984).

0768 Archambault, G.F. The legal liability when standards of
      quality are not met [editorial]. Hosp. Formul.,
      12(8):p544, (Aug. 1977).

0769 Austin, C.J.; Carter, H.S. Hospital information systems
      and quality assurance. Hosp. Health Serv. Adm.,
      26(5):p42-62, (Fall 1981).

0770 Baird, J. Quality circles may substantially improve
      hospital employees' morale. Mod. Health Care, 11(9):p70,
      72, 74, (Sep. 1981).

0771 Banner, M.T. Administrative reviews: pharmacy.
      Hospitals, 49(7):p137-40, (Apr. 1, 1975).

0772 Birkett, D.P. The medical director in the nursing home.
      Aged Care Serv. Rev., 2(3):p1, 14-23, (1980).

0773 Black, J.R. Organization development in health care.
      Quality assurance programs. J. Am. Podiatry Assoc.,
      73(10:p17-20, (Jan. 1983).

0774 Blaes, S.M. Hospital and staff: working together for
      quality patient care. J. Kans. Med. Soc.,
      81(11):p527-30, (Nov. 1980).

0775 Borden, L.P. Patient education and the quality assurance
      process. QRB, 11(4):p123-7, (Apr. 1985).

0776 Bradford, L.W. Quality assurance--considerations in the
      expression of professional evaluations from examinations
      [letter]. J. Forensic Sci., 30(4):p981-5, (Oct. 1985).

0777 Brazil, A. Quality assurance coordinator: what are the qualifications? Tex. Hosp., 35(9):p30-1, (Feb. 1980).

0778 Brazil, A. Cooperate to communicate. Tex. Hosp., 35(13):p46, (May 1980).

0779 Brook, R.H.; Davies-Avery, A. Trade-off between cost and quality in ambulatory care. QRB, 3(11):p4-7, (Nov. 1977).

0780 Brown, D.E. Concurrent review, prompt feedback forestall problems. Hosp. Peer Rev., 4(3):p35-7, (Mar. 1979).

0781 Chase, T.B. Quality assurance as a positive motivator. Radiol. Manage., 4(2):p16, (Mar. 1982).

0782 Chayet, N.L.; Reardon, T.M. Trouble in the medical staff: a practical guide to hospital initiated quality assurance. Am. J. Law Med., 7(3):p301-20, (Fall 1981).

0783 Clemenhagen, C. Obstacles in quality assurance activities [editorial]. Dimens. Health Serv., 62(5):p4-5, (May 1985).

0784 Clemenhagen, C.J. Quality assurance in the hospital--making it work. Can. Med. Assoc. J., 133(1):p17-9, (Jul. 1, 1985).

0785 Collins, P. Hospital aims quality assurance risk management education at staff. Hospitals, 55(11):p93-5, (Jun. 1, 1981).

0786 Communication encouraged to ensure quality in hospitals. Hosp. Peer Rev., 6(9):p108-11, (Sep. 1981).

0787 Couch, J.B. Hospital corporate liability for inadequate quality assurance in Pennsylvania. J. Leg. Med., 2(1):p14-46, (Oct. 1980).

0788 Cunningham, R.M., Jr. Quality patient care and the hospital trustee. QRB, 2(4):p3-10, (Apr. 1976).

0789 del Bueno, D. What employees can do: the educator's responsibility. Cross Ref. Manpower Educ. Careers, 7(1):p4-5, (Jan-Feb. 1977).

0790 Demby, N.A. Quality assurance and marketing. Dent. Clin. North Am., 29(3):p605-14, (Jul. 1985).

0791 Der Yuen, D. A large community hospital's experience with an obstetrics-gynecology risk management committee: quality assurance. Am. J. Obstet. Gynecol., 154(6):p1206-10, (Jun. 1986).

0792 Dietz, J.W.; Phillips, J.L. The quality assurance
      committee in the hospital structure. QRB, 6(1):p8-12,
      (Jan. 1980).

0793 Donabedian, A. Quality assurance: corporate
      responsibility for multihospital systems. QRB,
      12(1):p3-7, (Jan. 1986).

0794 Donovan, R.J., Jr.; Bader, B.S. The systems approach to
      patient safety: role of the medical staff. QRB,
      5(4):p16-20, (Apr. 1979).

0795 Don't get "one-year" by making the mistake of thinking
      that JCAH has "backed off." Second Opin. Health Care
      Issues, 2(6):p39-40, (Jun. 1981).

0796 Edwardson, S.R: Anderson, D.I. Hospital nurses'
      valuation of quality assurance. University of Minnesota
      School of Nursing, Minneapolis. 13(7-8):p33-9, (Ju@-Aug.
      1983).

0797 Elder, M.Q. Hospital/community relations: perceive,
      relate to the public. Hospitals, 50(7):109-10,113-6,
      (Apr. 1, 1976).

0798 Evenson, B.0. Teaching quality assurance. Nurse Educ.,
      5(2):p8-12, (Mar-Apr. 1980).

0799 Ferguson, C.G. Quality assurance--do you know the legal
      implications? Dimens. Health Serv., 61(11):p27-8, (Nov.
      1984).

0800 Ferguson, C.G. Quality assurance documentation--its
      legal disclosure rights. Dimens. Health Serv.,
      62(2):p27,46, (Feb. 1985).

0801 Fine, R.B. Conceptual perspectives on the organization
      design task and the quality assurance function.
      Nurs. Health Care, 7(2):p100-4, (Feb. 1986).

0802 Flensborg, P. For U.R. coordinators: expanding your
      role in quality assurance. Hosp. Peer Rev., 4(7):p97-8,
      (Jul. 1979).

0803 Foglesong, D.H. Using a quality assurance audit. The
      impact of a staff development offering on nursing
      Practice. J. Contin. Educ. Nurs., 14(6):p12-5, (Nov-Dec.
      1983).

0804 Fox, L.A. The quality assurance administrator: who will
      it be? Top Health Rec. Manage., 1(2):p1-3, (Dec. 1980).

0805 Frank, R.E. On the scene: Barnes Hospital. An
      administrator looks at circles. Nurs. Adm. Q,
      6(3):p27-30, (Spring 1982).

0806 Friend, G. Hospital inservice education: through the
      quality assurance program. Hosp. Top., 56(2):p10-12,
      (Mar-Apr. 1978).

0807 Friend, G. QA/RM program streamlines work, merges
      functions. Hosp. Peer Rev., 4(11):145-6, (Nov. 1979).

0808 Gardner, C. I.V. therapy quality assurance provides risk
      management. NITA, 8(3):p199-204, (May-Jun. 1985).

0809 Gardner, L.P. Coordinating quality assurance
      activities: one facility's experience with utilization
      review and audit. QRB, 4(6):p26, (Jun. 1978).

0810 Garrell, M. Malpractice, quality assurance, and
      continuing education: a linkage past due. Conn. Med.,
      45(3):p175-6, (Mar. 1981).

0811 Gaston, S.R. The role of leadership in the quality of
      fracture care. Bull. Am. Coll. Surg., 60(11):p16-23,
      (Nov. 1975).

0812 Gerber, R.L. Quality assurance in radiation therapy:
      clinical and physical aspects. Manpower requirements in
      training and certification of technologists and
      dosimetrists. Int. J. Radiat. Uncol. Biol. Phys., 10
      Suppl. 1:p127-30, (Jun. 1984).

0813 Goldberg, B.A. The duty of hospitals and hospital
      medical staffs to regulate the quality of patient care.
      J. Kans. Med. Soc., 80(2):p75-81, (Feb. 1979).

0814 Goldberg, G.A. Implementing university hospital
      ambulatory care evaluation. J. Med. Educ.,
      50(5):p435-42, (May 1975).

0815 Goodspeed, S.W. Evaluating a hospital quality assurance
      plan. Hosp. Med. Staff, 10():p18-24, (Sep. 1981).

0816 Gothlin, J.H. [Analysis of a quality assurance
      program]. Radiol. Diagn., 27(1):p45-50, (1986).

0817 Harmon, C.A. Involving staff in nursing quality
      assurance. QRB, 6(11):p26-30, (Nov. 1980).

0818 Harris, L.J. Quality assurance: a safe working
      environment for hospital nurses. AAOHN J., 34(5):p237-8,
      (May 1986).

0819 Heimanson, R. Quality assurance in the OR. Getting a program started. AORN J., 44(2):p172-4,176, (Aug. 1986).

0820 Hendrix, K.K.; Baltz, A. A visual aid to quality assurance: a simple management tool to track quality assurance activities. QRB, 7(7):p23-7, (Jul. 1981).

0821 Hetherington, R.W. Quality assurance and organizational effectiveness in hospitals. Health Serv. Res., 17(2):p185, (Summer 1982).

0822 Hicks, A.M. Administrative reviews: governance. Hospitals, 49(7):p41-3, (Apr. 1, 1975).

0823 Holbrook, R.F.; Dunn, L.J., Jr. Medical malpractice litigation: the discoverability and use of hospitals' quality assurance committee records. Med. Malpract. Cost Containment J., 1(2):p109-31, (Jul. 1979).

0824 Honovich, D. Planning: the key to success. Tex. Hosp., 37(9):p28, (Feb. 1982).

0825 Hospital quality circles improve quality and productivity. Hosp. Peer Rev., 6(9):p101-3, (Sep. 1981).

0826 Hovind, O.B. Quality assurance and training for quality control. Med. Lab. Sci., 40(3):p275-7, (Jul. 1983).

0827 Howie, H. Trustees take on quasi-legal role. Health Care, 21(12):p16, (Dec. 1979).

0828 Huckabay, L.M. The significance of administrative control in quality assurance. Nurs. Adm. Q., 1(3):p51-5, (Spring 1977).

0829 Hunter, S.A.; Dunlop, C.R. Developing a quality assurance plan in a medical center. QRB, 6(9):p11-5, (Sep. 1980).

0830 Isaac, D.N. Suggestions for organizing a quality assurance program. QRB, 9(3):p68-72, (Mar. 1983).

0831 Johnson, D.E. Quality circles put workers in charge of their productivity. Mod. Health Care, 11(9):p68-9, 74, (Sep. 1981).

0832 Jones, M. Nurses can change the social systems of hospitals. Am. J. Nurs., 78(6):p1012-4, (Jun. 1978).

0833 Judkins, S.B. Staff involvement in quality assurance. Dimens. Crit. Care Nurs., 1(5):p298-300, (Sep-Oct. 1982).

0834 Kaderbhai, F.A. Workstudy & its place in effective patient care. Kenya Nurs. J., 5(2):p50-4, (Dec. 1976).

0835 Kagan, R.M. Organizational change and quality assurance in a psychiatric setting. QRB, 10(9):p269-77, (Sep. 1984).

0836 Kahn, J. Quality assurance professionals: a national profile. Dimens. Health Serv., 63(1):p14, (Feb. 1986).

0837 Kaluzny, A.D. Quality assurance as a managerial innovation: a research perspective. Health Serv. Res., 17(3):p253-68, (Fall 1982).

0838 Kane, R.L. Administrative reviews: ambulatory care. Hospitals, 49(7):p85-8, (Apr. 1, 1975).

0839 Kelly, P. Differentiating roles in quality assurance. Dimens. Crit. Care Nurs., 3(2):p104-9, (Mar-Apr. 1984).

0840 Kinsella, C.R. Administrative reviews: nursing. Hospitals, 49(7):p101-5, (Apr. 1, 1975).

0841 Kirchner, E. Quality assurance at work: improving library services. Calgary General Hospital. Dimens. Health Serv., 62(1):p26-7, (Jan. 1985).

0842 Klapp, D. Quality assurance training for pharmacy students [letter]. Am. J. Hosp. Pharm., 37(7):p922,924, (Jul. 1980).

0843 Klopfer, A.H. Improving quality assurance in hospitals. Conn. Med., 45(7):p443-4, (Jul. 1981).

0844 Knowlton, H.C. Making the ancillary audit work. Hosp. Med. Staff, 6(11):p19-24, (Nov. 1977).

0845 Kresky, B.; Henry, M.C. Responsibilities for quality assurance in prehospital care. QRB, 12(7):p230-5, (Jul. 1986).

0846 Kress, G.C., Jr.; Silversin, J.B. Internal marketing and quality assurance through patient feedback. J. Am. Dent. Assoc., 110(1):p29-34, (Jan. 1985).

0847 Kuehnert, P. The staffing mess: who can we turn to? RN. 44(5):p101-6, (May 1981).

0848 Kuramoto, A.M.; Sandahl, B.B. A quality assurance workshop for maternal child nurses. MCN. 5(2):p87-94,142, (Mar-Apr. 1980).

0849 Lamnin, M. The dynamics of quality assurance. Top Hosp. Pharm. Manage., 1(3):p1-9, (Nov. 1981).

0850   Lane, G.H.; Cronin, K.M.; Peirce, A.G.   Teaching diploma
       students how to utilize the ANA Quality Assurance Model.
       J. Nurs. Educ., 21(9):p42-5, (Nov. 1982).

0851   Lang, D.A.   Softening the 'perverse' effects of quality
       assurance.   Hosp. Med. Staff, 10(11):p23-8, (Nov. 1981).

0852   Laurie-Shaw, B.; Stove, V.   Quality assurance - what can
       it do for the nurse?   AARN News Lett., 38(10):p19-20,
       (Nov. 1982).

0853   LaViolette, S.   Quality assurance activities revamped.
       Mod. Health Care, 9(3):p16, (Mar. 1979).

0854   Lazes, P.M.; Wasilewski, Y.; Redd, J.D.   Improving
       outpatient care through participation: the Newark
       experiment in staff and patient involvement.   Int. J.
       Health Educ., 20(1):p61-8, 70, (1977).

0855   Leach, J.; Nagy, S.; Cercone, R.   Adopting a quality
       assurance program.   Dimens. Health Serv., 58(4):p30,32,
       (Apr. 1981).

0856   Lindstrom, R.   Part two: Implementing a shared quality
       assurance program.   Dimens. Health Serv., 56(3):p32-4,
       (Mar. 1979).

0857   Lippitt, G.L.   Trends in developing effective inservice
       education for HSOs.   Health Care Educ., 9(3):p1, 11, 13
       passim, (Aug.-Sep. 1980).

0858   Luke, R.D.; Boss, R.W.   Barriers limiting the
       implementation of quality assurance programs.   University
       of Colorado Health Science Center, Denver.
       Health Serv. Res., 16(3):p305-14, (Fall 1981).

0859   Maciorowski, L.F.; Larson, E.; Keane, A.   Quality
       assurance.   Evaluate thyself.   J. Nurs. Adm.,
       15(6):p38-42, (Jun. 1985).

0860   Marcus, M.   Quality assurance and prepaid programs.
       Dent. Clin. North Am., 29(3):p497-506, (Jul. 1985).

0861   Marshik-Gustafson, J.; Kopher, S.; Terze, M.   Planning is
       the key to successful QA programs.   Hospitals,
       55(11):p67-8, 71-3, (Jun. 1, 1981).

0862   Martin, N.S.   Clinical management models: staff
       education curriculum for quality assurance.   Superv.
       Nurse, 10(11):p24-8, (Nov. 1979).

0863   McConkey, R.   What's your quality assurance IQ?   Trustee,
       28(12):p16,18, (Dec. 1975).

0864 McGee, P.A. Who is responsible for quality control in the C.S.R.? Hosp. Adm. Can., 18(12):p19-20, (Dec. 1976).

0865 McSherry, C.K. Quality assurance: the cost of utilization review and the educational value of medical audit in a university hospital. Surgery, 80(1):p122-9, (Jul. 1976).

0866 Metzger, N. Despite unionization, administrators can control policy, cost, quality. Hosp. Prog., 58(9):p36,38,40 passim, (Sep. 1977).

0867 Milgrom, P.; Chapko, M.; Milgrom, L.; Weinstein, P. Quality assurance and the role of self-evaluation and continuing education. Dent. Clin. North Am., 29(3):p531-44, (Jul. 1985).

0868 Miller, J.R.; Lewis, F.M. Closing the gap in quality assurance: A tool for evaluating group leaders. Health Educ. Q., 9(1):p55-66, (Spring 1982).

0869 Mitchell, M. Administrative reviews: manpower and education. Hospitals, 49(7):p69-71, (Apr. 1, 1975).

0870 Moore, R.D.; Klein, W.F. On the scene: quality control circles at Barnes Hospital. Nurs. Adm. Q., 6(3):p23-7, (Spring 1982).

0871 Morse, E.V.; Gordòn, G.; Moch, M. Hospital costs and quality of care: an organization perspective. Milbank Mem. Fund. Q., 52(3):p315-46, (Sum. 1974).

0872 Mulroy, T.R. How directors can meet their responsibility of patient care quality. Trustee, 33(6):p13-6, (Jun. 1980).

0873 Nelson, R.E.; Barnes, G.T.; Witten, D.M. Economic analysis of a comprehensive quality assurance program. Radiol. Technol., 49(2):p129-34, (Sep-Oct. 1977).

0874 Nelson, S. Quality assurance: a country hospital administrator's experience. Byron District Hospital, New South Wales. Aust. Clin. Rev., (5):p15-7, (Jun. 1982).

0875 Nodolny, M.D. Primary nursing care...as a method for improving the quality of patient care. Hosp. Top., 57(4):p10,13-4,17, (Jul-Aug. 1979).

0876 Orlikoff, J.E. The use of outside consultants for QA--why, when, how. Hosp. Med. Staff, 10(11):p29-34, (Nov. 1981).

0877 Penkhus, M.L.; Schear, W.A. Quality assurance council administers, evaluates hospital program. Hosp. Prog., 62(11):p48-51, (Nov. 1981).

0878 Peterson, S. The quality assurance network. Tex. Hosp., 37(12):p12-3, (May 1982).

0879 Pfeffer-Kloss, L.L. Managing quality assurance information: organizational and staffing consideration. Top Health Rec. Manage., 1(2):p5-11, (Dec. 1980).

0880 Pharmacists meet monthly to discuss findings of QA audits. Hospitals, 54(23):p39-40, (Dec. 1, 1980).

0881 Porter, K.W. An 'inhouse PSRO' success story. Trustee, 28(9):p28-30, (Sep. 1975).

0882 Post, R.S. Comments on a pragmatic route to quality assurance. University Hospitals of Cleveland. QRB, 7(12):p4-5, (Dec. 1981).

0883 Prybil, L.D. Accountability vested in trustees. Hospitals, 50(7):p48-50, (Apr. 1, 1976).

0884 Purgatorio-Howard, K. Improving a quality sssurance program. Nurs. Manage., 17(4):p38-42, (Apr. 1986).

0885 Quality assurance as a management function: introduction to this issue and a report on the quality assurance management institute. QRB, 7(7):p2-3, (Jul. 1981).

0886 Reerink, E. National organization for quality assurance in hospitals. Med. Educ., 14(5 Suppl.):p52-5, (Sep. 1980).

0887 Reeves, D.M.; Underly, N. Nursing executive committee sets standards for clinical practice. Hospitals, 55(13):p71-2, 80, (Jul. 1, 1981).

0888 Restuccia, J.D.; Holloway, D.C. Methods of control for hospital quality assurance systems. Health Serv. Res., 17(3):p241-51, (Fall 1982).

0889 Rifkin, M.; Lynne, C.; Williams, R.; Hilsenbeck, C. Managing quality assurance activities in a large teaching hospital. QRB, 7(8):p27-32, (Aug. 1981).

0890 Rifkin, M.; Lynne, C.; Williams, R.; Hilsenbeck, C. Tracking quality assurance problems in a large teaching hospital. QRB, 7(9):p25-9, (Sep. 1981).

0891 Rinaldi, L. Managing a hospital audit committee. Superv. Nurse, 8(6):p60-2, (Jun. 1977).

0892 Rodin, A.E.; Calhoun, K.P.; Bledsoe, S.D. Building
      blocks to comprehensive quality assurance. Hosp. Med.
      Staff, 9(10):p26-31, (Oct. 1980).

0893 Rosen, H.M.; Feigin, W., Sr. Quality assurance and data
      feedback. Manage. Rev., 8(1):p67-74, (Winter 1983).

0894 Rovinsky, J.J. Structure and function of a hospital
      audit and quality review committee. J. Hosp. Dent.
      Pract., 9(3):p89-90, (Jul-Sep. 1975).

0895 Saternus, K.S.; Staak, M. [Sudden death in medical
      practice. Quality assurance and control as a task of
      forensic medicine]. Dtsch. Med. Wochenschr.,
      109(23):p893-8, (Jun. 8, 1984).

0896 Schor, E.L. Teaching quality assurance at an HMO. J.
      Med. Educ., 55(2):p129-31, (Feb. 1980).

0897 Shannon, M.; McIver, B.; MacLeod, S. Quality of care
      program relies on medical records staff. Dimens.
      Health Serv., 57(9):p36-7, (Sep. 1980).

0898 Shimeld, A. A five point approach to staff development
      for quality assurance. Can. J. Occup. Ther.,
      49(2):p53-6, (Apr. 1982).

0899 Sibley, H. Industrywide management plan can affect
      quality, cost of care. Hospitals, 53(2):p73-6, (Jan. 16,
      1979).

0900 Sniff, D. The evolution of a quality assurance program.
      QRB, 6(1):p26-9, (Jan. 1980).

0901 Sommers, L.S.; Sholtz, R.; Shepherd, R.M.; Starkweather,
      D.B. Physician involvement in quality assurance. Med.
      Care, 22(12):p1115-38, (Dec. 1984).

0902 Southwick, A.F.; Slee, D.A. Quality assurance in health
      care. Confidentiality of information and immunity for
      participants. J. Leg. Med., 5(3):p343-97, (Sep. 1984).

0903 Spaeth, R.G. Liability, role of trustees affected by QA
      standard, says adminstrator. Hosp. Peer Rev.,
      5(5):p53-4, (May 1980).

0904 Spencer, D.S. Contribution of hospital management firms
      to quality, cost-effective health care. Top. Health
      Care Financ., 6(4):p1-9, (Summer 1980).

0905 Stearns, G.; Fox, L.A. Assessing quality assurance and
      risk management activities: a profile analysis. QRB,
      5(10):p26-9, (Oct. 1979).

0906 Stearns, G.; Fox, L.A. A three-phase plan for integrating quality assurance activities. QRB, 6(1):p13-6, (Jan. 1980).

0907 Stoelwinder, J.U.; Clayton, P.S. Hospital organization development: changing the focus from "better management" to "better patient care". J. Appl. Behav. Sci., 14(3):p400-14, (Jul-Aug. 1978).

0908 Stromberg, R.E. The trustee's role in quality assurance. Trustee, 30(11):p25-7, (Nov. 1977).

0909 Summary report of Working Group on Training for Quality Assurance, World Health Organization, Regional Office for Europe. Meeting held in Udine, Italy, 25-28 June 1985. J. Adv. Nurs., 11(4):p487-9, (Jul. 1986).

0910 Thompson, R.E. Relating continuing education and quality assurance activities. QRB, 7(1):p3-6, (Jan. 1981).

0911 Tilson, J.Q. The hospital trustee and quality assurance. Conn. Med., 45(4):p245, (Apr. 1981).

0912 Tolpin, B.B. The role of the consumer in quality assurance. Dent. Clin. North Am., 29(3):p595-604, (Jul. 1985).

0913 Troyer, G.; Salman, S. Committees can help oversee hospital's QA activities. Hospitals, 55(11):p87-91, (Jun. 1, 1981).

0914 Turner, G.P.; Mapa, J. Board takes action in quality assurance role. Hospitals, 54(9):p109-10,112-3, (May 1, 1980).

0915 Understanding and meeting the quality assurance standard of the Joint Commission on Accreditation of Hospitals. Part II. Second Opin. Health Care Issues, 2(2):p9-16, (Feb. 1981).

0916 Van Sluyter, C.K. Organizing for patient safety and liability control. QRB, 5(4):p21-4, (Apr. 1979).

0917 Van Vorst, C.B. Quality assurance: the buck stops with the board. Trustee, 32(5):p25-6,28, (May 1979).

0918 Vogel, D.P.; Gurwich, E.; Compagna, K.; Sula, J.; Eck, T.A.; Hutchinson, R.A. Pharmacy unit devises quality assurance plan. Hospitals, 54(11):p83-5, (Jun. 1980).

0919 Wallace, R.F.; Donnelly, M. Computing quality assurance costs. Hosp. Prog., 56(5):p53-7, (May 1975).

0920 Ward sisters discuss the process of administration and
      its application to promote quality patient care.
      Jamaican Nurse, 15(1):p7, 9, (May 1975).

0921 Warner, A.M. Thoughts about the cost of quality
      assurance. QRB, 9(2):p39-41, (Feb. 1983).

0922 Warner, R.L. Finding the perfect person for integrated
      QA program. Hosp. Peer Rev., 5(7):p80-1, (Jul. 1980).

0923 Watkinson, S.A. Economic aspects of quality assurance.
      Radiography, 51(597):p133-40, (May-Jun. 1985).

0924 White, J.; Baker, R. Coordinating a quality assurance
      program. Dimens. Health Serv., 58(11):p43-4, (Nov.
      1981).

0925 Who controls quality of "temporary registry nurses?
      Hosp. Peer Rev., 4(2):17-20, (Feb. 1979).

0926 Williamson, J.W. Information management in quality
      assurance. Nurs. Res., 29(2):p78-82, (Mar-Apr. 1980).

0927 Wilner, S.; Winickoff, R.N.; Schoenbaum, S.C.; Coltin,
      K.L. The role of patient interventions in ambulatory
      quality assurance programs. Health Educ. Q.,
      9(1):p42-54, (Spring 1982).

0928 Winickoff, R.N.; Wilner, S.; Neisuler, R.; Barnett, G.O.
      Limitations of provider interventions in hypertension
      quality assurance. Am. J. Public Health, 75(1):p43-6,
      (Jan. 1985).

0929 Wolverton, L.M. Data retrieval in the new quality
      assurance program. J. Am. Med. Rec. Assoc.,
      52(2):p68-71, (Apr. 1981).

0930 Zelman, W.N.; Jessee, W.F. Budgeting quality assurance
      activities. QRB, 9(2):p42-7, (Feb. 1983).

Overviews

0931 Accreditation may hinge on QA, experts maintain.
      Hosp. Risk Manage., 2(11):p137-8, (Nov. 1980).

0932 Adair, M.; Griffin, K.M. Quality assurance: a
      professional quest for speech-language pathologists and
      audiologists. ASHA, 21(10):p871-4, (Oct. 1979).

0933 Affeldt, J.E. New Q.A. standard allows flexibility,
      innovation. Hosp. Med. Staff, 8(6):p7-9, (Jun. 1979).

0934 Affeldt, J.E. Accreditation problems: new quality
assurance standard. Hospitals, 53(14):p14, (Jul. 16,
1979).

0935 Affeldt, J.E. Accreditation problems: How much will it
cost hospitals seeking accreditation to comply with
JCAH's new quality assurance standard? Hospitals,
53(16):p14, (Aug. 16, 1979).

0936 Affeldt, J.E. Accreditation problems: quality assurance
standard issued. Hospitals, 53(24):p15, (Dec. 16, 1979).

0937 Affeldt, J.E. JCAH responds to legal questions raised
over QA standard. Hosp. Peer Rev., 5(4):p42-3, (Apr.
1980).

0938 Affeldt, J.E. The new quality assurance standard of the
Joint Commission on Acreditation of Hospitals.
West. J. Med., 132(2):p166-70, (Feb. 1980).

0939 Albinsson, G. Quality and cost of hospital services.
World Hosp., 14(4):p255-60, Nov. 1978).

0940 Andrew, R.R. Quality assurance in private hospitals.
Aust. Clin. Rev., (6):p11-5, (Sep. 1982).

0941 Andrews, G. Quality assurance in health care.
World Hosp., 17(1):p18-23, (Feb. 1981).

0942 Angrist, A.A. Impersonal medical care. Role of the
pathologist in its evolution. Am. J. Clin. Pathol.,
64(1):p136-41, (Jul. 1975).

0943 Ashton, K. Off the record. Nurs. Times, 74(9):p346-9,
(Mar. 2, 1978).

0944 Aurousseau, P. Quality and cost of hospital services.
World Hosp., 14(4):p236-7, (Nov. 1978).

0945 Backe, B. [Quality assurance and quality control of
health care services] Kvalitetssikring og
kvalitetskontroll i institusjonshelsevesenete
Tidsskr Nor Laegeforen, 105(17-18):p1246-9, (Jun. 20,
1985).

0946 Barnes, G. Hospital liability--no fat left to trim.
Dimens. Health Serv., 59(3):p38-40, (Mar. 1982).

0947 Barr, A. Letter: Reallocation of resources. Lancet,
2(7976):p105, (Jul. 10, 1976).

0948 Batsakis, J.G.; Lawson, N.S.; Gilbert, R.K. Introduction
to the report on the Quality Assurance Programs of the
College of American Pathologists, 1980.
Am. J. Clin. Pathol., 74(4Suppl):p505-7, (Oct. 1980).

0949 Berg, J.K.; Kelly, J.T. Psychosocial health care and
quality assurance activities. J. Fam. Pract.,
11(4):p641-3, (Oct. 1980).

0950 Black, D. Client-oriented medicine. Ciba Found Symp.,
(44):p169-83, (1976).

0951 Block, M.B. "Excellent versus adequate care" that is the
question! [editorial]. Ariz. Med., 35(6):p417-8, (Jun.
1978).

0952 Blunt, L.L. Hygiene perspectives on quality assurance.
J. Oreg. Dent. Assoc., 53(4):p26-8, (Summer 1984).

0953 Brink, L. Quality care: a fact of life. Times,
22(6):p6-9, (Jul. 1981).

0954 Brown, A. Centre of excellence? Nurs. Mirror,
151(24):p8, (Dec. 11, 1980).

0955 Bunker, J.P.; Gerber, W.G. Holistic health care and
California's Board of Medical Quality Assurance.
West J. Med., 131(6):p484-5, (Dec. 1979).

0956 Buske, S.M. Quality assurance. Same Day Surg.,
4(2-3):p17-8, (Feb.-Mar. 1980).

0957 Cahn, C.; Richman, A. Quality assurance in psychiatry.
The position of the Canadian Psychiatric Association.
Can. J. Psychiatry, 30(2):p148-58, (Mar. 1985).

0958 Caldeira da Silva, J.M. Quality and cost of hospital
services. World Hosp., 14(4):p253-4, (Nov. 1978).

0959 Caldera, K.G.; Joy, L.; McGrath, B. Quality assurance.
Mass. Nurse, 50(4):p5, (Apr. 1981).

0960 Cam, R.S. Interviews: quality of nursing care and its
determinants. Phillip. J. Nurs., 51(2):p44-7, (Apr.-Jun.
1981).

0961 Collaboration for quality health care: education of
beginning practitioners of nursing and utilization of
graduates. NLN Publ., (14-1654):piii-viii,1-111, (1977).

0962 Consumer expresses concerns over quality care.
RNAO News, 32(1):p6, (Jan.-Feb. 1976).

0963 Conversations with consultants: falling standards and sagging morale. Br. Med. J., 1(5959):p675-6, (Mar. 22, 1975).

0964 Cooley, R.L.; Lubow, R.M. Quality assurance: its role in military dentistry. Milit. Med., 149(1):p21-3, (Jan. 1984).

0965 Cost considerations of the new standard. Perspect. Accredit., (3):p10, (May-Jun. 1979).

0966 Couch, J.B. Hospital corporate liability for inadequate quality assurance in Pennsylvania. J. Leg. Med.(Chicago), 2(1):p14-46, (Oct. 1980).

0967 Cousins, N. Anatomy of an illness (as perceived by the patient). N. Engl. J. Med., 295(26):p1458-63, (Dec. 23, 1976).

0968 de Beer, J. Apartheid and mental health care [letter]. Lancet, 2(8050):p1222-3, (Dec. 10, 1977).

0969 Delisle, G.R. Let's keep caring, curing, quality, cost in proper perspective. Mich. Hosp., 16(12):p15-7,30, (Dec. 1980).

0970 Dennis, W.B. JCAH may require quality assurance, says CS head [interview]. Purch. Adm., 5(6):p18,38, (Jun. 1981).

0971 Diamond, H.; Luft, L.L. A selected bibliography of literature on quality assurance for community mental health centers. QRB, 6(4):p27-31, (Apr. 1980).

0972 Diddie, P.J. Quality assurance--a general hospital meets the challenge. J. Nurs. Adm., 6(6):p6-8,12-6, (Jul.-Aug. 1976).

0973 Dinel, B. Quality is our most important product. Can. J. Hosp. Pharm., 28(2):p49-50, (Mar.-Apr. 1975).

0974 Dische, S. Quality assurance in radiation therapy: European experience--present and future clinical efforts. Int. J. Radiat. Oncol. Biol. Phys., (10 Suppl.1):p55, (Jun. 1984).

0975 Dunea, G. Inspecting the hospitals. Br. Med. J., [Clin. Res.], 284(6319):p890-1, (Mar. 20, 1982).

0976 DuVerlie, E. Trends in quality assurance activities in France. QRB, 12(7):p258-63, (Jul. 1986).

0977 Egelston, E.M. New JCAH standard on quality assurance. Nurs. Res., 29(2):p113-4, (Mar.-Apr. 1980).

0978 Egelston, E.M. New JCAH quality assurance standard: preliminary requirements emerge. Hosp. Peer Rev., 4(5):p67-9, (May 1979).

0979 Eichhorn, S. Quality and cost of hospital services. World Hosp., 14(4):p226-31, (Nov. 1978).

0980 Ellis, B. Critical challenges lie ahead for the new JCAH president. Hosp. Med. Staff, 6(10):p34-41, (Oct. 1977).

0981 Everett, G.D. Quality assurance and cost containment in teaching hospitals: implications for a period of economic restraint. QRB, 11(2):p42-6, (Feb. 1985).

0982 Evolution of quality assurance reflected in new standard. Staff, Joint Commission on Accreditation of Hospitals. QRB, 5(6):p2-3, (Jun. 1979).

0983 Fainter, J. Action and reaction: how facilities of the Hospital Corporation of America improved patient care. QRB, 4(2):p4-7, (Feb. 1978).

0984 Firshein, J. PA HMOs undergo @xpanded quality-assurance review. Hospitals, 60(5):p76, (Mar. 5, 1986).

0985 Friedman, B.I. Quality assurance and nuclear medicine: the challenge of change. J. Nucl. Med., 27(8):p1366-72, (Aug. 1986).

0986 Friedman, E. Burn care in U.S. hospitals-how much? How good? Hospitals, 51(23):p53-8, (Dec. 1, 1977).

0987 Gallegos, G. Audits ensure QA at three hospitals [interview]. Hosp. Peer Rev., 6(10):p121-2, (Oct. 1981).

0988 Garletts, A. Quality control maintained in community hospitals [interview]. Hosp. Peer Rev., 6(6):p64-5, (Jun. 1981).

0989 Gertman, P.M. The future of quality assurance and PSROs. Med. Care, 19(3):p253-4, (Mar. 1981).

0990 Gonzales, Sister. How to cope with the goal of all pharmacists: better patient care. Pharm. Times, 44(6):p68-71, (Jun. 1978).

0991 Groah, L.W. [Quality assurance: audits and standards, and the operating room nurse]. Rev. Enferm, 6(56 Suppl.):p4-7, (Mar. 1983).

0992 Guidelines for quality assurance in the hospital practice of internal medicine. Aust. Clin. Rev., (6):p24-6, (Sep. 1982).

0993 Hammond, M. The hospital as a bureaucracy and the possibility of quality care. SA Nurse J., 45(2):p8-10, (Feb. 1978).

0994 Harris survey on "Hospital Care in America." Hosp. Prog., 59(8):p28-9, (Aug. 1978).

0995 Haywood, K. Our introduction to quality assurance. Aust. Nurses J., 13(3):p56-7, (Sep. 1983).

0996 Health Services Review Organization: Veterans Administration. Proposed regulations. Fed. Regist., 46(144):p38540-7, (Jul. 28, 1981).

0997 Hershey, N. Providers learn hard lessons from major court decisions. Hosp. Med. Staff, 9(11):p2-7contd, (Nov. 1980).

0998 Hickey, J. Health care system becoming public utility. Mich. Med., 76(14):p274, (May 1977).

0999 Hillsman, J.T.; Albertini, T.F.; Crawford, B.L. Dental quality assurance. A federal overview. Dent. Clin. North Am., 29(3):p477-82, (Jul. 1985).

1000 Hirsh, H.L. Patient hospital care--changing times. Med. Trial Tech. Q., 24(2):p157-63, (Fall 1977).

1001 Holroyd, B.R.; Knopp, R.; Kallsen, G. Medical control. Quality assurance in prehospital care. JAMA, 256(8):p1027-31, (Aug. 22-29, 1986).

1002 Horty, J.F. The wrong Smith costs a hospital +90,000. Mod. Health Care, 5(6):p52, (Dec. 1976).

1003 Hospital organization: effectiveness of patient care. Soc. Secur. Bull., 39(4):p28-9,33, (Apr. 1976).

1004 Hsia, L. Quality assurance and peer review. J. Nurse Midwife, 29(4):p233-4, (Jul.-Aug. 1984).

1005 Huenemann, R.L. Leadership and quality in nutritional care: our role in today's world. J. Am. Diet Assoc., 78(2):p124-8, (Feb. 1981).

1006 Hughes, E.N. Politics and patient care. Hosp. Trustee, 4(4):p16-8, (Jul.-Aug. 1980).

1007 Inzinga, M. Legislative issues and health care trends--quality assurance. 8(4):p81-4, (Summer 1984).

1008 Jones, P.K. Financial 'heyday' of health care is past. But what about quality assurance under DRG's? Pa. Nurse, 39(7):p7-8, (Jul. 1984).

1009 Kane, R.A. Assuring quality of care and quality of life in long term care. QRB, 7(10):p3-10, (Oct. 1981).

1010 Kane, R.L.; Jorgensen, L.A.; Teteberg, B.; Kuwahara, J. Is good nursing-home care feasible? JAMA, 235(5):p516-9, (Feb. 2, 1976).

1011 Karlins, M.; Knudsen, M. State hospital review boards in Minnesota. Hosp. Community Psychiatry, 27(9):p641-3, (Sep. 1976).

1012 Kinzer, D.M. A revival for quality assurance--but when? QRB, 11(11):p323-6, (Nov. 1985).

1013 Kline, M.M.; Tracy, M.L.; Davis, S.L. Quality assurance in public health. Nurs. Health Care, 1(4):p192-6, (Nov. 1980).

1014 Klyop, J.S. The dental profession's commmitment to quality assurance. Dent. Clin. North Am., 29(3):p521-30, (Jul. 1985).

1015 Knutson, R.A. The young physician versus the aging system. Bull NY Acad. Med., 52(1):p70-4, (Jan. 1976).

1016 Korsak, A. Risk management: new concept calls for definitional refinement in use of term. Hospitals, 52(22):p48,50, (Nov. 16, 1978).

1017 Kraft, M.R. Quality assurance. J. Gerontol Nurs., 9(6):p326-7,330-1,357, (Jun. 1983).

1018 Rugler, D.; Nash, T.; Weinberger, G. Patient/resident care management and quality assurance. QRB, 10(4):p109-11, (Apr. 1984).

1019 Kulwiec, M. Quality control plus quality assurance: equals customer insurance. Quintessence Dent. Technol., 5(6):p605-8, (Jun. 1981).

1020 Lamont, G.X. The cost containment-quality of care issue. Hosp. Top., 58(3):p6-10, (May-Jun. 1980).

1021 Lang, D.A. Prospective quality assurance [editorial]. QRB, 10(5):p143-5, (May 1984).

1022 Lanham, G. Quality assurance in USA. World Hosp., 17(1):p13-7, (Feb. 1981).

1023 Laughlin, J.S. Development of quality assurance in radiation therapy in North America. Int. J. Radiat. Oncol. Biol. Phys., (10Suppl1):p9-1, (Jun. 1984).

1024 Lebreton, P.P. Strategic factors in hospital nursing practice. Nurs. Health Care, 1(4):p197-207, (Nov. 1980).

1025 Legge, D. Quality assurance in US hospitals: a view from Australia. Aust. Clin. Rev., (7):p29-36, (Dec. 1982).

1026 Legge, D.G.; Hutton, P.A. Quality assurance in hospital medicine: a report. Aust. NZ J. Med., 11(6):p687-96, (Dec. 1981).

1027 Lempenau, M.C. Soviet hospital stay a grim experience. Hosp. Financ. Manage., 30(5):p54-7, (May 1976).

1028 Lentchner, E. Government's role in dental quality assurance. NY State Dent. J., 50(6):p354-6, (Jun.-Jul. 1984).

1029 Litt, I.F.; Cohen, M.I. Prisons, adolescents, and the right to quality medical care: the time is now. Am. J. Public Health, 64(9):p894-7, (Sep. 1974).

1030 Looney, D.H.; Gibson, C. Standards of practice: Nutritional quality assurance in acute-care hospitals. J. Am. Diet. Assoc., 79(1):p64-5, (Jul. 1981).

1031 Maestrini, V.; Riley, M.A. Quality assurance in nursing. Emphasis Nurs., 1(1):p19-20, (1985).

1032 Management of nursing care: Quality care in a small facility. Health Serv. Manager, 9(8):p6-7, (Aug. 1976).

1033 Manjoro, J.W. Quality assurance in radiography. Quality assurance in the developing countries. Radiography, 51(597):p145, (May-Jun. 1985).

1034 Margan, I. Quality and cost of hospital services. World Hosp., 14(4):p270-3, (Nov. 1978).

1035 Marram, G. Principles and processes in instituting the change to primary nursing. NLN Publ., (52-1695):p18-24, (1977).

1036 Martin, A.E.; Mann, J.L. Clinical pharmacy services: Part II--the issues. Can. J. Hosp. Pharm., 34(6):p173-7,191, (Nov.-Dec. 1981).

1037 Martin, P.J. Quality assurance in Australia. Aust. Nurses J., 9(7):p45-9, (Feb. 1980).

1038 Martin, R.J. Quality assurance and clinical microbiology. Med. Lab. Sci., 40(3):p269-74, (Jul. 1983).

1039 Mass, D. Quality assurance for the sake of public accountability [editorial]. Am. J. Med. Technol, 47(12):p952, (Dec. 1981).

1040 Matoth, Y. Quality assurance--an Israeli point of view. QRB, 7(2):p7-9, (Feb. 1981).

1041 Mattson, M.R. Quality assurance: a literature review of a changing field. Hosp. Community Psychiatry, 35(6):p605-16, (Jun. 1984).

1042 McGrail, W. Hospital association examines legal perils of JCAH standard [interview]. Hosp. Peer Rev., 5(4):p41-2, (Apr. 1980).

1043 McGuill, G. Quality assurance is for nurses too! Alaska Nurse, 28(1):p4, (Jan. 1979).

1044 McSherry, C.K. Quality assurance and surgical practice. Surg. Clin. North Am., 62(4):p751-9, (Aug. 1982).

1045 Medical care of the elderly. Report of the Working Party of the Royal College of Physicians of London. Lancet, 1(8021):p1092-4, (May 21, 1977).

1046 Meisenheimer, C.G. Incorporating JCAH standards into a quality assurance program. Nurs. Adm. Q., 7(3):p1-8, (Spring 1983).

1047 Merlino, J.; London, E.; Turner, S. Hospital crisis. Consum. Health Perspect., 7(8):p2-5, (May 1981).

1048 Miccio, B.L. Rate setting promotes interdepartmental cooperation in QA. Hospitals, 55(11):p83-5, (Jun. 1981).

1049 Miller, J.N. Why dangerous doctors keep doctoring. Read. Dig., 120(717):p102-8, (Jan. 1982).

1050 Miringoff, M.L. Incomplete technology and the organizational dynamics of a state mental hospital. Adm. Ment. Health, 3(2):p133-45, (Spring 1976).

1051 Moaninch, M.; Weedman, R.D.; Jones, R.E. The JCAH consolidated standards: questions and answers. Hosp. Community Psychiatry, 30(10):p690-3, (Oct. 1979).

1052 Morris, A.L.; Bentley, J.M.; Bomba, M.R. Response of general practitioners to a national dental office evaluation program. Office of Quality Assurance. J. Am. Dent. Assoc., 111(5):p799-801, (Nov. 1985).

1053 New JCAH quality assurance standard for hospitals. Perspect. Accredit., (3):p5-6, (May-Jun 1979).

1054 New JCAH standard stirs malpractice fears.
      Med. World News, 21(4):p30-2, (Feb. 18, 1980).

1055 New QA standard approved. Perspect. Accredit., (3):p1-3,
      (May-Jun. 1979).

1056 New quality assurance standard of the JCAH. QRB,
      5(6):p4-5, (Jun. 1979).

1057 Newmark, G.L. Can quality be equated with cost?
      Hospitals, 50(7):p81-2,84-6, (Apr. 1, 1976).

1058 Nuallain, C.O. Quality and cost of hospital services.
      World Hosp., 14(4):p242-4, (Nov. 1978).

1059 Ostrow, P.C. Quality assurance requirements of the Joint
      Commission on Accreditation of Hospitals.
      Am. J. Occup. Ther., 37(1):p27-31, (Jan. 1983).

1060 Paine, L.H. General report and commentary: the
      realities of quality assurance. QRB, 12(4):p152-6, (Apr.
      1986).

1061 Palmer, H.; Hillestad, B. Quality and cost of hospital
      services. World Hosp., 14(4):p249-52, (Nov. 1978).

1062 Phelps, C.E. NHI won't control costs, quality, or
      access. Hosp. Prog., 58(10):p79-85, (Oct. 1977).

1063 Pimlott, J.F.; Chambers, L.W.; Feller, S.J.; Scherer,
      F.K. Dental hygiene quality assurance: definitions,
      issues, and directions for Canada. Can. Dent. Hyg.,
      19(1):p20-3, (Spring 1985).

1064 Posatko, R.C. The soaring cost of a day in the
      hospital. Pa. Med., 84(5):p29-32, (May 1981).

1065 Pratt, R. National quality assurance program--Royal
      Australian Nursing Federation. Aust. Clin. Rev.,
      (15):p22-5, (Dec. 1984).

1066 Quaethoven, P. Quality and cost of hospital services.
      World Hosp., 14(4):p232-3, (Nov. 1978).

1067 Quality assurance: five experts examine the issues
      [interview]. J. Am. Dent. Assoc., 104(5):p608-17, (May
      1982).

1068 Quality and cost of hospital services. World Hosp.,
      14(4):p264-9, (Nov. 1978).

1069 Quality assurance. Top Hosp. Pharm. Manage., 1(3):p1-99,
      (Nov. 1981).

1070 Reed, E.A. Quality assurance: the JCAH standard.
AORN J., 35(7):p1287-90, (Jun. 1982).

1071 Reerink, E. InterCom: European attitudes toward
accreditation and quality assurance. QRB, 5(5):p24, (May
1979).

1072 Regan, W.A. Hospital responsible for uniform quality of
care. Hosp. Prog., 62(11):p60,63, (Nov. 1981).

1073 Regan, W.A. Hospitals nursing and poor medical care.
Okla. Nurse, 52(3):p7, (Mar. 1977).

1074 Reichaman, S. Accountability through corporate
responsibility in community hospitals. AHME, 8(1):p1-2,
(Spring 1975).

1075 Report on the Quality Assurance Programs of the College
of American Pathologists. Am. J. Clin. Pathol.,
74(4Suppl):p505-605 (Oct. 1980).

1076 Rhodes, D. Wanted: uniform quality assurance standards
for registries. Nurs. Careers, 2(4):p1,5,19-20,
(Jul.-Aug. 1981).

1077 Rinaldi, L.A. Quality assurance '81--satisfying JCAH.
Nurs. Manage., 12(9):p23-4, (Sep. 1981).

1078 Roberts, J.S.; Walczak, R.M. Toward effective quality
assurance: the evolution and current status of the JCAH
QA standard. QRB, 10(1):p11-5, (Jan. 1984).

1079 Rose, V. What would Florence say? Nurs. Mirror,
139(16):p74, (Oct. 17, 1974).

1080 Rubsamen, D.S. Sounding board. Even more legal controls
on the physician's hospital practice. N. Engl. J. Med.,
292(17):p917-9, (Apr. 24, 1975).

1081 Runnells, G. Quality assurance a must for central
service, expert says [interview]. Hospitals, 55(23):p49,
(Dec. 1, 1981).

1082 Salmore, R. JCAH is coming. Nurs. Manage., 13(7):p41-2,
(Jul. 1982).

1083 Samuels, T.M. EtO quality assurance Q's and A's.
Hosp. Top, 60(1):p48, (Jan.-Feb. 1982).

1084 Sanazaro, P.J. The private initiative in PSRO.
Hospitals, 53(1):p61-4, (Jan. 1, 1979).

1085 Sanazaro, P.J. The PSRO program: start of a new chapter [editorial]? N. Engl. J. Med., 296(16):p936-8, (Apr. 21, 1977).

1086 Satisfaction guaranteed. Health Serv. Manager, 9(1):p5, (Jan. 1976).

1087 Saypol, G.M. Medical malpractice, Threat to quality care. NY State J. Med., 75(3):p427-30, (Feb. 1975).

1088 Scarf, C.G.; Weaver, C.J.; Duckett, S.J.; Schmiede, A.M. Quality assurance in Australian hospitals. Med. J. Aust., 1(8):p328-31, (Apr. 21, 1979).

1089 Schade, C.P.; Garland, M.F.; Seggar, J.K., Jr. Care in free clinics [letter]. Am. J. Public Health, 67(4):p382-3, (Apr. 1977).

1090 Schega, W. [Quality assurance in medicine. A contribution of surgery]. Dtsch. Med. Wochenschr., 109(2):p43-5, (Jan. 13, 1984).

1091 Schmidt, P.R. Twenty-ninth annual Welch Memorial Lecture. Can. J. Radiogr. Radiother. Nucl. Med., 11(5):p275-81, (Sep.-Oct. 1980).

1092 Schmincke, W. Quality and cost of hospital services. World Hosp., 14(4):p238-9, (Nov. 1978).

1093 Schoen, M.H. Social, economic, and political forces in quality assurance. Dent. Clin. North Am., 29(3):p449-55, (Jul. 1985).

1094 Schriner, F.; Martin, P.; Bigge, R. Quality assurance in nursing: what others are doing. Kans Nurse, 55(12):p24,27, (Jan. 1981).

1095 Schumacher, D.N. Hospitals and PSROs: can quality compete with cost? QRB, 7(11):p2-3, (Nov. 1981).

1096 Schurmeier, L.J. How to tell if your hospital is well run. Trustee, 34(4):p43-4, (Apr. 1981).

1097 Schwartz, H. Accountability: not all it's cracked up to be. Internist, 22(2):p5-6, (Mar. 1981).

1098 Scibetta, L.P. What do people think about their hospitals? Hosp. Top., 60(3):p8-14, (May-Jun. 1982).

1099 Shanahan, M. Quality assurance update: Medical education on cost and quality. QRB, 6(4):p6-7, (Apr. 1980).

1100 Shanahan, M. Update on international activities in
      quality assurance. QRB, 19(9):p281-2, (Sep. 1984).

1101 Sigal, S.N. A hospital "maven" speaks her mind.
      Imprint, 22(4):p34-5,47, (dec. 1975).

1102 Simola, H. Quality and cost of hospital services.
      World Hosp., 14(4):p235, (Nov. 1978).

1103 Slaven, T.M. How courts measure standards of care.
      Hosp. Med. Staff, 7(12):p23-9, (Dec. 1978).

1104 Smits, H.L.; McMahon, L.P. Approaches to quality
      assurance: the federal role. Bull. NY Acad. Med.,
      62(1):p39-45, (Jan.-Feb. 1986).

1105 Soares, D.P. Quality assurance standards for purchasing
      and inventory control. Am. J. Hosp. Pharm.,
      42(3):p610-20, (Mar. 1985).

1106 Sommers, S.C.; Carter, M.; Palmer, E. Beginnings of the
      New York State Mental Hygiene Medical Review Board
      1976-1980. Am. J. Forensic Med. Pathol., 1(4):p361-4,
      (Dec. 1980).

1107 Spasoff, R.A.; Lane, P.; Steele, R. Quality of care in
      hospital emergency departments and family physicians'
      offices. Can. Med. Assoc., 117(3):p229-32, (Aug. 6,
      1977).

1108 Spellberg, M.A. Editorial: Quality medical care.
      Am. J. Gastroenterol., 63(4):p345-6, (Apr. 1975).

1109 Statement of quality assurance of pharmacy services
      approved by the Canadian Society of Hospital Pharmacists
      May 1975. Can. J. Hosp. Pharm., 28(5):p162, (Sep.-Oct.
      1975).

1110 Steggles, W.A. Quality assurance--an update.
      Ont. Dent., 59(12):p19-20, (Dec. 1982).

1111 Stehbens, W.E. Good medicine: the place of pathology.
      NZ Med. J., 86(596):p271-4, (Sep. 28, 1977).

1112 Stern, S.K. Quality assurance in dentistry: a study of
      the state of the art. QRB, 5(9):p25-31, (Sep. 1979).

1113 Stern, S.K. Quality assurance: ADA perspective.
      J. Hosp. Dent. Pract., 14(2):p76-9, (1980).

1114 Stolte, J.B. Quality and cost of hospital services.
      World Hosp., 14(4):p247-8, (Nov. 1978).

1115 Sweeney, S.B. Manpower utilization and quality control. Lamp, 37(5):p5-10, (May 1980).

1116 Szucs, G.F. Federal certification of hospitals has substantial impact on quality of care. Forum, 2(1):p26-9, (Jan.-Feb. 1978).

1117 Tabatabai, C. On the quality of anesthesia care: an introduction to the special section. QRB, 7(3):p8-9, (Mar. 1981).

1118 Tan, I.K.; Jacob, E. Quality assurance in the Third World--the Singapore experience. Ann. Clin. Biochem., 21(Pt3):p193-207, (May 1984).

1119 Terkla, L.G.; Ueno, H. [Quality assurance in dentistry--recent topic in American dentistry]. Shikai Tenbo, (1):p157-66, (Jan. 1980).

1120 The evolution of quality assurance professionals in Australia. Aust. Clin. Rev., 6(20):p46-8, (Mar. 1986).

1121 The NHS is dead: long live the NHS [letter]. Br. Med. J., 2(6050):p1502-3, (Dec. 18, 1976).

1122 The views of the patient [editorial]. Lancet, 2(8035):p439-40, (Aug. 27, 1977).

1123 Thompson, R. Medical care in the '80s. Quality assurance. J. Tenn. Med. Assoc., 74(11):p801-6, (Nov. 1981).

1124 Tibbitts, S.B. Cost containment and quality assurance. J. Fla. Med. Assoc., 69(3):p195-7, (Mar. 1982).

1125 Tobin, E. Proposed JACH quality assurance standards offer flexibility, require results. Hosp. Peer Rev., 4(2):p22-3, (Feb. 1979).

1126 Tucker, J.H.; Rogers, J. New federal regulations, professional standards review organization, JCAH and criteria development. Med. Rec. News, 46(1):p25-37, (Feb. 1975).

1127 U.R., audit impact of PSRO's said improving. Hosp. Peer Rev., 3(12):p163-4, (Dec. 1978).

1128 Umbdenstock, R.J.; Mohr, B.J. New JCAH standards stress quality and flexibility. Trustee, 32(12):p16-9, (Dec. 1979).

1129 VA creating medical inspector's post. US Med., 16(13):p1,16-7, (Jul. 1980).

1130 Vail, J.D.; Jacobs, M.E. Quality assurance: the pieces of the puzzle. 1. (Continuing education credit). <u>AANA</u>, 54(2):p171-6, (Apr. 1986).

1131 Vaisrub, S. Editorial: Pseudopatients and pseudoresearch. <u>JAMA</u>, 232(1):p59, (Apr. 7, 1975).

1132 van Maanen, H.M. Improvement of quality of nursing care: a goal to challenge in the eighties. <u>J. Adv. Nurs.</u>, 6(1):p3-9, (Jan. 1981).

1133 Vetere, C. Quality and cost of hospital services. <u>World Hosp.</u>, 14(4):p246, (Nov. 1978).

1134 Walczak, R. J.C.A.H.'s new quality assurance standard: requirements aired. <u>Hosp. Peer Rev.</u>, 4(9):p113-8, (Sep. 1979).

1135 Wallace, J.L. Family practice forum. In defense of the emergency room. <u>J. Fam. Pract.</u>, 2(5):p389, (Oct. 1975).

1136 Watkin, B. Do we manage to care? <u>Nurs. Mirror</u>, 141(14):p48-50, (Oct. 2, 1975).

1137 Weissburg, A.A. How Medicare limits quality. <u>J. Natl. Assoc. Priv. Psychiatr. Hosp.</u>, 10(1):p73-5, (Fall 1978).

1138 West, D. A look at quality assurance in Florida. <u>QRB</u>, 9(10):p310-1, (Oct. 1983).

1139 Wheelock, R.D. Reconciliation and the hospital patient. <u>Hosp. Prog.</u>, 56(10):p60-3, (Oct. 1975).

1140 Wiley, L. Good patient care: can you give it in the real world? <u>Nursing</u>, 7(9):p105-6,108-9, (Sep. 1977).

1141 Williams, K.N.; Brook, R.H. Foreign medical graduates and their impact on the quality of medical care in the United States. <u>Milbank Mem. Fund Q.</u>, 53(4):p549-81, (Fall 1975).

1142 Wilson, L.L. The implications of quality assurance in Australia. <u>NZ Med. J.</u>, 94(691):p181-4, (Sep. 9, 1981).

1143 Wiseman, J. Accountability: health quality assurance. <u>Nurs. Times</u>, 79(1):p16-8, (Jan. 5-11, 1983).

1144 Wittrock, J.W. Does accreditation foster quality assurance [letter]. <u>J. Dent. Educ.</u>, 45(12):p785, (Dec. 1981).

1145 Wolkstein, I. The ninth Arthur C. Beall, Jr., MD.,
      Commemorative Lectures. Health technology: the hope and
      the fear. <u>Med. Instrum.</u>, 12(3):p200-1, (May-Jun. 1978).

1146 Young, M.G. Competence and quality assurance in
      medicine. <u>Tex. Med.</u>, 82(8):p64-8, (Aug. 1986).

1147 Zambito, R.F. Quality assurance of hospital dental
      care: the hospital and quality of care.
      <u>J. Hosp. Dent. Pract.</u>, 14(2):p80-4, (1980).

1148 Zaremski, M.J. Hospital corporate liability: the walls
      continue to tumble. <u>Medicoleg. News</u>, 9(2):p13-5,20,
      (Apr. 1981).

CHAPTER 3:

UTILIZATION REVIEW REFERENCES

Theory and Concept

1149 Bartek, W. Utilization review creates terms. Tex. Hosp.,
      41(3)p7, (Aug. 1985).

1150 Berg, R.N. Utilization and quality control peer review
      organizations--a rose by any other name...? J. Med. Assoc. Ga.,
      71(11):p793-6, (Nov. 1982).

1151 Boaz, R.F. Utilization review and containment for hospital
      utilization: some implications of providing care in the "most
      appropriate setting". Med. Care, 17(4):p315-30, (Apr. 1979).

1152 Brodie, D.C.; Benson, R.A. Drug Utilization Review and Drug
      Usage as a Determinant of the Quality of Health Care. Final
      report. 29 Jun. 74-28 Dec. 75. Sponsor(s): Los Angeles
      County-Univ. of Southern California Medical Center, National
      Center for Health Services Research, Rockville, Md.,
      NTIS Order No.: PB-253 731/4, p.224, (Jan. 28, 1976).

1153 Brodie, D.C.; Smith, W.E. Constructing a conceptual model of
      drug utilization review. Hospitals, 50(6)p143-4,146,148,
      passim, (Mar. 16, 1976).

1154 Brook, R.H.; Lohr, K.N. Efficacy, effectiveness, variations,
      and quality. Boundary-crossing research. Med. Care,
      23(5):p710-22, (May 1985).

1155 Brown, D.E.; Levy, J.D. Utilization review altered to
      advantage. Hospitals, 54(5):p83-6, (Mar. 1 1980).

1156 Connelly, D.; Steele, B. Laboratory utilization. Problems and
      solutions [editorial]. Arch. Pathol. Lab. Med., 104(2):p59-62,
      (Feb. 1980).

101

1157 Curran, W.J. Law-medicine notes. Medical standards and medical ethics in utilization review for nursing homes. N. Engl. J. Med., 308(8):p435-6, (Feb. 24, 1983).

1158 DiBlase, D. Hospital utilization review pays off: experts. Bus. Insur., 20(7):p12,14,18, (Feb. 17, 1986).

1159 DiBlase, D. Psychiatric care focus of utilization review. Bus. Insur., 20(7):p17, (Feb 17, 1986).

1160 Dorney, D.C. Setting resource utilization standards in a Community Mental Health Center. QRB, 8(11):p14-21, (Nov. 1982).

1161 Dunea, G. Decibels and utilization review [editorial]. JAMA, 238(6):p514, (Aug 8, 1977).

1162 Eisenberg, J.M. The use of ancillary services: a role for utilization review? Med. Care, 20(8):p849-61, ISSN 0025-7079, (Aug. 1982).

1163 Epstein, A.M.; McNeil, B.J. Relationship of beliefs and behavior in test ordering. Am. J. Med., 80(5):p865-70, (May 1986).

1164 Falcone, A.R. Capitalizing on prospective reimbursement with a new utilization system. QRB, 10(10):p316-24, (Oct. 1984).

1165 Felder, L.H. Utilization--the name of the game. J. Med. Assoc. Ga., 73(4):p227-8, (Apr. 1984).

1166 Gertman, P.M.; Manuel, B. A scientific approach to second opinions: editorial comment [editorial]. Obstet. Gynecol., 56(4):p411-2, (Oct. 1980).

1167 Giordano, F.L. Values conflict in utilization review in the military [editorial]. Milit. Med., 150(4):p221-2, (Apr. 1985).

1168 Goldowsky, S.J. Editorial: Wither utilization review? RI.Med. J., 59(1):p25,32, (Jan. 1976).

1169 Grimaldi, P.L.; Micheletti, J.A. Utilization and quality review under the prospective rate system. QRB, 10(2):p30-7, (Feb. 1984).

1170 Grimaldi, P.L.; Micheletti, J.A. PRO objectives and quality criteria. Hospitals, 59(3):p64-7, (Feb 1, 1985).

1171 Gurevitz, H. All marriages are not in heaven made: the joining of quality assurance and utilization review. J. Natl. Assoc. Priv. Psychiatr. Hosp., 8(3):p17-20, (Fall 1976).

1172 Handel, B. Hospital utilization review--an essential element in
      health care cost containment. Employee Benefits J., 9(3:)p8-12,
      30, (Sept. 1984).

1173 Huber, S.L.; Patry, R.A. Internal standards: rationale for use
      in a drug utilization review program. Drug Intell. Clin.
      Pharm., 15(10):p789-92, (Oct. 1981).

1174 Kahan, R.; Tobin, R.G. Utilization review can be tool for
      improvement. Hospitals, 52(6):p89-90, 94, (Mar. 16, 1978).

1175 Kane, R.L.; Rubenstein, L.Z.; Brook, R.H.; VanRyzin, J.;
      Masthay, P.; Schoenrich, E.; Harrell, B. Utilization review in
      nursing homes: making implicit level-of-care judgments
      explicit. Med. Care, 19(1):p3-13, (Jan. 1981).

1176 Katz, P.S. Integrating quality assurance, utilization review,
      and risk management activities for the small hospital. QRB,
      12(3):p114-5, (Mar. 1986).

1177 Kearns, P.M. Utilization review expanded into quality assurance
      program. Hospitals, 54(17):p62-3, (Sept. 1, 1980).

1178 Keys, P.W. Drug-use review and risk management.
      Am. J. Hosp. Pharm., 38(10):p1533-4, (Oct. 1981).

1179 Korjus, J.H. Utilization review--utility or futility? Am. Arch
      Rehabil. Ther., 27(3):p23-6, (Fall 1979).

1180 Levin, J.M. Effect of utilization review on surgical training
      with reference to the increasing importance of the ward service
      in this changing environment [editorial]. Am. J. Surg.,
      145(2):p191-2, (Feb. 1983).

1181 Liljestrand, J.S. Test your skills: utilization review. Hosp.
      Peer. Rev., 4(12):p162-3, (Dec. 1979).

1182 Magraw, R.M. Formal quality-assessment and utilization-review
      programs: their effects on the basic transactions of medical
      education. Bull. N.Y. Acad. Med., 52(1):p105-18, (Jan. 1976).

1183 McCurdy, T.R.; Chase, D.C. Utilization review: P.S.R.O. and the
      oral surgeon. Oral Surg. Oral Med. Oral Pathol., 42(3):p271-7,
      (Sept. 1976).

1184 Moore, J.M. Utilization review: the Blue Cross perspective.
      QRB, 4(6):p29-31, (Jun. 1978).

1185 Mutter, C.B. Peer medical utilization review: conformity or
      avoidance? J. Fla. Med. Assoc., 67(11):p1029-30, (Nov. 1980).

1186 Nelson, A.R. Relation between quality assessment and utilization review in a functioning PSRO. N. Engl. J. Med., 292(13):p671-5, (Mar. 27, 1975).

1187 Noble, S.; Willoughby, P.W. Drug utilization review for oncology drugs: background and issues. Top Hosp. Pharm. Manage., 1(3):p65-79, (Nov. 1981).

1188 Reisine, S.T.; Bailit, H.L. History and organization of pretreatment review, a dental utilization review system. Public Health Rep., 95(3):p282-90, (May-Jun. 1980).

1189 Richards, G. Business spurs UR growth. Hospitals are coming under increased scrutiny from outside utilization review. Hospitals, 58(5):p96,98-100, (Mar. 1, 1984).

1190 Rogers, E.; Blamey, K. DRGs and utilization review--do they work? Top Health Rec. Manage., 4(3):p88-98, (Mar. 1984).

1191 Schueler, A. Utilization review for Medicare. Does it open a new gap in services? Am. J. Nurs., 77(1):p110-1, (Jan. 1977).

1192 Schwarz, F. Least restrictive alternative and utilization review: meeting requirements in a single system. Hosp. Community Psychiatry, 32(3):p204-6, (Mar. 1981).

1193 Sieverts, S. The uses of utilization review [editorial]. N. Engl. J. Med., 299(11):p601-2, (Sept. 14, 1978).

1194 Stolar, M.H. Opportunity for clinical pharmacy in concurrent and prospective drug-use review [editorial]. Am. J. Hosp. Pharm., 39(6):p985, (Jun. 1982).

1195 Stolar, M.H. The case for prospective and concurrent drug utilization review. American Society of Hospital Pharmacists, Bethesda, Maryland. QRB, 8(6):p6-10, (Jun. 1982).

1196 Studnicki, J.; Stevens, C.E. The impact of a cybernetic control system on inappropriate admissions. QRB, 10(10):p304-11, (Oct. 1984).

1197 Thompson, R.E. From "medical audit" and "UR" to effective use of patient care data. IMJ, 158(1):p19-24, (Jul. 1980).

1198 Tippett, J.; Smith, B. Developing a utilization review model for community mental health centers. Hosp. Community Psychiatry, 26(3):p65-6, (Mar. 1975).

1199 Traditional utilization review methods--much ado about nothing. Second Opinion Health Care Issues, 1(8):p1-3, (Oct. 1980).

1200 Tremblay, J. Drug-use review and risk management: another view [letter]. Am. J. Hosp. Pharm. (UNITED STATES), 39(4):p578-80, (Apr. 1982).

1201 Tremblay, J.; LeBlanc, P.P. A comment on "Peer Review in Ambulatory Care" [letter]. Med. Care, 17(11):p1154-5, (Nov. 1979).

1202 Utilization review regulations stir controversy and concern. J. Okla. State Med. Assoc., 68(3):p98-9, (Mar. 1975).

1203 Wertheimer, A.I. The defined daily dose system (DDD) for drug utilization review. Hosp. Pharm., 21(3):p233-4,239-41,258, (Mar. 1986).

1204 Wymelenberg, S. Aggressive utilization review shortens stays, lower cost. Hospitals, 52(9):p75-6,78, (May 1, 1978).

1205 Zaslow J. Medicare and the physician: utilization review. Leg. Aspects Med. Pract., 6(3)p41-3, (Mar. 1978).

Programs, Techniques & Procedures

1206 A drug utilization review program with teeth in it. Hosp. Formul., 12(3)p194-5, (Mar. 1977).

1207 Allen, C.V. A personal system for utilization review management. Med. Group Manage., 32(5)p14-21, 32, (Sep.-Oct. 1985).

1208 Bachman, D.C. Meniscectomy review: various focuses for evaluating care of meniscectomy patients. QRB, 5(9)p2-5, (Sept. 1979).

1209 Bailit, H.L.; Clive, J. The development of dental practice profiles. Med. Care, 19(1)p30-46, (Jan. 1981).

1210 Balmasov, A.A.; Kondrashev, A.K.; Erokhov, B.A.; Lisanov, A.G.; Zebode, V.G. (Development and introduction of the Bed Reserve Subsystem) Razrabotka i vnedrenie podsistemy "Koechnyi fond". Sov Zdravookhr, (8)p16-22, (1985).

1211 Barnard, C.; Esmond, T. DRG-based reimbursement: the use of concurrent and retrospective clinical data. Med. Care, 19(11)p1071-82, (Nov. 1981).

1212 Behling, R.J. A pharmacist's primer on drug utilization review. Am. Pharm., 21(6)p33-6, (Jun. 1981).

1213 Bergman, U.; Christenson, I.; Jansson, B.; Wiholm, B.E.
Auditing hospital drug utilization by means of defined daily
doses per bed-day. A methodological study. Eur. J. Clin.
Pharmacol, 17(3)p183-7, (1980).

1214 Binns, T.B. Drug utilization and therapeutic audit. Br. J.
Clin. Pharmacol, 9(3)p227-8, (Mar. 1980).

1215 Blanchard, R.J.; Downs, A.R. Clinical audit of surgery in a
large teaching hospital. Can. J. Surg., 23(3)p278-82, (May
1980).

1216 Block, W.E. Applying utilization review procedures in a
community mental health center. Hosp. Community Psychiatry,
26(6)p358-62, (Jun. 1975).

1217 Budkin, A.; Jacobs, W.A.; Smith, C.D.; Daily, J.D.; Button,
J.H.; Berman, R.L. An automated PSRO-utilization review system.
J. Med. Syst., 6(2)p139-47, (Apr. 1982).

1218 Butler, R.J. Quality assurance in hospital dental practice.
Aust. Dent. J., 29(4)p257-9, (Aug. 1984).

1219 Chase, C.R.; Merz, B.A.; Mazuzan, J.E. Computer assisted
patient evaluation (CAPE): a multi-purpose computer system for
an anesthesia service. Anesth. Analg., 62(2)p198-206, (Feb.
1983).

1220 Dancey, J.W. Drug utilization review at Lions Gate Hospital.
Can. J. Hosp. Pharm., 31(2)p55-7, (Mar.-Apr. 1978).

1221 DesHarnais, S.; Kibe, N.M.; Barbus, S. Blue Cross and Blue
Shield of Michigan hospital laboratory on-site review project.
Inquiry, 20(4)p328-33, (Winter 1983).

1222 Dexter, C. Utilization review in an alcoholism treatment
program. QRB, 5(11)p13-6, (Nov. 1979).

1223 Dodds, J.J. Utilization review: surveillance reduces
admissions. Hospitals, 48(23)p52-5, (Dec. 1, 1974).

1224 Dollard, V.M. Utilization review and continuing care program in
an HMO. Top Health Rec. Manage., 6(4)p66-71, (Jun. 1986).

1225 Dunn, R.T. Computer assistance for utilization review. Med.
Rec. News, 48(4)p62-9, (Aug. 1977).

1226 Echols, R.M.; Kowalsky, S.F. The use of an antibiotic order
form for antibiotic utilization review: influence on
physicians' prescribing patterns. J. Infect. Dis.,
150(6)p803-7, (Dec. 1984).

1227   Edwards, A.B.   Care level and timeliness review--an approach to curbing inappropriate hospital utilization. Top Health Care Financ., 7(3)P47-60, (Spring 1981).

1228   Fielding, J.E.   A utilization review program in the making. Bus. Health, 2(7)p25-8, (Jun. 1985).

1229   Garg, M.L.; Kleinberg, W.M.; Schmitt, B.; Barzansky, B.M.   A new methodology for ancillary services review. Med. Care, 23(6)p809-15, (Jun. 1985).

1230   Gertman, P.M.; Restuccia, J.D.   The appropriateness evaluation protocol: a techique for assessing unnecessary days of hospital care. Med. Care, 19(8)p855-71, (Aug. 1981).

1231   Goldberg, G.A.; Holloway, D.C.   Emphasizing "level of care" over "length of stay" in hospital utilization review. Med. Care, 13(6)p474-85, (Jun. 1975).

1232   Goldensohn, S.S.   Cost, utilization, and utilization review of mental health services in a prepaid group practice plan. Am. J. Psychiatry, 134(11)p1222-6, (Nov. 1977).

1233   Goldstein, J.; Miller, L.V.   The use of radiographic studies in a teaching hospital. J. Med. Syst., 4(3-4)p347-54, (1980).

1234   Groves, R.E.   Therapeutic drug-use review for the Florida Medicaid program. Am. J. Hosp. Pharm., 42(2)p316-9, (Feb. 1985).

1235   Guest, K.; McLean, A.J.; Wellington, C.V.   Drug assay services and therapeutic drug use in a general hospital. Med. J. Aust., 1(4)p167-70, (Feb. 23, 1980).

1236   Guidelines for Hospital Patient Care Evaluation, Patient Care Audit and Utilization Review. NTIS Order No.: HRP-0018181, 27p, (Jun. 1975).

1237   Hall, J.   Utilization review I: an outline of the method. Aust. Clin. Rev., (3)p3-4, (Nov. 1981).

1238   Heineman, H.S.; Watt, V.S.   All-inclusive concurrent antibiotic usage review: a way to reduce misuse without formal controls. Infect. Control, 7(3)p168-71, (Mar. 1986).

1239   Hekster, Y.A.; Friesen, W.T.; Boerema, J.B.   Record-linked audit of drug utilization data in a hospital: antimicrobial use on a urology ward. J. Clin. Hosp. Pharm., 6(4)p277-83, (Dec. 1981).

1240   Helling, D.K.; Hepler, C.D.; Herman, R.A.   Comparison of computer-assisted medical record audit with other drug use review methods. Am. J. Hosp. Pharm, 36(12)p1665-71, (Dec. 1979).

1241 Hermansen, M.C.; Blodgett, F.M. Prospective evaluation of routine admission urinalyses. Am. J. Dis. Child, 135(2)p126-30, (Feb. 1981).

1242 Hirt, F.D.; Solomon, J.R. Utilizing Utilization Review: a model medical care evaluation. J. Am. Health Care Assoc., 2(3)p25-30, (May 1976).

1243 Hlynka, J.N.; Smith, W.E., Jr.; Brodie, D.C. Developing drug-use profiles from drug-charge records. Am. J. Hosp. Pharm., 36(10)p1347-51, (Oct. 1979).

1244 Hoffmann, R.P. Anti-infective utilization review in a community hospital based on published guidelines. Hosp. Pharm., 13(9)p461, 465, 468 passim, (Sep. 1978).

1245 Hoffmann, R.P. Using the PAS system for hospital drug utilization review. Hosp. Prog., 60(1)p54-6, 68, (Jan. 1979).

1246 Hollmann, M. Chemotherapeutic-bacteriological interdependences observed by use of a clinical anti-infective drug monitoring system. Eur. J. Clin. Pharmacol, 17(2)p101-9, (Feb. 1980).

1247 Homer, C.G. Methods of hospital use control in health maintenance organizations. Health Care Manage. Rev., 11(2)p15-23, (Spring 1986).

1248 Huber, S.L.; Patry, R.A. Internal standards: rationale for use in a drug utilization review program. Drug Intell. Clin. Pharm., 15(10)p789-92, (Oct. 1981).

1249 Hunter, S.A. Retrospective utilization review as a focused method of evaluation. QRB, 6(2)p11-2, (Feb. 1980).

1250 Ingman, S.R.; Claus, L.M. Preadmission assessments for geriatric patients. QRB, 7(9)p3-5, (Sep. 1981).

1251 John, G.W. Drug utilization review: a cost-effective method that doesn't tie up costly pharmacy staff time [interview]. Cost Containment, 4(11)p7-8, (Jun. 8, 1982).

1252 John, G.W.; Spieler, J.L., Jr. Drug utilization review: a practical approach. Hosp. Pharm., 16(11)p587-90, 595-8, (Nov. 1981).

1253 Kabat, H.F.; Kidder, S.W.; Marttila, J.K.; Stewart, J.E. Bureau of Quality Assurance, Rockville, Md. Drug Utilization Review in Skilled Nursing Facilities. A Manual System for Performing Sample Studies of Drug Utilization. GPO Order No.: 017-026-00045-3, 125p, (Nov. 1975).

1254 Kabat, H.F.; Marttila, J.; Stewart, J. Use of protocols. Drug utilization review in skilled nursing facilities. J. Am. Pharm. Assoc., 15(1)p34-7, (Jan. 1975).

1255 Kane, R.L.; Olsen, D.M.; Thetford, C.; Byrnes, N. The use of utilization review records as a source of data on nursing home care. Am. J. Public Health, 66(8)p778-82, (Aug. 1976).

1256 Kane, R.L.; Rubenstein, L.Z.; Brook, R.H.; VanRyzin, J.; Masthay, P.; Schoenrich, E.; Harrell, B. Utilization review in nursing homes: making implicit level-of-care judgments explicit. Med. Care, 19(1)p3-13, (Jan. 1981).

1257 Kilarski, D.J.; Schneider, P.J.; Teil, S.M.; Lemay, A.P. Use review of intravenous infusion devices. Am. J. Hosp. Pharm., 38(10)p1517-8, (Oct. 1981).

1258 Kincaid, W.H. Changing physician behavior: the peer data method. QRB, 10(8)p238-42, (Aug. 1984).

1259 Kleffel, D. Utilization Review Project for Home Health Agencies. NTIS Order No.: HRP-0006956, 18p., (Nov. 1975).

1260 Kleffel, D.; Wilson, E. Utilization Review and a Statistical Information Program for Home Health Agencies. NTIS Order No.: HRP-0014984, 204p, (Jun. 1975).

1261 Knapp, D.A. Developing criteria for drug prescribing review--a SIG project (letter). Am. J. Hosp. Pharm., 36(11)p1465, 1470, (Nov. 1979).

1262 Komaroff, A.L.; Sherman, H.; Ervin, C.T.; Pass, T.M. Protocols and "auditable" checklists in ambulatory medical care. QRB, 5(2)p22-6, (Feb. 1979).

1263 Kramer, P.M.; Martin, B.A. The Clarke Institute experience with electroconvulsive therapy: I. Development of a clinical audit procedure. Can. J. Psychiatry, 29(8)p648-51, (Dec. 1984).

1264 Krischer, J.P.; Cheung, A.; Bush, P.; Sleight, S.M. Drug utilization review in the Veterans Administration. QRB, 8(10)p11-9, (Oct. 1982).

1265 Kuhnmuench, P.; Hill, C. Utilization review in the internal medicine department of an HMO clinic. QRB, 8(11)p22-9, (Nov. 1982).

1266 Lamin, M. Nonantibiotic drug utilization review. QRB, 10(7)p218-21, (Jul. 1984).

1267 Legge, D. Medical care review in Australia: 2 A focus on the process and outcome of medical care. Aust. Clin. Rev. (3)p29-37, (Nov. 1981).

1268   Leist, E.R.   A blueprint for antibiotic utilization review.
       Hosp. Med. Staff, 10(5)p19-24, (May 1981).

1269   Manion, C.V.; Hassanein, K.   A hospital use evaluation by
       numerical taxonomy.   Comput. Biomed. Res., 13(6)p567-80, (Dec.
       1980).

1270   Martin, R.D.   A method for documenting and displaying
       problem-focused activities.   QRB, 7(4)p24-7, (Apr. 1981).

1271   Mashford, M.L.; Robertson, M.B.   Surveying antibiotic use in a
       general teaching hospital.   Med. J. Aust., 2(10)p515-8, (Nov.
       17, 1979).

1272   McConnell, T.S.; Berger, P.R.; Dayton, H.H.; Umland, B.E.;
       Skipper, B.E.   Professional review of laboratory utilization.
       Hum. Pathol., 13(4)p399-403, (Apr. 1982).

1273   McCormick, R.A.; Ramirez, L.F.   Clinician-interactive
       computerized utilization review for mental health care.   QRB,
       12(4)p121-7, (Apr. 1986).

1274   McManus, C.D.; Smalley, D.L.; Sanders, D.E.   Monitoring
       laboratory services through concurrent review.   QRB, 8(2)p5-9,
       (Feb. 1982).

1275   Mehl, B.   Use of electronic data processing for drug utilization
       review.   QRB, 5(1)p13-6, (Jan. 1979).

1276   Mitchell, N.L.   A suggested schema for utilization review for a
       Community Mental Health Center.   J. Natl. Med. Assoc.,
       69(4)p237-9, (Apr. 1, 1977).

1277   Morgan, J.P.   Watching the monitors: "PAID" prescriptions,
       fiscal intermediaries and drug-utilization review.   N. Engl. J.
       Med., 296(5)p251-6, (Feb. 3, 1977).

1278   Moss, J.; Wyatt, G.; Christopherson, D.; Routh, S.   A
       prospective drug utilization review on the prescribing of oral
       and parenteral cephalosporins.   Hosp. Formul., 17(12)p1589-91,
       1596-8, 1601, (Dec. 1982).

1279   Mott, P.D.   Hospital utilization by health maintenance
       organizations.   Separating apples from oranges.   Med. Care,
       24(5)p398-406, (May 1986).

1280   Mullin, R.L.   Utilization review based on practitioner
       profiles.   J. Med. Syst., 7(5)p409-12, (Oct. 1983).

1281   Mushlin, A.I.   The analysis of clinical practices: shedding
       light on cost containment opportunities in medicine.   QRB,
       11(12)p378-84, (Dec. 1985).

1282   O'Donnell, L. Manchester Memorial Hospital utilization review
       program. Med. Rec. News, 46(2)p20-2, (Apr. 1975).

1283   Opit, L.J.; Selwood, T.S. Caesarean-section rates in Australia:
       a population-based audit. Med. J. Aust., 2(13)p706-9, (Dec. 29,
       1979).

1284   Pelletier, L.L., Jr. Hospital usage of parenteral antimicrobial
       agents: a gradated utilization review and cost containment
       program. Infect. Control, 6(6)p226-30, (Jun. 1985).

1285   Perler, J.M. Utilization review for the PPO. Hosp. Forum,
       25(6)p23-5, (Nov.-Dec. 1982).

1286   Reed, D.M.; Hepler, C.D.; Helling, D.K. Antibiotic use review
       in ambulatory care using computer-assisted medical record audit.
       Am. J. Hosp. Pharm., 39(2)p280-4, (Feb. 1982).

1287   Reisine, S.T.; Bailit, H.L. History and organization of
       pretreatment review, a dental utilization review system. Public
       Health Rep., 95(3)p282-90, (May-Jun. 1980).

1288   Rishpon, S.; Lubacsh, S.; Epstein, L.M. Reliability of a method
       of determining the necessity for hospitalization days in Israel.
       Med. Care, 24(3)p279-82, (Mar. 1986).

1289   Salsberry, P.; Glynn K. A PPS for Medicaid: one state's
       approach. Nurs. Manage., 16(1)p35-9, 42-5, (Jan. 1985).

1290   Scarafile, P.D.; Campbell, B.D.; Kilroy, J.E.; Mathewson, H.O.
       Computer-assisted concurrent antibiotic review in a community
       hospital. Am. J. Hosp. Pharm., 42(2)p313-5, (Feb. 1985).

1291   Schwartz, J.I.; Kennedy, T.J. Computer-assisted
       practitioner-response system for studying the use of cimetidine.
       Am. J. Hosp. Pharm., 39(7)p1198-201, (Jul. 1982).

1292   Schwarz, F. Least restrictive alternative and utilization
       review: meeting requirements in a single system. Hosp.
       Community Psychiatry, 32(3)p204-6, (Mar. 1981).

1293   Shannon, R.C.; DeMuth, J.E. Application of federal indicators
       in nursing-home drug-regimen review. Am. J. Hosp. Pharm.,
       41(5)p912-6, (May 1984).

1294   Spencer, J.H., Jr.; Mattson, M.R. Criteria for admission to a
       psychiatric hospital: a guide to their use. QRB, 5(12)p8-15,
       (Dec. 1979).

1295   State Welfare ADP Application, Medicaid Management
       Information Subsystem Detail Design Specifications for the State
       of New Hampshire, Section V. Surveillance and Utilization Review
       Subsystem. NTIS Order No.: PB-243 572/5, 1063p., (Apr. 30,
       1975).

1296 Stephany, T.M. Utilization review in a hospice program. _J. Community Health Nurs._, 2(1)p13-20, (1985).

1297 Stewart, J.E. Manual Drug Utilization Review System for Skilled Nursing Facilities. _Thesis_, 311p, (Mar. 1975).

1298 Studnicki, J.; Honemann, D. Analyzing inpatient hospital duration and intensity: a methodology. _QRB_, 8(9)p15-26, (Sep. 1982).

1299 Sussman, E.J.; Eisenberg, J.M.; Williams, S.V. Diagnostic services utilization review at a university medical center. _Health Care Manage. Rev._, 6(4)p65-8, (Fall 1981).

1300 Thompson, R.E. A patient care review model to suit both hospitals and PSROs. _Hospitals_, 54(16)p61-3, (Aug. 16, 1980).

1301 Tobin, R.G. Audit disclosure: length of stay problems for utilization review. _QRB_, 4(6)p23-5, (Jun. 1978).

1302 Tremblay, J. (The clinical pharmacist and drug utilization review) Le pharmacien-clinique et la revision de l'utilisation mdicamenteuse. _Union Med. Can._, 108(12)p1425-30, (Dec. 1979).

1303 Vaughan, W.P.; Waalkes, T.P.; Lenhard, R.E., Jr.; Watkins, S.P.; Sadler, W.P.; Stout, D.A.; Carney, S.P.; DelCarmen, B.V.; Herring, D.F. Patterns of care in oncology: an approach to medical and utilization audit. _Prog. Clin. Biol. Res._, 120p139-50, (1983).

1304 Walter, R.S. The hottest new thing in utilization review. _Med. Econ._, 60(4)p177, 180-1, (Feb. 21, 1983).

1305 Weaver, P.G. The bed utilization review index. _Dimens. Health Serv._, 52(1)p14-5, (Jan. 1975).

1306 West, S.K.; Brandon, B.M.; Stevens, A.M.; Zauber, A.; Chase, G.; Stolley, P.D.; Rumrill, R.E. Drug utilization review in an HMO. I. Introduction and examples of methodology. _Med. Care_, 15(6)p505-14, (Jun. 1977).

1307 Withersty, D.J.; Spradlin, W.W. A system to document medical records for utilization review. _Hosp. Community Psychiatry_, 28(12)p881, 885, (Dec. 1977).

1308 Witte, K.W.; Leeds, N.H.; Pathak, D.S.; Campagna, K.D.; West, D.P.; Spunt, A.L. Drug regimen review in skilled nursing facilities by consulting clinical pharmacists. _Am. J. Hosp. Pharm._, 37(6)P820-4, (Jun. 1980).

1309 Wright, G.; Goldberg, M.; Mark, H.; Petrillo, M.K.; Wiesel, B.
Utilization review of increase ambulatory-based surgery.
Application for surgical tooth extraction. QRB, 9(4)p100-6,
(Apr. 1983).

1310 Yaffe, R. Analyzing hospital discharge data to support
utilization review and quality assurance activities. Top
Health Rec. Manage., 2(3)p31-44, (Mar. 1982).

1311 Zegans, L.S.; Geller, J.; Flynn, H.; Swartzburg, M.;
Schowalter, J. Utilization review of the late adolescent
patient in a mental health center: steps toward the development
of criteria for the adequacy of assessment and treatment.
J. Nerv. Ment. Dis., 164(3)p198-209, (Mar. 1977).

1312 Zeleznik, C.; Gonnella, J.S. Jefferson Medical College Student
Model Utilization Review Committee. J. Med. Educ.,
54(11)p848-51, (Nov. 1979).

1313 Zilz, D. Drug utilization review at University of Wisconsin
Hospitals. Hosp. Formul., 13(10)p806-7, (Oct. 1978).

1314 Zimmerman, M.H.; Schlein, P.; Fuller, N.A.; Carrier, E.
Professional Standards Review Organization studies length of
stay for cataract extraction in District of Columbia hospitals.
Public Health Rep., 96(5)p439-41, (Sep.-Oct. 1981).

Research: Studies and Data

1315 A study of the utilization of skull radiography in 9
accident-and-emergency units in the U.K. A national study by
the Royal College of Radiologists. Lancet, 2(8206)p1234-6,
(Dec. 6, 1980).

1316 Adler, N.E.; Milstein, A. Evaluating the impact of physician
peer review: factors associated with successful PSROs. Am. J.
Public Health, 73(10)p1182-5, (Oct. 1983).

1317 Akhter, M.N. PRO review of hospital admissions of Medicare
patients. Mo. Med., 82(3)p123-6, (Mar. 1985).

1318 Ambrosioni, E.; Costa, F.V.; Marata, A.M. Evaluation of
rationality of use of antibiotics in a department of internal
medicine and possibility of correction. Prog. Clin. Biol. Res.,
35p183-93, (1979).

1319 Anderson, H.R.; Bailey, P.; West, S. Trends in the hospital
care of acute childhood asthma 1970-8: a regional study. Br.
Med. J., 281(6249)p1191-4, (Nov. 1, 1980).

1320 Aycock, E.K. PRN drug use in nursing homes. Am. J. Hosp. Pharm., 38(1)p105, (Jan. 1981).

1321 Bailit, H.L.; Balzer, J.A.; Clive, J. Evaluation of a focused dental utilization review system. Med. Care, 21(5)p473-85, (May 1983).

1322 Barnes, B.A.; O'Brien E.; Comstock, C.; D'Arpa, D.G.; Donahue, C.L. Report on variation in rates of utilization of surgical services in the Commonwealth of Massachusetts. JAMA, 254(3)p371-5, (Jul. 19, 1985).

1323 Barriere, S.L.; Conte, J.E., Jr. Aminoglycoside use monitored by clinical pharmaceutical services. Am. J. Hosp. Pharm., 36(9)p1209-11, (Sep. 1979).

1324 Benedict, S. Medical Care Evaluation Studies for Utilization Review in Skilled Nursing Facilities. NTIS Order No.: HRP-0009651, 62 p., (Jun. 1975).

1325 Bernstein, L.R.; Barriere, S.L.; Conte, J.E., Jr. Utilization of antibiotics: analysis of appropriateness of use. Ann. Emerg. Med., 11(8)p400-3, Aug. 1982.

1326 Boone, C.R.; Coulton, C.J.; Keller, S.M. The impact of early and comprehensive social work services on length of stay. Soc. Work Health Care, 7(1)p1-9, (Fall 1981).

1327 Calogero, M.A.; Hill, D.B. Periodic medical review: the impact in Pennsylvania. Med. Care, 20(1)p85-96, (Jan. 1982).

1328 Casewell, M. Correlation of antibiotic utilization on a urological ward with antibiotic policy. Prog. Clin. Biol. Res., 35p171-9 (1979).

1329 Charlwood, R.; Gibbons, K. The nutritional management of obese patients--a utilization review. Aust. Clin. Rev., 6(20)p49-52, (Mar. 1986).

1330 Chinn, F.J. Medicaid recipient lock-in program--Hawaii's experience in six years. Hawaii Med. J., 44(1)p9-18, (Jan. 1985).

1331 Cleary, P.D.; Jette, A.M. The validity of self-reported physician utilization measures. Med. Care, 22(9)p796-803, (Sep. 1984).

1332 Clemans, S.; Hamlin, R.H. PSRO: An Evaluation of the Professional Standards Review Organization. Volume 8. The Costs of Utilization Review Programs in Hospitals and PSRO's. Final rpt., NTIS Order No.: PB-275 512/2, 402 p., (Oct. 1977).

1333 Clendenning, M.K.; Wolfe, H.; Shuman, L.J.; Huber, G.A. The effect of a target date based utilization review program on length of stay. Med. Care, 14(9)p751-64, (Sep. 1976).

1334 Cohen, E.; Bernier, D.; Tam S.; Schimel, D.; Postel, A.H.; Scheidt, S.; Stamm, J.B. Data quality and DRGs: an assessment of the reliability of federal beneficiary discharge data in selected Manhattan hospitals. J. Community Health, 10(4)p238-46, (Winter, 1985).

1335 Connell, F.A.; Blide, L.A.; Hanken, M.A. Clinical correlates of small area variations in population-based admission rates for diabetes. Med. Care, 22(10)p939-49, (Oct. 1984).

1336 Counahan, R. An àudit of regional paediatric in-patient practice. Part I--Statistics. Ir. Med. J., 74(9)p248-50, (Sep. 1981).

1337 Covell, B.; Angus, M.M. A comparison of the characteristics of elderly patients admitted to acute medical and geriatric wards. Health Bull, 38(2)p64-70, (Mar. 1980).

1338 Crane, V.S. Rational use of drugs should be emphasized in utilization review. Tex. Hosp., 39(6)p26, (Nov. 1983).

1339 Cummins, R.O.; LoGerfo, J.P.; Inui, T.S.; Weiss, N.S. High-yield referral criteria of posttraumatic skull roentgenography. Response of physicians and accuracy of criteria. JAMA, 244(7)p673-6, (Aug. 15, 1980).

1340 Curry, C.E., Jr.; Antal, E.G.; Keys, P.W.; Duffy, M.G. Audit of phenytoin prescribing for outpatients. Am. J. Hosp. Pharm., 38(8)p1158-60, (Aug. 1981).

1341 Detmer, D.E.; Nevers, L.E.; Sikes, E.D., Jr. Regional results of acute appendicitis care. JAMA, 246(12)p1318-20, (Sep. 18, 1981).

1342 Dexter, C. Utilization review in an alcoholism treatment program. QRB, 5(11)p13-6, (Nov. 1979).

1343 Dini, M.; Fua, C.; Renga, G. Enquiry on the antibiotic usage at Ancona Regional Hospital. Prog. Clin. Biol. Res., 35p59-61, (1979).

1344 Durkin, J.W., Jr.; Bennett, J.B. Ectopic pregnancy: its occurrence in two community hospitals using medical audit techniques for review. W. Va. Med. J., 76(11)p287-90, (Nov. 1981).

1345 Eastaugh, S.R. Cost of elective surgery and utilization of ancillary services in teaching hospitals. Health Serv. Res., 14(4)p290-308, (Winter 1979).

1346   Echols, R.M.; Kowalsky, S.F. The use of an antibiotic form for
        antibiotic utilization review: influence on physicians'
        prescribing patterns. J. Infect. Dis., 150(6)p803-7, (Dec.
        1984).

1347   Eisenberg, J.M.; Williams, S.V. Limited usefulness of the
        proportion of tests with normal results in review of diagnostic
        services utilization. Clin. Chem., 29(12)p2111-3, (Dec. 1983).

1348   Eiser, C.; Eiser, J.R. Mothers' experiences on the postnatal
        ward. Child Care Health Dev., 11(6)p349-54, (Nov-Dec. 1985).

1349   Elliott, R.V.; Kahn, K.A.; Kaye, R. Physicians measure up. A
        study of 13 surgical procedures. JAMA, 245(6)p595-600, (Feb.
        13, 1981).

1350   Evans, J.G.; Wandless, I.; Prudham, D. A prospective study of
        fractured proximal femur: hospital differences. Public Health,
        94(3)p149-54, (May 1980).

1351   Evens, R.G.; Jost, R.G.; Evens, R.G., Jr. Economic and
        utilization analysis of magnetic resonance imaging units in the
        United States in 1985. AJR, 145(2)p393-8, (Aug. 1985).

1352   Faden, F.B.; Goldman, H.H. Appropriateness of placement of
        patients in state and county mental hospital. Ment. Health
        Stat. Note, (152)p1-7, (Jul. 1979).

1353   Farina, M.L.; Levati, A.; Tognoni, G. A multicenter study of
        ICU drug utilization. Intensive Care Med., 7(3)p125-131, (Apr.
        1981).

1354   FitzGerald, G.A.; Beggan, M.; Drury, M.I. Sources of referral,
        costs and length of hospital stay in a teaching hospital:
        impact of a day care facility. Ir. Med. J., 74(9)p265-70, (Sep.
        1981).

1355   Fitzpatrick, C. Three-year review of admissions to a child
        psychiatry unit. Ir. Med. J. (IRELAND), 74(6)p169-70, (Jun.
        1981).

1356   Fowkes, F.G.; Davies, E.R.; Evans, K.T.; Green, G.; Hartley, G.;
        Hugh, A.E.; Nolan, D.J.; Power, A.L.; Roberts, C.J.; Roylance,
        J. Multicentre trial of four strategies to reduce use of a
        radiological test. Lancet, 1(8477)p367-70, (Feb. 15, 1986).

1357   Gardner, L.P. Coordinating quality assurance activities: one
        facility's experience with utilization review and audit. QRB,
        4(6)p26, (Jun. 1978).

116

1358 Gaskins, R.R.; Davis, F.A.; Greer, J.G. PSRO: An Evaluation of
      the Professional Standards Review Organization. Volume 9.
      Acute Care Utilization Review Costs Associated with Medicare
      Fiscal Intermediaries. Medicaid State Agencies, and State
      Licensing and Certification Agencies. NTIS Order No.:
      PB-278 155/7, 278 p., (Oct. 1977).

1359 Gertman, P.M.; Egdahl, R.E. The dynamics of utilization
      review: a case study of 44 Massachusetts hospitals.
      Ann. Surg., 188(4)p544-51, (Oct. 1978).

1360 Gertman, P.M.; Monheit, A.C.; Anderson, J.J.; Eagle, J.B.;
      Levenson, D.K. Utilization review in the United States:
      results from a 1976-1977 national survey of hospitals.
      Med. Care, 17(8 Suppl)pi-iii, 1-148, (Aug. 1979).

1361 Goldfarb, M.G.; Hornbrook, M.C.; Higgins, C.S. Determinants of
      hospital use: a cross-diagnostic analysis. Med. Care,
      21(1)p48-66, (Jan. 1983).

1362 Goldstein, R.S.; Contreras, M.; Craig, G.A.; Cheung, O.T.
      Tuberculosis--a review of 498 recent admissions to hospital.
      Can. Med. Assoc. J., 126(5)p490-2, (Mar. 1, 1982).

1363 Greene, V.L.; Monahan, D.J. Inconsistency in level of care
      assignment decisions in skilled nursing facilities. Am. J.
      Public Health, 71(9)p1036-9, (Sep. 1981).

1364 Greer, J.G.; Bodin, L.O.; Robeson, F.E.; Pfaffenberger, R.
      PSRO: An Evaluation of the Professional Standards Review
      Organization. Volume 10. Acute Care Utilization Review Costs;
      Synthesis of Components and Estimates for a Fully Implemented
      Program. Final rpt., NTIS Order No.: PB-277 470/1, 75 p.,
      (Oct. 1977).

1365 Guernsey, B.G.; Hokanson, J.A.; Ingrim, N.B.; Fuchs, J.E.;
      Sanders, A.G.; Doutre, W.H.; Bryant, S.G. A utilization review
      of digoxin assays: sampling patterns and use. Hosp. Pharm.,
      19(3)p187-92,196-200, (Mar. 1984).

1366 Guernsey, B.G.; Ingrim, N.B.; Hokanson, J.A.; Fuchs, J.E., Jr.;
      Prohaska, C.; Doutre, W.H.; Bryant, S.G.; Sigler, K.A. A
      utilization review of theophylline assays: sampling patterns
      and use. Drug Intell. Clin. Pharm., 18(11)p906-12, (Nov. 1984).

1367 Helling, D.K.; Norwood, G.J.; Donner, J.D. An assessment of
      prescribing using drug utilization review criteria. Drug
      Intell. Clin. Pharm., 16(12)p930-4, (Dec. 1982).

1368 Hladik, W.B. III; Dujovne, C.A. One hundred digitalis blood
      levels. A utilization review. Eur. J. Clin. Pharmacol,
      15(6)p411-5, (Jul. 1979).

1369 Holt, R.J.; Gaskins, J.D. Neuroleptic drug use in a
      family-practice center. Am. J. Hosp. Pharm.,
      38(11)p1716-9, (Nov. 1981).

1370 Horgan, C.M. Specialty and general ambulatory mental health
      services. Comparison of utilization and expenditures.
      Arch. Gen. Psychiatry, 42(6)p565-72, (Jun. 1985).

1371 Horn, S.D.; Roveti, G.C.; Kreitzer, S.L. Length of stay
      variations: a focused review. QRB, 6(2)p6-12, (Feb. 1980).

1372 Horn, S.D.; Schumacher, D.N. Comparing classification methods:
      measurement of variations in charges, length of stay, and
      mortality. Med. Care, 20(5)p489-500, (May 1982).

1373 Huber, G.A. Statistically developed criteria used for
      utilization review screening. Health Care Syst., 14(5)p1-2,
      (Sep-Oct. 1975).

1374 Huckleberry, S.D. Antibiotic cost-containment. Drug Intell.
      Clin. Pharm., 20(7-8)p589-9, (Jul-Aug. 1986).

1375 Huebler, L.A.; Christian, J.A.; Marcella, L.W. Reducing length
      of stay provides key to improvement in Veterans Administration
      Medical Center. QRB, 6(2)p20-4, (Feb. 1980).

1376 Hull, J.H.; Brown, H.S., Jr.; Yarborough, F.F.; Murray, W.J.
      Drug utilization review of medicaid patients: therapeutic
      implications and opportunities. NC Med. J., 36(3)p162-3, (Mar.
      1975).

1377 Ireland, A.W.; Harris, J.; Scarf, C.G. Cholelithiasis:
      length-of-stay analysis in two series of surgical patients.
      Med. J. Aust., 2(13)p691-3, (Dec. 29, 1979).

1378 Ives, T.J.; Parry, J.L.; Gwyther, R.E. Serum drug level
      utilization review in a family medicine residency program.
      J. Fam. Pract., 19(4)p507-12, (Oct. 1984).

1379 Kiesler, C.A.; Sibulkin, A.E. Episodic rate of mental
      hospitalization: stable or increasing? Am. J. Psychiatry,
      141(1)p44-8, (Jan. 1984).

1380 Kimelblatt, B.J.; Lerro, R.C.; Franchak, N.; Potter, S.K.;
      Greasley, D.M.; Silverman, H.M.; Simon, G.I. Use review of
      cimetidine injection. Am. J. Hosp. Pharm., 39(2)p311,
      (Feb. 1982).

1381 King, R.W.; Suthers, M.B. Creatinine phosphokinase levels in
      coronary care. An example of utilization review. Aust. Clin.
      Rev. (1)p10-1, (May 1981).

1382 Kirstein, L.; Weissman, M.M. Utilization review of treatment of suicide attempters: chart review as patient care evaluation. Am. J. Psychiatry, 132(8)p851-5, (Aug. 1975).

1383 Kirstein, L.; Weissman, M.M.; Rrusoff, B. Utilization review and suicide attempts. Exploring discrepancies between experts' criteria and clinical practice. J. Nerv. Ment. Dis., 160(1)p49-56, (Jan. 1975).

1384 Klapp, D.; Harrison, W.L. Evaluation of albumin use by medical audit. Am. J. Hosp Pharm., 36(9)p1205-9, (Sep. 1979).

1385 Knapp, D.E.; Knapp, D.A.; Speedie, M.K.; Yaeger, D.M.; Baker, C.L. Relationship of inappropriate drug prescribing to increased length of hospital stay. Am. J. Hosp. Pharm., 36(10)p.1334-7, (Oct. 1979).

1386 Knoben, J.E. Drug utilization review. Current status and relationship to assuring quality medical care. Drug Intell. Clin. Pharm., 10(4)p222-8, (Apr. 1976).

1387 Leopold, D.A.; Lagoe, R.J. Patterns of otolaryngologic surgery utilization in Syracuse, NY. Arch Otolaryngol. Head Neck Surg., 112(6)p623-, (Jun. 1986).

1388 Levin, J.M. Effect of utilization review on surgical training with reference to the increasing importance of the ward service in this changing environment [editorial]. Am. J. Surg., 145(2):p191-2, (Feb. 1983).

1389 Martinez, D.R.; Reitz, J.A.; Miller, W.A.; Nolly, R.J. Drug utilization review of parenteral clindamycin therapy. Hosp. Formul., 19(4)p308-16, (Apr. 1984).

1390 McCaughan, B.C.; May, J. Appendicectomy audit. Aust. NZ J. Surg., 53(1)p89-91, (Feb. 1983).

1391 Morse, M.L.; Leroy, A.A.; Gaylord, T.A.; Kellenberger, T. Reducing drug therapy-induced hospitalization: impact of drug utilization review. Drug Inf. J., 16(4)p199-202, (Oct-Dec. 1982).

1392 Moskowitz, M.A. Evaluating doctors' office testing patterns. Clin. Lab. Med., 6(2)p387-94, (Jun. 1986).

1393 Muno, F.J., Jr.; Chen, G.T. Utilization review report. Hosp. Formul., 19(11)p1070-3, (Nov. 1984).

1394 Murphy, W.A.; Totty, W.G.; Gado, M.; Levitt, R.G.; Lee, J.K.; Evens, R.G. Utilization characteristics of a superconductive MR system undergoing initial clinical trial. J. Comput. Assist. Tomogr., 9(2)p258-62, (Mar-Apr. 1985).

1395 Myers, R.A.; Britten, J.S.; Grassi, R.T.; Kietur, L.M.; Weitzel, C.J. Short-stay study--utilization review. J. Trauma, 23(3)p238-40, (Mar. 1983).

1396 Newble, D.I.; Wangel, A.G.; Nelson, A.W. An audit of investigational services within general medical units. Aust. Clin. Rev., (2)p9-11, (Aug. 1981).

1397 Nishimura, M.; Egawa, H.; Suzuki, H.; Kobayashi, T.; Baba, K.; Matsui, K.; Yoshimura, T. A study of utilization review in hospitals--focusing on medical statistics. Sangyo Ika Daigaku Zasshi, 8 Suppl.p401-16, (Mar. 20, 1986).

1398 Parker, W.A.; Reid, L.W. Serum digoxin level (SDL) utilization review. Can. J. Hosp. Pharm., 31(3)p97-9, (May-Jun. 1978).

1399 Phillips, L.A. Emergency services utilization of skull radiography. Neurosurgery, 4(6)p580-2, (Jun. 1979).

1400 Phillips, L.A. Comparative evaluation of the effect of a high yield criteria list upon skull radiography. JACEP, 8(3)p106-9, (Mar. 1979).

1401 Rederscheid, P. Utilization: does this patient belong in CCU? Nurs. Manage., 17(8)p46I-46L, (Aug. 1986).

1402 Redmond, F.C. Study on the use of the seclusion room. QRB, 6(8)p20-3, (Aug. 1980).

1403 Restuccia, J.D. The effect of concurrent feedback in reducing inappropriate hospital utilization. Med. Care, 20(1)p46-62, (Jan. 1982).

1404 Restuccia, J.D.; Gertman, P. A comparative analysis of appropriateness of hospital use. Health Aff., 3(2)p130-8, (Summer 1984).

1405 Rihn, T.L.; DeBalko, J.N.; Keys, P.W. Audit of lidocaine use. Am. J. Hosp. Pharm., 38(7)p1017-21, (Jul. 1981).

1406 Sabath, L.D.; Notto, D.A. Analysis of factors influencing antibiotic usage in hospitals. Prog. Clin. Biol. Res., 35p65-74, (1979).

1407 Sandrick, K.M. Blue Cross and Blue Shield of Michigan's efforts to change practice patterns. QRB, 10(11)p349-52, (Nov. 1984).

1408 Sargenti, C.; Zelman, L.; Beauclair, T.; Garrard, E.; Boehm, R. Evaluation of appropriateness and interpretation of serum theophylline assays. Drug Intel. Clin. Pharm., 19(5)p380-4, (May 1985).

1409 Satoh, Y.; Ichiwata, T.; Tsukui, J.; Yashiro, J.; Ryu, S.;
Kasai, S.; Ishigami, K.; Ibonai, T.; Nakamura, A.; Ohki, K.
Statistical observations of the use of dental materials at Nihon
University Dental Hospital. J. Nihon Univ. Sch. Dent.,
25(1)p41-55, (Mar. 1983).

1410 Seifert, R.; Jamieson, J.; Gardner, R., Jr. Use of
anticholinergics in the nursing home: an empirical study and
review. Drug Intell. Clin. Pharm., 17(6)p470-3, (Jun. 1983).

1411 Seshadri, R.S.; Odell, W.R.; Roxby, D.; Morley, A.A. Effective
use of blood in elective surgical procedures. Med. J. Aust.,
2(11)p575-8, (Dec. 1, 1979).

1412 Shackford, S.R.; Hollingworth-Fridlund, P.; Cooper, G.F.;
Eastman, A.B. The effect of regionalization upon the quality of
trauma care as assessed by concurrent audit before and after
institution of a trauma system: a preliminary report.
J. Trauma, 26(9)p812-20, (Sep. 1986).

1413 Shapiro, M.; Rosner, B.; Townsend, T.R.; Kass, E.H. Aspects of
antimicrobial drug use in general hospitals. Prog. Clin.
Biol. Res., 35p161-70, (1979).

1414 Shapiro, S. Survey of Quality Assurance and Utilization Review
Mechanisms in Prepaid Group Practice Plans and Medical Care
Foundations. NTIS Order No.: HRP-0014362, 93 p., (Jan. 1976).

1415 Shapiro, S.; West, S.K.; Brandon, B.M.; Chase, G.A.; Stolley,
P.D. Drug Utilization Review in a Health Maintenance
Organization. Final rept. 1 Nov. 71-31 Oct. 76. NTIS Order
No.: PB-284 583/2, 451 p., (Nov. 30, 1977).

1416 Sheridan, E.P.; Teplin, L.A. Recidivism in different patients:
differences between community mental health center and state
hospital admissions. Am. J. Psychiatry, 138(5)p688-90, (May
1981).

1417 Shock, J.A.; Jones, W.N.; Bootman, J.L.; Goldman, S. Drug
utilization review of nifedipine. Hosp. Formul., 19(1)p45-6,48,
(Jan. 1984).

1418 Sloane, P.D. Nursing home candidates: hospital inpatient trial
to identify those appropriately assignable to less intensive
care. J. Am. Geriatr. Soc., 28(11)p511-4, (Nov. 1980).

1419 Studnicki, J.; Honemann, D. Analyzing inpatient hospital
duration and intensity, Part II. Results of a pilot study.
QRB, 9(5)p139-46, (May 1983).

1420 Thibault, G.E.; Mulley, A.G.; Barnett, G.O.; Goldstein, R.L.; Reder, V.A.; Sherman, E.L.; Skinner, E.R. Medical intensive care: indications, interventions, and outcomes. N. Engl. J. Med., 302(17)p938-42, (Apr. 24, 1980).

1421 Tolentino, P. Recent variations in the use of antibiotics, with particular regard to a major pediatric hospital. Prog. Clin. Biol. Res., 35p103-7, (1979).

1422 Walton, J.R.; Shapiro, B.A. Appropriate utilization of bronchial hygiene therapy: development and evaluation of a cost-effective respiratory therapy program. QRB, 7(1)p21-5, (Jan. 1981).

1423 Wareham, D.V.; Deliganis, S.G. Rational fluid and electrolyte therapy utilization review. Part One. Drug Intell. Clin. Pharm., 10(6)p339-45, (Jun. 1976).

1424 Wareham, D.V.; Deliganis, S.G. Rational fluid and electrolyte therapy utilization review. Part II. Drug Intell. Clin. Pharm., 11(9)p549-53, (Sep. 1977).

1425 Weaver, P.G. Bed utilization index after five days. Dimens. Health Serv., 57(2)p23-4, (Feb. 1980).

1426 Wells, K.B.; Manning, W.G., Jr.; Duan, N.; Newhouse, J.P.; Ware, J.E., Jr.; Benjamin, B. The sensitivity of mental health care use and cost estimates to methods effects. Med. Care, 22(9)p783-8, (Sep. 1984).

1427 Westphal, M.; Frazier E.; Miller, M.C. Changes in average length of stay and average charges generated following institution of PSRO review. Health Serv. Res., 14(4)p253-65, (Winter 1979).

1428 Witte, K.W.; Nelson, A.A., Jr.; Hutchinson, R.A. Effect of pharmacist consultation on rational antimicrobial therapy. Am. J. Hosp. Pharm., 37(6)p829-32, (Jun. 1980).

1429 Young, W.W.; Swinkola, R.B.; Hutton, M.A. Assessment of the AUTOGRP patient classification system. Med. Care, 18(2)p228-44, (Feb. 1980).

Management

1430 A response to DRG reimbursement: overhauling the hospital's/medical staff's utilization review program. Second Opin. Health Care Issues, 4(6)p31-3, (Jun. 1983).

1431 A 'suggested' utilization review committee plan and (available) HEW guidelines concerning U.R. J. Am. Health Care Assoc., 1(1)p10-21, (Jul. 1975).

1432 Ankrum, A.D. Who's in charge of utilization review? Hosp. Peer Rev., 3(5)p60-1, (May 1978).

1433 Bailit, H.L.; Balzer, J.A.; Clive, J. Evaluation of a focused dental utilization review system. Med. Care, 21(5)p473-85, (May 1983).

1434 Bender, F.H.; DeMatteo, C.S. Cost Containment through P & T committee drug utilization review. Hosp. Formul., 19(8)p699-700,705-7, (Aug. 1984).

1435 Black, F.O.; Johnson, J.; Myers, E.N.; Perkun, O. Quantification of standards for length-of-stay based upon optimal patient care and standard medical practice. Otolaryngol. Head Neck Surg., 89(1)p27-33, (Jan.-Feb. 1981).

1436 Boyle, D.A. Letter: Utilization review coordinator. JAMA, 236(13)p1453, (Sep. 27, 1976).

1437 Bruhn, P.S.; Howes, D.H. Service Line management. New opportunities for nursing executives. J. Nurs. Adm., 16(6)p13-8, (Jun. 1986).

1438 Conneen, T.F. Utilization Review Chairman speaks to the staff. J. Maine Med. Assoc., 68(6)p189-91, (Jun. 1977).

1439 Craddick, J.W. The medical management analysis system: a professional liability warning mechanism. QRB, 5(4)p2-8, (Apr. 1979).

1440 Does utilization review cost more than it saves? Employ. Benefit Plan Rev. , 31(3)p20,22, (Sep. 1976).

1441 Douglas, R.M.; Catchlove, E.; Reid, D.P.; Young, J.F. Publication of utilization data. Its effect on clinical decisions. Med. J. Aust., 2(12)p580-3, (Dec. 11-25, 1982).

1442 Ferguson, J.S. The utilization review committee. Va. Nurse Q., 42(2)p52-5,57, (Summer 1974).

1443 German, T.L. The physician advisor: genesis and rules. J. Med. Assoc. Ga., 70(9)p657-8, (Sep. 1981).

1444 Given, C.W.; Morrill, C.E.; Lachance, R.; Gifford, W.; Bedell, A.; Kowaleski, E.; Haddock, D. Defining the information content of health data systems. Primary Care, 12(3)p515-33, (Sep. 1985).

1445 Goldberg, G.A.; Hein, L.M.; Rosales, S.M.; Alexander, J.F.
Criteria and flowsheet for utilization review by level of care.
West. J. Med., 126(4)p318-23, (Apr. 1977).

1446 Hall, J. Utilization review: II. A commentary on some
problems. Aust. Clin. Rev., (4)p4-5, (Mar. 1982).

1447 Hancock, C. Monitoring. 2. A question of efficiency.
Nurs. Mirros, 156(4)p47-8, (Jan. 26, 1983).

1448 Health Care Financing Administration--Medicare and Medicaid;
Utilization review. Proposed rule. Fed. Regist.,
45(43)p13940-53, (Mar. 3, 1980).

1449 Henderson, W.J.; Ichinose, C.; Goto, U.; Tom, B.; Stewart, J.;
Sage, W.; Judd, C.; Gresham, S.; Thompson, H.; McDonald, B.A.;
Kim, M. Hawaii Med. J., 34(1)p15-20, (Jan. 1975).

1450 Hirt, F.D.; Solomon, J.R. Utilization review: a model medical
care evaluation. J. Am. Health Care Assoc., 2(3)p25-30, (May
1976).

1451 Hoffmann, R.P. A strategy to reduce drug expenditures with a
drug utilization review program. Hosp. Pharm., 19(1)p7-8,11-2,
(Jan. 1984).

1452 Holbrook, F.K. Computerization aids utilization review.
Hospitals, 49(17)p53-5, (Sep. 1, 1975).

1453 Hoyt, J.P. An effective utilization review program using
accurate management information. Healthc. Comput. Commun.,
2(1)p36-9, (Jan. 1985).

1454 Huber, G.A.; Wolfe, H.; Hardwick, C.P. Evaluating computerized
screening as an aid to utilization review. Inquiry,
11(3)p188-95, (Sep. 1974).

1455 Hutchinson, S.; Malamud, J.; Stearns, N.S.; Moulton, B.
Preselecting literature for routine delivery to physicians in a
community hospital-based patient care related reading program.
Bull Med. Libr. Assoc., 69(2)p236-9, (Apr. 1981).

1456 Jacoby, J.E. Physicians must maintain involvement in
utilization review [letter]. QRB, 11(4)p106-7, (Apr. 1985).

1457 Jones, B. Priorities in utilization review. Hosp. Peer Rev.,
3(4)p50-1, (Apr. 1978).

1458 Kidder, S.W. The cost benefit of drug reviews in long-term care
facilities. Am. Pharm., NS22(7)p63-7, (Jul. 1982).

1459 Lange, M. Searching for the bottom line via review. Tex. Med.,
79(10)p64-5, (Oct. 1983).

1460 LeBrun, P. Payers step up roles in discharge planning. Hospitals, 59(12):p98,102, (Jun. 16, 1985).

1461 Lipp, C.S. The effect of the prospective payment system on hospital QA/UR systems. QRB, 10(9)p283-7, (Sep. 1984).

1462 Little, J.C.; Austing, R.H. Some guidelines for the analysis and design of a computerized utilization review and reporting system. Med. Rec. News, 48(4)p6,8-9, 12-5 passim, (Aug. 1977).

1463 McGowan, J.E., Jr. Continuing education for improving antibiotic usage. QRB, 5(1)p32-5, (Jan. 1979).

1464 McSherry, C.K. Quality assurance: the cost of utilization review and the educational value of medical audit in a university hospital. Surgery, 80(1)p122-9, (Jul. 1976).

1465 Meyers, V.W.; Hober, F. Utilization review within PPS. Health Care Strateg. Manage., 2(5)p15-7, (May 1984).

1466 Micheletti, J.A.; Shlala, T.J. PROs and PPS: nursing's role in utilization management. Nurs. Manage., 16(10)p37-42, (Oct. 1985).

1467 Monroe, R.D.; Grant, E.A. Upgrading financial planning and reporting in response to DRG requirements. Top Health Care Financ., 11(3)p63-71, (Spring 1985).

1468 Moody-Williams, J.D. DRG committee helps UR and QA efforts. QRB, 10(3)p89-90, (Mar. 1984).

1469 Newmark, G.L. Organizing for utilization review. Hospitals, 49(6)p22, (Mar. 16, 1975).

1470 O'Brien, J.R. Organizing QA and UR activities under a DRG-based system. QRB, 9(9)p276-7, (Sep. 1983).

1471 Part 405--Federal health insurance for the aged and disabled. Utilization review: conditions of participation. Med. Rec. News, 46(2)p63-70, (Apr. 1975).

1472 Pattee, J.J. Utilization review committee as a peer review mechanism. J. Am. Geriatr. Soc., 28(4)p190-1, (Apr. 1980).

1473 Pattee, J.J. Update on the medical director concept. Am. Fam. Physician, 28(6)p129-33, (Dec. 1983).

1474 Physicians' cost cuts spur PPO's success. Hospitals, 59(6)p65, (Mar. 16, 1985).

1475 Raymond, D. Department review: a PSRO aproach from the hospital's perspective. QRB, 6(8)p11-5, (Aug. 1980).

1476 Restuccia, J.D. Minimal use of physician advisors improves utilization review process [interview]. Hosp. Peer Rev., 7(6)p68-70, (Jun. 1982).

1477 Ryckman, D.; Sourapas, J.K. Medical records: a new challenge under prospective DRG reimbursement. Top Health Care Financ., 11(3)p47-58, (Spring 1985).

1478 Savings Claimed for the Oklahoma Hospital Utilization Review System Were Overstated. NTIS Order No.: HRP-0902900/0, 32p., (Jan. 11, 1980).

1479 Schaeffer, P.M. The utilization review coordinator--a different kind of nurse. Nursing, 6(2)p95-8, (Feb. 1976).

1480 Schmitz, H.H.; Schoenhard, W.C., Jr. Automated utilization review is timely, accurate, efficient. Hosp. Prog., 57(7)p73-7,98, (Jul. 1976).

1481 Schumacher, D.N.; Chan, C. Medical staff and hospital administration uses of discharge abstract data. QRB, 7(6)p26-35, (Jun. 1981).

1482 Sherber, J. Review ensures quick response to faulty care. Hospitals, 54(15)p55-7, (Aug. 1, 1980).

1483 Sieverts, S. The assurance of appropriate medical care: the role of Blue Cross and Blue Shield. Bull N.Y. Acad. Med. (UNITED STATES), 58(1)p49-55, (Jan.-Feb. 1982).

1484 Snider, M.E. Utilization review for Medicare. Is this a good use of nurses' time? Am. J. Nurs., 77(1)p107-9, (Jan. 1977).

1485 Spencer, J.H., Jr.; Mattson, M.R. Utilization review and resident education. Hosp. Community Psychiatry, 30(4)p269-72, (Apr. 1979).

1486 Studnicki, J.; Honemann, D. Payment source as a variable in utilization research: a selected literature review. QRB, 9(9)p258-66, (Sep. 1983).

1487 Sway, E.M. Analysis of regulations governing utilization review by skilled nursing facilities. Med. Rec. News, 46(3)p56-63, (Jun. 1975).

1488 TA2--Guidelines for the Review Coordinator in PSRO Programs and/or Utilization Review Activities. NTIS Order No.: HRP-0901212, 9p., (Nov. 7, 1975).

1489 Thompson, K.S.; Cheng, E.H. A computer package to facilitate compliance with utilization review requirements. Hosp. Community Psychiatry, 27(9)p653-6, (Sep. 1976).

1490 Tom, B.C.; Gresham, S.C.; Goto, U.; Henderson, W.J.; Judd, C.S., Jr.; McDonald, B.A. Pay the peers. Utilization review with a team approach and payment of physician reviewers. JAMA, 235(7)p738-41, (Feb. 16, 1976).

1491 Tremblay, J. Creating an appropriate climate for drug use review. Am. J. Hosp. Pharm., 38(2)p212-5, (Feb. 1981).

1492 Turley, R.M.; Edwardson, S.R. Can ICUs be used more efficiently? J. Nurs. Adm., 15(7-8)p25-8, (Jul.-Aug. 1985).

1493 Utilization review: the revised regulations. J. Med. Assoc. Ga., 64(3)p65, (Mar. 1975).

1494 Utilization review regulations. Questions and answers. Tex. Med., 71(3)p107-8, (Mar. 1975).

1495 Utilization review may separate winners from losers. Hosp. Peer Rev., 7(11)p133-5, (Nov. 1982).

1496 Walkley, P.H., Jr. Auditing the utilization review coordinator's performance. Med. Rec. News, 46(5)p30-3, (Oct. 1975).

1497 Wilson, L.L. Formal assessment--springboard for continuing education. Med. J. Aust., 1(12)p609-10, (Jun. 13, 1981).

1498 Zeleznik, C.; Gonnella, J.S. Jefferson Medical College Student Model Utilization Review Committee. J. Med. Educ., 54(11)p848-51, (Nov. 1979).

1499 Zoebelein, E. Maximizing UR and QA resources through innovative models of practice. QRB, 10(8)p253-5, (Aug. 1984).

Overviews

1500 Anderson, J. Industry looks at utilization review. Ala. J. Med. Sci., 22(4):p403-7, (Oct. 1985).

1501 Annual Utilization Review, 1969-1974. Health Planning NTIS Order No.: HRP-003731, p31, (Feb 1975).

1502 Ashby, J.L., Jr. The impact of hospital regulatory programs on per capita costs, utilization, and capital investment. Inquiry, 21(1):p45-59, (Spring 1984).

1503 Baltaxe, H.A. Cost and utilization of the new cardiac imaging modalities [editorial]. Cathet. Cardiovasc. Dia., 11(2):p113-4, (1985).

1504 Bice, T.W. Health planning and regulation effects on hospital costs. Annu. Rev. Public Health, 1p:137-61, (1980).

1505 Breeden, B. Utilization review. Va. Nurse Q., 42(1):p68-71,73, (Spring 1974).

1506 Carpenter, R.A. Business and industry's role - a working partnership with providers. J. Fla. Med. Assoc., 69(3):p198-201, (Mar. 1982).

1507 Corder, M.P.; Lachenbruch, P.A.; Lindle, S.G.; Sisson, J.H.; Johnson, P.S.; Kosier, J.T. A financial analysis of Hodgk lymphoma staging. Am. J. Public Health, 71(4):p376-80, (Apr. 1981).

1508 Curran, W.J. Law-medicine notes. Medical standards and medical ethics in utilization review for nursing home. N. Engl. J. Med., 308(8):p435-6, (Feb. 24, 1983).

1509 Diblase, D. Utilization review costs, not benefits. Bus. Insur., 20(16):p7, (Apr. 21, 1986).

1510 Dittman, D.A.; Magee, R.P. Optimal investigation policies under selected PSRO procedures. Med. Care, 18(10):p103-47, (Oct. 1980).

1511 Edelston, J.M.; Valentine, S.T.; Ginoza, D. PPA contracting: a California experience. Hospitals, 59(19):p81-3, (Oct. 1, 1985).

1512 Eisenberg, J.M. Prospects for Cost Containment Through Utilization Review in the United Kingdom, NTIS Order No.: HRP-0031143/1, p25, (Mar. 1979).

1513 Faulkner, P.L.; Nevick, R.; Williams, S.V.; Pascale, L.A.; Poyss, L.; Eisenberg, J.M. Many diagnostic tests may be unnecessary. Hospitals, 55(8):p57-9, (Apr. 16, 1981).

1514 Federal judge halts state from auditing judgements of utilization review boards [news]. Hospitals, 52(21):p18-9, (Nov. 1, 1978).

1515 Fetter, R.B.; Shin, Y.; Freeman, J.L.; Averill, R.F.; Thompson, J.D. Case mix definition by diagnosis-related groups. Med. Care, 18(2 Suppl.):piii,1-53, (Feb. 1980).

1516 Fielding, J.E. Lessons from health care regulation. Annu. Rev. Public Health, 4:p91-130, (1983).

1517 Frey, R.J. Minnesota coalition on health care costs--private utilization review. Minn. Med., 64(4):p225, (Apr. 1981).

1519 Friedman, D.; Schwartzbard, A.; Velcek, F.T.; Klotz, D.H.;
     Kottmeier, P.K. The government and the inguinal hernia.
     J. Pediatr. Surg., 14(3):p356-9, (Jun. 1979).

1520 Froh, R. Changing patterns in health benefits design.
     Nurs. Econ., 4(3):p117-21, (May-Jun. 1986).

1521 Gardner, S.F.; Kyzr-Sheeley, B.J.; Sabatino, F. Big business
     embraces alternate delivery. Hospitals, 59(6):p81-4,
     (Mar. 16, 1985).

1522 Goldstein, R.L.; Stanton, B.; Burwell, L. PSRO performance: the
     1977 and 1978 evaluations of Professional Standards Review
     Organizations. QRB, 5(10):p3-7, (Oct. 1979).

1523 Hansen, A.S. Utilization review. Employee Benefit Plan Rev.,
     37(5):p24-6,32, (Nov. 1982).

1524 HEW seeks to revamp utilization review plan. Purch. Adm.,
     4(5):p11, (Jun. 1980).

1525 Himler, G. PSRO. Cost versus quality. N.Y. State J. Med.,
     79(12):p1863-5, (Nov. 1979).

1526 Hoyt, J.D.; Davies, J.M. A response to the Task Force on
     Supportive Care. Law Med. Health Care, 12(3):p103-5,134-5,
     (Jun. 1984).

1527 Huff, J.W. Hospital utilization review under Medicare. J. Med.
     Assoc. Ga., 64(8):p322-3, (Aug. 1975).

1528 Jackson-Beeck, M. The need for psychiatric utilization review.
     Healthspan, 2(6):p17-9, (Jun. 1985).

1529 Kaiser, J.; Townsend, E.J. A community support system's use of
     state hospitalization: is it still necessary? Hosp.
     Community Psychiatry, 32(9):p625-8, (Sept. 1981).

1530 Katz, P.S. Prospective payment and mental health. QRB, 10(11):
     p355-8, (Nov. 1984).

1531 Kaufmann, J.S. Editorial: Drug utilization review. N.C. Med.
     J., 36(3):p168-9, (Mar. 1975).

1532 Kittrell, A. Employers turn to managed care, utilization review
     to control costs [news]. Mod. Healthc., 16(10):p96,98, (May 9,
     1986).

1533 Korcok, M. Will DRG payments creep into all U.S. health
     insurance plans? Can. Med. Assoc. J., 130(7):p912-5, (Apr. 1,
     1984).

1534 Krinsky, L.W.; Carone, P.A. Is cost containment a myth? J.
     Asthma Res., 16(3):p85-92, (Apr. 1979).

1535 Krischer, J.P.; Cheung, A.; Bush, P.; Sleight, S.M. Drug
     utilization review in the Veterans Administration. QRB,
     8(10):p11-9, (Oct. 1982).

1536 Legge, D. Peer review in the U.S.A.: an historical perspective.
     Med. J. Aust., 1(13):p709-11, (Jun. 1).

1537 Lewis, S. Speculations on the impact of prospective pricing and
     DRGs. West J. Med., 140(4):p638-44, (Apr. 1984).

1538 Ludlam, J.E. Payment systems, cost management, and malpractice.
     Hospitals, 58(21):p102-4, (Nov. 1, 1984).

1539 Mandsager, R.L. The fate of peer review: IFMC or elsewhere?
     J. Iowa Med. Soc., 73(1):p15-6, (Jan. 1983).

1540 Margolis, J.A.; McDermott, J.F., Jr.; Vaughan, W.T., Jr.
     Residential treatment centers: peer review by APA and CHAMPUS.
     Hosp. Community Psychiatry, 35(5):p482-6, (May 1984).

1541 McGarvey, M.R. The relationship between the Professional
     Standards Review Organizations and the State Health Department.
     Bull. N.Y. Acad. Med., 58(1):p114-21, (Jan.-Feb. 1982).

1542 Moorefield, J.L. Privately initiated assurance programs: the
     insurance industry's role. Bull. N.Y. Acad. Med., 58(1):p56-62,
     (Jan.-Feb. 1982).

1543 Murchison, G.C. The medical community looks at review. Ala. J.
     Med. Sci., 22(4):p704-9, (Oct. 1985).

1544 Nationwide utilization review groups get results. Employee
     Benefit Plan Rev., 38(7):p34,36,38, (Jan. 1984).

1545 Ness, C.O. Utilization review, in conjunction with redesign,
     saves employer 27% over projected 1984 costs. Employee
     Benefit Plan Rev., 40(3):p104,106,108, (Sept. 1985).

1546 Nyberg, J.; Wolff, N. DRG panic. J. Nurs. Adm., 14(4):p17-21,
     (Apr. 1984).

1547 Osifo, N.G.; Ogbuebele, H.U. Hospital drug use review in a
     developing country. Am. J. Hosp. Pharm., 38(7):p1037-9, (Jul.
     1981).

1548 Palmer, D.B. Some cons of PROs [editorial]. Arch. Ophthalmol.,
     103(3):p343-5, (Mar. 1985).

1549 Paradisi, F.; Cioffi, R.; Cristiano, P.; Caruso, G.;
     Caiazza, M.; Corona G. Antibiotic utilization in a general
     hospital: and overview. Prog. Clin. Biol. Res., 35:p129-37,
     (1979).

1550 Pearson, D.A.; Abernethy, D.S. A qualitative assessment of previous efforts to contain hospital costs. J. Health Polit. Policy Law, 5(1):p120-41, (Spring 1980).

1551 Powills, S. Atlanta coalition tackles UR. Hospitals, 59(8):p120-2, (Apr. 16, 1985).

1552 Rice, T.; De Lissovoy, G.; Gabel, J.; Ermann, D. The state of PROs: results from a national survey. Health Aff., 4(4): p25-40, (Winter 1985).

1553 Richards, G. Business spurs UR growth. Hospitals are coming under increased scrutiny from outside utilization review. Hospitals, 58(5):p96,98-100, (Mar. 1, 1984).

1554 Rosen, H.M.; Feigin, W., Sr. Quality assurance and data feedback. Health Care. Manage. Rev., 8(1):p67-74, (Winter 1983).

1555 Rothberg, D.L.; Gertman, P.M. The use of attitudinal data for public policy: the case of unnecessary hospital use. Med. Care, 19(1):p47-54, (Jan. 1981).

1556 Rucker, T.D.; Visconti, J.A. Relative drug safety and efficacy: any help for the practitioner? Am. J. Pharm., 36(8):p1099-101, (Aug. 1979).

1557 Rzasa, C.B. Prospective rate system for Medicare reimbursement. QRB, 9(6):p158-60, (Jun. 1983).

1558 Sack, R.A. The effect of utilization on health care costs. Am. J. Obstet. Gynecol., 137(2):p270-5, (May 15, 1980).

1559 Schlicke, C.P. Joint Commission adopts new utilization review standard. Bull. Am. Coll. Surg., 62(9):p15-6, (Sept. 1977).

1560 Schroer, K.A.; Taylor, E. PPAs: fewer start-ups but better operations. Hospitals, 59(17):p68-9,72-3, (Sept. 1, 1985).

1561 Shah, N.M.; Turner, G.P. Medical QA activities: incorporating essential elements. Dimens. Health Serv., 63(1):p25-8, (Feb. 1986).

1562 Shahoda, T. Preadmission review cuts hospital use. Hospitals, 58(15):p54-5, (Aug. 1, 1984).

1563 Shaw, J. Utilization review effort gaining ground. Am. Med. News, 25(18):p3,13, (May 14, 1982).

1564 Spies, J.J. Utilization review and risk sharing--two key measures for cost control in an IPA. Employ. Benefit Plan Rev., 32(8): p32-3, (Feb. 1978).

1565 Stone, DA. Health care cost containment in West Germany.
      J. Health Polit. Policy Law, 4(2):p176-99, (Summer 1979).

1566 Thompson, R.W. Hospitals and review. Ala. J. Med. Sci.,
      22(4):p400-2, (Oct. 1985).

1567 Utilization review and the AMA challenge. J. Psychiatr. Nurs.,
      13(3):p40, (May-Jun. 1975).

1568 Utilization review. Conn. Med., 41(8):p509-10, (Aug. 1977).

1569 Vladeck, B.C. Restructuring the financing of health care: more
      stringent regulation of utilization. Bull. N.Y. Acad. Med.,
      60(1):p89-97, (Jan.-Feb. 1984).

1570 Vraciu, R.A. Hospital strategies for the eighties: a mid-decade
      look. Health Care Manage. Rev., 10(4):p9-19, (Fall 1985).

1571 Wilcox, D.P. Pressure to serve two masters. Tex. Med.,
      82(6):p67-9, (Jun. 1986).

1572 Wills, C. Korner in the community. Nurs. Times, 82(16):p30-1,
      (Apr. 16-22, 1986).

1573 Wirtschafter, D. The impact of DRGs on medical management.
      Ala. J. Med. Sci., 21(1):p86-95, (Jan. 1984).

1574 Yeater, D.C. Are you keeping up with health care cost
      containment management strategies? Occup. Health Nurs.,
      32(4):p193-8, (Apr. 1984).

1575 Zuidema, G.D. The problem of cost containment in teaching
      hospitals: the Johns Hopkins experience. Surgery, 87(1):p41-5,
      (Jan. 1980).

CHAPTER 4:

RISK MANAGEMENT REFERENCES

Theory and Concept

1576   Allen, P.   Risk management program protects against financial
       loss. Dimens Health Serv., 63(5):p24-5, (Jun. 1986).

1577   Alt, S.   HCA's insurance captive contains premiums and risk
       management costs. Mod. Healthc., 8(5):p61-2, (May 1978).

1578   Baram, M.S.   Charting the future course for corporate management
       of health risks. Am. J. Public Health, 74(10):p1163-6,
       (Oct. 1984).

1579   Birnbaum, D.   Risk management vs. infection control committees.
       Dimens Health Serv., 58(12):p16-7,19, (Dec. 1981).

1580   Cain, C.   Loss control cornerstone of risk management plan.
       Bus. Insur., 20(15):p135-6, (Apr. 14, 1986).

1581   Carpenter, J.K.   Risk management.   II. Workers' compensation.
       Top Health Care Financ., 9(4):p5-18, (Summer 1983).

1582   Connolly, D.R.   Insurer perspectives on causation and financial
       compensation. Regul. Toxicol. Pharmacol., 6(2):p80-8,
       (Jun. 1986).

1583   Davis, W.P., III; Atkins, T.; Henkel, C.E.; McGovern, B.J.
       Top Health Care Financ., 1(4):p1-106, (Summer 1975).

1584   Ejvegard, R.; Grimvall, A.   Consent and responsibility in
       risk management. Prog. Clin. Biol. Res., 208:p53-7, (1986).

1585   Fifer, W.R.   Risk management: the art of preventing 'people
       failure'. Trustee, 30(9):p52-3, (Sep. 1977).

133

1586 Follesdal, D. Risk: philosophical and ethical aspects.
Department of Philosophy, Stanford University, CA 94305.
Prog. Clin. Biol. Res., 208:p41-52, (1986).

1587 Glass, L.S. The physician as expert witness. Alaska Med.,
27(4):pfollowing 107, (Oct.-Dec. 1985).

1588 Grayson, M.A. Risk management: new focus for traditional
functions. Hosp. Med. Staff, 7(5):p12-7, (May 1978).

1589 Holzer, J.F. Analysis of anesthetic mishaps. Current concepts
in risk management. Inst. Anesthesiol. Clin., 22(2):p91-116,
(Summer 1984).

1590 Jones, D.B. Risk management: one way to fight malpractice
suits. Tex. Med., 81(6):p64-6, (Jun. 1985).

1591 Joseph, E. Patient rights--key to risk management in mental
health settings. QRB, 6(11):p4-6, (Nov. 1980).

1592 Katz, D.M. Divided loyalties of health risk management.
Natl. Underwrit. [Life Health], 88(32):p4,6, (Aug. 11, 1984).

1593 Katz, P.S. Integrating quality assurance, utilization review,
and risk management activities for the small hospital. QRB,
12(3):p114-5, (Mar. 1986).

1594 Kolozyn, H. What is risk management? Occup. Health (Lond),
29(9):p380-2, (Sep. 1977).

1595 Korsak, A. Risk management: new concept calls for definitional
refinement in use of term. Hospitals, 52(22):p48,50, (Nov. 16,
1978).

1596 Lamnin, M. Risk management: an ounce of prevention.
Top Hosp. Pharm. Manage., 5(4):p1-8, (Feb. 1986).

1597 Long, M.J. An integrated theory of provider behavior in Health
Maintenance Organizations. J. Community Health,
8(2):p119-29, (Winter 1982).

1598 Magiera, J.J. The value of risk management today. Tex. Hosp.,
35(11):p10-2, (Apr. 1980).

1599 Maroncelli, R.D.; Heard, J.M.; Herrington, L.F.; Kaun-Till,
G.L.; Graves, F.B.; Rauber, A.P. Georgia Poison Control Center,
Atlanta 30335. Vet. Hum. Toxicol, 27(6):p512-5, (Dec. 1985).

1600 Monagle, J.F. Risk management is linked with quality of care.
Hospitals, 54(17):p57-9, (Sep. 1, 1980).

1602 Moon, J.E.   The great risk: ignoring risk management.
      Ala. J. Med. Sci., 17(3-4):p332-4, (Jul.-Oct. 1980).

1603 Morrison, A.B.   The changing expectations of society and the
      influence thereof on individual and societal decisions regarding
      foods.   Fundam. Appl. Toxicol., 4(3Pt2):pS284-92, (Jun.
      1984).

1604 Oppman, C.D.   Risk management components.   Hosp. Risk Manage.,
      4(6):p82-4, (Jun. 1982).

1605 Orlikoff, J.E.; Lanham, G.B.   Integrated approach improves
      quality assurance, risk management activities.   Hospitals,
      54(17):p59-61, (Sep. 1, 1980).

1606 Orlikoff, J.E.; Lanham, G.B.   Why risk management and quality
      assurance should be integrated.   Hospitals, 55(11):p54-5, (Jun.
      1, 1981).

1607 Philipson, L.L.   Risk acceptance criteria and their
      development.   J.H. Wiggins Company, Redondo, Beach, California.
      J. Med. Syst., 7(5):p437-56, (Oct. 1983).

1608 Quinlan, A.; Krolikowski, F.J.; Dunham, W.G.; Reuter, K.   Risk
      management enhances quality care and protection from liability.
      Pathologist, 40(6):p29-32, (Jun. 1986).

1609 Risk management: threat or opportunity?
      Health Care Secur. Saf. Manage., 1(7-8):p5-9, (Nov.-Dec. 1980).

1610 Risk management: why nurses need it.   Health Serv. Manager,
      11(3):p6-7,10, (Mar. 1978).

1611 Rubin, H.W.; Staples, S.C.   Risk management is more than buying
      insurance policies.   Hosp. Financ. Manage., 32(8):p20-2,24,
      (Aug. 1978).

1612 Sax, A.   Physicians and hospital managers: partners in risk
      management.   Hospitals, 53(2):p41,44,46 passim, (Jan. 16, 1979).

1613 Sax, A.B.   Patient relations in risk management.   QRB,
      5(4):p14-5, (Apr. 1979).

1614 Schmitt, J.P.   Risk management--it's more than just insurance.
      Health Financ. Manage., 37(3):p10-1,14-7,20-2, (Mar. 1983).

1615 Self-insuring against medical malpractice damages.
      Top Health Care Financ., 7(2):p37-47, (Winter 1980).

1616 Sielicki, A.P., Jr.   Current philosophy of risk management.
      Top Health Care Financ., 9(3):p1-7, (Spring 1983).

1617 Sielicki, A.P., Jr. Risk management philosophy and techniques--an overview. Top Health Care Financ., 9(4):p1-4, (Summer 1983).

1618 Singleton, W.T. Psychological aspects of risk management. Institut de Medecin Sociale et Preventive Universite de Geneve. Prog. Clin. Biol. Res., 208:p31-40, (1986).

1619 Stewart, K.P. The physician's stake in risk management. Hosp. Med. Staff, 6(9):p30-4, (Sep. 1977).

1620 Taylor, M.R. The role of law in risk management: a framework for managing uncertainty. Fundam. Appl. Toxicol., 4(3Pt2):pS408-17, (Jun. 1984).

1621 Todhunter, J.A. Societal considerations in implementing risk management decisions: towards improving the process. Sci. Total Environ., 51:p63-68, (May 1986).

Programs, Techniques & Procedures

1622 Allen, P. Risk management program protects against financial loss. Dimens. Health Serv., 63(5):p24-5, (Jun. 1986).

1623 Anaesthetists and the reporting of adverse drug reactions. Br. Med. J. [Clin. Res.], 292(6525):p949, (Apr. 5, 1986).

1624 Anzian, G. A risk management program. Tex. Hosp., 40(7):p8-9, (Dec. 1984).

1625 Bannon, T.; Mier, C.H. Department devises dietary safety program. Hospitals, 54(8):p77-8, (Apr. 16, 1980).

1626 Beck, B.; Hardwick, K. A concurrent surgical miniaudit procedure: use of generic outcome screening criteria to detect anesthesia and other perioperative problems. QRB, 7(3):p21-4, (Mar. 1981).

1627 Bernstein, J.E. A complete approach to health risk management. Risk Manage., 32(10):p58-62, (Oct. 1985).

1628 Betz, R.P.; Levy, H.B. An interdisciplinary method of classifying and monitoring medication errors. Am. J. Hosp. Pharm., 42(8):p1724-32, (Aug. 1985).

1629 Blake, P. Incident investigation: a complete guide. Nurs. Manage., 15(11):p36-41, (Nov. 1984).

1630 Bloom, A. Risk management in medical groups. Med. Group Manage., 30(2):p10-2, (Mar-Apr. 1983).

1631 Boone, C.W. Well-planned program credited with drop in
      malpractice claims. Hospitals, 56(7):p37, (Apr. 1,
      1982).

1632 Brunn, I.O.; Campbell, J.S.; Hutzel, R.L. Evaluation of
      occupational exposures: a proposed sampling method.
      Am. Ind. Hyg. Assoc. J., 47(4):p229-35, (Apr. 1986).

1633 Burnhill, M.S. Risk management in pregnancy termination. Clin.
      Obstet. Gynaecol., 13(1):p145-56, (Mar. 1986).

1634 Carpenter, J.K. Risk management. II. Workers' compensation.
      Top Health Care Financ., 9(4):p5-18, (Summer 1983).

1635 Chavigny, K.H. Nosocomial data collection: making it
      meaningful. Part 3: Interfacing infection control with other
      hospital surveillance systems. Infect. Control Urol. Care,
      7(2):p13-7, (1982).

1636 Connaway, N.I. Incident reports in home health agencies.
      Home Healthc. Nurse, 4(3):p9-10, (May-Jun. 1986).

1637 Cooper, J.B. Toward prevention of anesthetic mishaps. Int.
      Anesthesiol. Clin., 22(2):p167-83, (Summer 1984).

1638 Craddick, J.W. The medical management analysis system: a
      professional liability warning mechanism. QRB, 5(4):p2-8, (Apr.
      1979).

1639 Crane, E.J.; Reckard, J.M. Hospital liability, risk management,
      and the medical record. Top Health Rec. Manage., 2(1):p49-59,
      (Sep. 1981).

1640 CSMS patient risk prevention plan. CSMS Council. Conn. Med.,
      44(9):p573-5, (Sep. 1980).

1641 Cushing, M. Incident reports: for your eyes only? Am. J.
      Nurs., 85(8):p873-4, (Aug. 1985).

1642 Davis, J.B.; Bader, B.S. The systems approach to patient safety.
      QRB, 5(2):p17-21, (Feb. 1979).

1643 Du Pont's occupational health and safety program. Am. Ind. Hyg.
      Assoc. J., 41(6):pA46,A48,A50 passim, (Jun. 1980).

1644 Durkin, E.; Korsak, A. A risk management primer for medical
      record practitioners. Med. Rec. News, 51(3):p37-41, (Jun.
      1980).

1645 Edwards, C. Quality assessment in the emergency room of a
      small, rural hospital. QRB, 10(4):p119-23, (Apr. 1984).

1646 Eichhorn, J.H.; Cooper, J.B.; Cullen, D.J.; Maier, W.R.; Philip, J.H.; Seeman, R.G. Standards for patient monitoring during anesthesia at Harvard Medical School. JAMA, 256(8):p1017-20, (Aug. 22-29, 1986).

1647 Fife, D.D.; Solomon, P.; Stanton, M. A risk/falls program: code orange for success. Nurs. Manage., 15(11):p50-3, (Nov. 1984).

1648 Flamm, W.G.; Winbush, J.S. Role of mathematical models in assessment of risk and in attempts to define management strategy. Fundam. Appl. Toxicol., 4(3 Pt. 2):pS395-401, (Jun. 1984).

1649 Freilich, H. Public hospital system institutes loss-control program. Hospitals, 54(10):p10,14, (May 16, 1980).

1650 Freilich, H.; Farkas, S. Rapid incident identification, systematic vollow-up key to preventive risk managing. Hospitals, 56(16):p53-4, (Aug. 16, 1982).

1651 Gardner, C. I.v. therapy quality assurance provides risk management. NITA, 8(3);p199-204, (May-Jun. 1985).

1652 Garrison, H.; Griggs, T. The interagency incident management system: an important element in successful prehospital emergency medical care. NC Med. J., 45(11):p714-6, (Nov. 1984).

1653 Goetz, A.; Bernstein, J. Computer developments in health risk management. Corp. Comment, 1(1):p26-33, (Jun. 1984).

1654 Grose, V.L. Managing medical malpractice risk via system science. J. Med. Syst., 6(1):p89-103, (Feb. 1982).

1655 Halpert, A.; Connors, J.P. Prevention of patient falls through perceived control and other techniques. Law Med. Health Care, 14(1):p20-4,12, (1986).

1656 Hart, M.A.; Sliefert, M.K. Monitoring patient incidents in a long term care facility. QRB, 9(12):p356-65, (Dec. 1983).

1657 Hayes, A.H., Jr. United States Food and Drug Administration approach to risk evaluation and risk management for foods. Regul. Toxicol. Pharmacol., 3(2):p152-7, (Jun. 1983).

1658 Hepplewhite, D.W. Reporting incidents with medical devices: procedures for radiologic technologists. Radiol. Technol., 57(4):p331-7, (Mar-Apr. 1986).

1659 Hibbert, J.; Craven, R.; Balinski, J. Instant problem solving. Nurs. Manage., 12(12):p37-8, (Dec. 1981).

1660 Hodgin, L. Sarnia General develops medication error report.
Dimens. Health Serv., 61(3):p25, (Mar. 1984).

1661 Holmberg, B. Occupational cancer risk management in Sweden.
Ann. NY Acad. Sci., 363:p255-60, (1981).

1662 Huber, G.A.; Wolford, J.A. Investigative reporting cuts risk at
psychiatric facility. Hospitals, 55(9):p73-6, (May 1, 1981).

1663 Hyman, W.A. Knowing your equipment: a vital element in risk
management. Tex. Hosp., 35(11):p48-9, (Apr. 1980).

1664 IL hospital reduces ER liability risks. Hospitals, 59(18):p66,
(Sep. 16, 1985).

1665 Innes, E.M. Maintaining fall prevention. QRB,
11(7):p217-21, (Jul. 1985).

1666 Jackson, M.M.; Lynch, P. Applying an epidemiological structure
to risk management and quality assurance activities.
QRB, 11(10):p306-12, (Oct. 1985).

1667 Jacoby, J.E. Risk management rounds: promoting quality care.
QRB, 9(3):p85-6, (Mar. 1983).

1668 Johnson, F.E. Internal medicine. MMTE risk Management
Committee. Minn. Med., 67(9):p491, (Sep. 1984).

1669 Jones, M.; Dodge, D. Training model helps staff eliminate
risks. Hospitals, 54(2):p40-2, (Jan. 16, 1980).

1670 Joseph, V.D.; Jones, S.K. Incident reporting: the cornerstone
of risk management. Nurs. Manage., 15(12):p22-3, (Dec. 1984).

1671 Kapp, M.B. Preventing malpractice suits in long term care
facilities. QRB, 12(3):p109-13, (Mar. 1986).

1672 Kennedy, J.R. Risk management for allied health departments.
QRB, 10(6):p175-80, (Jun. 1984).

1674 Keys, P.W. Drug-use review and risk management. Am. J. Hosp.
Pharm., 38(10):p1533-4, (Oct. 1981).

1675 Kinloch, K. For nurses only: should nursing administrators use
incident reports as a risk management tool? Can. Nurse,
78(10)p16-8, (Nov. 1982).

1676 Korsak, A. Risk management activities boost effectiveness of
self-insurance program. Hospitals, 52(4):p58,62, (Feb. 16,
1978).

139

1677 Korsak, A. Risk management: idea and effort widely supported, but appropriate methods debated. Hospitals, 53(7):p175-80, (Apr. 1, 1979).

1678 Kraus, N. Professional liability risk management and incident management in obstetrics. J. Nurse Midwife, 30(5):p295-6, (Sep-Oct. 1985).

1679 Kroll, J.; Mackenzie, T.B. When psychiatrists are liable: risk management and violent patients. Hosp. Community Psychiatry, 34(1):p29-36, (Jan. 1983).

1680 Kucera, W.R.; Ator, N. Risk management: 5 alternatives to commercial insurance. Hosp. Financ. Manage., 31(10):p26,28, 30-3, (Oct. 1978).

1681 Langdon, A.; Windle, L. Hospital incidents: how can they be reduced? Dimens. Health Serv., 60(12):p28-30, (Dec. 1983).

1682 Larkin, M. The need for I.V. teams is stronger than ever. NITA, 6(2):p82-3, (Mar-Apr. 1983).

1683 LaViolette, S. LA County focuses on prevention. Mod. Healthc., 9(12):p62, (Dec. 1979).

1684 Lee, P.S.; Pash, B.J. Preventing patient falls. Nursing, 13(2):p118-20, (Feb. 1983).

1685 Lenckus, D. Risk management techniques can reduce health claims. Bus. Insur., 20(7):p3-7, (Feb. 17, 1986).

1686 Lohman, J. Hospital safety strategies. Occup. Health Saf., 51(12):p46-7, (Dec. 1982).

1687 MacHattie, L. Workplace inspections: a vital part of your safety program. Dimens. Health Serv., 59(4):p26-7, (Apr. 1982).

1688 Massanari, R.M.; Hierholzer, W.J., Jr. Numbers that count: analytic methods for hospital epidemiology, Part 1. Am. J. Infect. Control., 14(4):p149-60, (Aug. 1986).

1689 McCollum, W.E. Multifacility program addresses both QA and risk management. Hospitals, 55(11):p96-7, (Jun. 1, 1981).

1690 McLain, N.B. Risk management in the operating room. AORN J., 31(5):p873-4,876-7, (Apr. 1980).

1691 McLain, N.B. Risk management in the emergency department. JEN, 7(6):p269-74, (Nov-Dec. 1981).

1692 McNulty, E.G. The comprehensive data base: a risk management tool. Hosp. Top., 60(1):p3-4, (Jan-Feb. 1982).

1693 Merryman, P. The incident report if in doubt, fill it out. Nursing, 15(5):p57-9, (May 1985).

1694 Miller, O.D. Risk management. II. Interruption of operations. Top Health Care Financ., 9(4):p51-60, (Summer 1983).

1695 Miller, S.A.; Skinner, K. Uncertainty and the estimation of human hazard: the science of food safety. Fundam Appl. Toxicol, 4(3 Pt. 2):pS426-33, (Jun. 1984).

1696 Murphy, M.J. Environmental risk assessment of industrial facilities: techniques, regulatory initiatives and insurance. Sci. Total Environ., 51:p185-96, (May 1986).

1697 Newbower, R.S.; Cooper, J.B.; Long, C.D. Learning from anesthesia mishaps: analysis of critical incidents in anesthesia helps reduce patient risk. QRB, 7(3):p10-6, (Mar. 1981).

1698 Oppman, C.D. Incident reporting systems: risk management components. Hosp. Risk Manage., 4(5):p68-70, (May 1982).

1699 Oulton, R. Use of incidence report data in a system-wide quality assurance/risk management program. QRB, 7(6):p2-7, (Jun. 1981).

1700 Pena, J.J.; Schmelter, W.R.; Ramseur, J.E. Computerized incident reporting and risk management. Hosp. Health Serv. Adm., 26(5):p7-11, (Fall 1981).

1701 Pierce, M.E. Reporting and following up on medication errors. Nursing, 14(1):p77,79,81, (Jan. 1984).

1702 Pollack, B.R. Risk management in the dental office. Dent. Clin. North Am., 29(3):p557-80, (Jul. 1985).

1704 Pollack, B.R.; Waldman, H.B. A risk management program for dental schools. J. Dent. Educ., 46(2):p93-6, (Feb. 1982).

1705 Punch, L. Risk management. Early-warning plan could detect neurological problem, cut liability. Mod. Healthc., 15(10):p64,66, (May 10, 1985).

1706 Raz, T.; Baretich, M.F. ARMIS: a microcomputer-based hospital risk management information system. J. Med. Syst., 9(5-6):p315-24, (Dec. 1985).

1707 Raz, T.; Baretich, M.F. ARMIS: a microcomputer-based hospital risk management information system. J. Med. Syst., 9(5-6):p315-24, (Dec. 1985).

1708 Rendell-Baker, L. Update anesthesia equipment to reduce risks.
Hospitals, 54(22):p49,52, (Nov. 16, 1980).

1709 Richards, G. Dial RM for investigation. Risk managers take on
the police work when claims arise. Hospitals, 57(8):p64-6,68,
(Apr. 16, 1983).

1710 Risk management reporting. Clin. Eng. Inf. Serv., 7(1):p3-8,
(Jan-Feb. 1983).

1711 Rodger, C.Z. Medical records role in risk management.
Mich. Hosp., 20(11):p36-7, (Nov. 1984).

1712 Salman, S.; Click, N. Risk manager must interact with infection
control expert. Hospitals, 54(6):p52-4, (Mar. 16, 1980).

1713 Sandrick, K.M. Approaches to cost and risk reduction taken by
three organizations. QRB, 9(3):p73-6, (Mar. 1983).

1714 Schrenzel, S.N. A risk management model for health costs.
Healthspan, 3(4):p19-23, (Apr. 1986).

1715 Schultz, F.W. Risk management. II. Property coverages. Top
Health Care Financ., 9(4):p37-50, (Summer 1983).

1716 Schultz, F.W. Risk management. II. Catastrophe liability. Top
Health Care Financ., 9(4):p25-35, (Summer 1983).

1717 Shotwell, H.P. Safety in the clinical laboratory.
Am. J. Med. Technol., 48(1):p61-3, (Jan. 1982).

1718 Sielicki, A.P., Jr. Evolution of risk financing techniques.
Top Health Care Financ., 9(3):p9-26, (Spring 1983).

1719 Siler, E. An integrated approach to liability.
Am. J. Infect. Control., 13(2):p90-2, (Apr. 1985).

1720 Smith, N.G. A systemwide quality assurance/risk management
program. Hosp. Med. Staff., 8(8):p40-4, (Aug. 1979).

1721 Sorrell, M.A., Jr. Risk management. II. The insurance
marketplace and competitive bidding. Top Health Care Financ.,
9(4):p61-7, (Summer 1983).

1722 Sorrell, M.A., Jr. Risk management. II. Other liability
considerations. Top Health Care Financ., 9(4):p19-23, (Summer
1983).

1723 Spaulding, J.A. Risk management: a hospital-wide approach.
Nurs. Manage., 13(4):p29-31, (Apr. 1982).

1724 Stock, R. Risk management: minimizing errors and liability.
Dimens. Health Serv., 63(1):p22-3, (Feb. 1986).

1725 Stofberg, J.; Kirschman, J.C. The consumption ratio of flavouring materials: a mechanism for setting priorities for safety evaluation. Food Chem. Toxicol., 23(9):p857-60, (Sep. 1985).

1726 Stolar, M.H.; Gabriel T.; Grant, K.L.; Koeller, J.; Letendre, D.E. Pharmacy-coordinated investigational drug services. Am. J. Hosp. Pharm., 39(3):p232-6, (Mar. 1982).

1727 Stollard, P. The codification and interpretation of hospital fire reports. Health Bull., 41(5):p238-47, (Sep. 1983).

1728 Swartzbeck, E.M. The problems of falls in the elderly. Nurs. Manage., 14(12):p34-8, (Dec. 1983).

1729 Talboom, S.J.; Elder, H.A. Nosocomial infection surveillance. QRB, 5(12):p2-7, (Dec. 1979).

1730 Tehan, J.; Colegrove, S.L. Risk management and home health care: the time is now. QRB, 12(5):p179-86, (May 1986).

1731 Tideiksaar, R. An assessment form for falls. J. Am. Geriatr. Soc., 32(7):p538-9, (Jul. 1984).

1732 Tilbury, M.S.; Ganley, S. The perioperative role: new avenue for risk management. Todays OR Nurse, 4(4):p16-9, (Jun. 1982).

1733 Webster, C.L. Risk management: hospital health insurance. Tex. Hosp., 35(11):p39, (Apr. 1980).

1734 Williams, C.W. Guide to hospital incident reports. Health Care Manage. Rev., 10(1):p19-25, (Winter 1985).

1735 Wrenn, A.J. The incident report as a risk management tool. Superv. Nurse, 12(1):p34-5, (Jan. 1981).

1736 Wright, R.E.; Gaudiosi, T.S. Risk management: a management-oriented program implemented through the medical director's office. QRB, 7(7):p10-2, (Jul. 1981).

1737 Yanish, D.L. Aggressive incident reporting saves hospitals millions of dollars. Mod. Healthc., 9(12):p64, (Dec. 1979).

1738 Young, R.L.; Du Vall, E.M. Chemotherapy exposure file. Am. J. Hosp. Pharm., 42(9):p1990-1, (Sep. 1985).

1739   Abramson, N.S.; Wald, K.S.; Grenvik, A.N.; Robinson, D.; Snyder,
        J.V.   Adverse occurrences in intensive care units.   JAMA,
        244(14):p158-4,   Oct. 3, 1980).

1740   Barbieri, E.B.   Patient falls are not patient accidents.   J.
        Gerontol. Nurs., 9(3):p165-73, (Mar. 1983).

1741   Beck, B.; Hardwick, K.; Ingram, B.; Taylor, A.   Improving the
        effectiveness of generic outcome screening criteria.   QRB,
        6(1):p5-7, (Jan. 1980).

1742   Beezley, D.; Tabel, C.; Kordick, M.   Support service evaluation:
        part II--defining the problem and its importance.   QRB, 6(4):
        p8-12, (Apr. 1980).

1743   Braff, J.; Way, B.B.; Steadman, H.J.   Incident reporting:
        evaluation of New York's pilot incident logging system.
        QRB, 12(3):p90-8, (Mar. 1986).

1744   Brantley, G.C.   A pilot study of risk management programs in
        large hospitals.   J. Am. Med. Rec. Assoc., 53(1):p68-72, (Feb.
        1982).

1745   Brown, B.   Study of patient-falls in a small, busy medical
        center.   Crit. Care Update, 10(8):p30-6, (Aug. 1983).

1746   Brown, G.C.   Medication errors: a case study.   Hospitals,
        53(20):p61-2,65, (Oct. 16, 1979).

1747   Brown, S.L.   Quantitative risk assessment of environmental
        hazards.   Annu. Rev. Public Health, 6:p247-67,
        (1985).

1748   Case history: the Mamay affair.   Rape by physicians--a risk
        management dilemma.   Hosp. Secur. Saf. Manage., 6(8):p12-5,
        (Dec. 1985).

1749   Cook, P.F.; Massie, D.   Incidents: acuity counts too.   Nurs.
        Manage., 15(12):p20, (Dec. 1984).

1750   Dandoy, S; Kirkman-Liff, B.; Krakowski, F.   Center for Health
        Services Administration at Arizona State University, Tempe.
        Arch. Intern. Med., 144(4):p720-3, (Apr. 1984).

1751   Der Yuen, D.   A large community hospital's experience with an
        obstetrics-gynecology risk management committee: quality
        assurance.   Am. J. Obstet. Gynecol., 154(6):p1206-10, (Jun.
        1986).

1753 Devoe, L.D.; Sholl, J.S. Postdates pregnancy. Assessment of
      fetal risk and obstetric management. J. Reprod. Med.,
      28(9):p576-80, (Sept. 1983).

1754 Dodge, D.D.; Dodson, B., Jr.; Helms, T.S. Developing a
      statewide loss control program: the experiences of the South
      Carolina Hospital Association. QRB, 5(4):p31-4, (Apr. 1979).

1755 Dossing, M.; Andreasen, P.B. Drug-induced liver disease in
      Denmark. An analysis of 572 cases of hepatotoxicity reported to
      the Danish Board of Adverse Reactions to Drugs.
      Scand. J. Gastroenterol., 17(2):p205-11, (Mar. 1982).

1756 Elnicki, R.A.; Schmitt, J.P. Contribution of patient and
      hospital characteristics to adverse patient incidents. Health
      Serv. Res., 15(4):p397-414, (Winter 1980).

1757 Gibbs, J. Bed area falls: a recent report. Aust. Nurses J.,
      11(10);p34-7, (May 1982).

1758 Gleicher, N. Cesarean section rates in the United States. The
      short-term failure of the National Consensus Development
      Conference in 1980. 252(23): p3273-6, (Dec. 21,
      1984).

1759 Guernsey, B.G.; Ingrim, N.B.; Hokanson, J.A.; Doutre, W.H.;
      Bryant, S.G.; Blair, C.W.; Galvan, E. Pharmacists' dispensing
      accuracy in a high-volume outpatient pharmacy service: focus on
      risk management. Drug Intell. Clin. Pharm., 17(10):p742-6,
      (Oct. 1983).

1760 Guernsey, B.G.; Ingrim, N.B.; Hokanson, J.A.; Doutre, W.H.;
      Bryant, S.G.; Blair, C.W.; Galvan, E. Pharmacists' dispensing
      accuracy in a high-volume outpatient pharmacy service: focus on
      risk management. Drug Intell. Clin. Pharm., 17(10):p742-6,
      (Oct. 1983).

1761 Hamory, B.H. Underreporting of needlestick injuries in a
      university hospital. Am. J. Infect. Control,
      11(5):p174-7, (Oct. 1983).

1762 Hampton, R.L.; Newberger, E.H. Child abuse incidence and
      reporting by hospitals: significance of severity, class, and
      race. Am. J. Public Health, 75(1):p56-60, (Jan. 1985).

1763 Heizer, D.E.; Hsieh, H. A study of choking/obstructed airway
      incidents. QRB, 9(3):p87-8, (Mar. 1983).

1764 Holsomback, T.C. The impact of risk management on hospital
      pharmacy. Top Hosp. Pharm. Manage., 5(2):p53-62, (Aug. 1985).

1765 Innes, E.M.; Turman, W.G. Evaluation of patient falls.
      QRB, 9(2):p30-5, (Feb. 1983).

1766 Jackson, M.M.; Dechairo, D.C.; Gardner, D.F. Perceptions and beliefs of nursing and medical personnel about needle-handling practices and needlestick injuries. Am. J. Infect. Control, 14(1):p1-10, (Feb. 1986).

1767 Jackson, M.M.; Lynch, P. Applying an epidemiological structure to risk management and quality assurance activities. QRB, 11(10):p306-12, (Oct. 1985).

1768 Johnson, F.E. MMIE malpractice claim review. Neurology. MMIE Risk Management Committee. Minn. Med, 68(3):p192, (Mar. 1985).

1769 Jones, I.H. Cause for complaint. Six. "A regrettable accident". Nurs. Times, 81(1):p34-5, (Jan. 2-8 1985).

1770 Jones, M.K. Patient violence. Report of 200 incidents. J. Psychosoc. Nurs. Ment. Health Serv., 23(6):p12, (Jun. 1985).

1771 Karki, M.; Mayer, C. Assessing reuse of disposables: an interdisciplinary challenge for the 1980s. Med. Instrum., 15(3):p153-5, (May-Jun. 1981).

1772 Korsak, A.J. Malpractice claims study assists claims investigation. Hospitals, 55(14):p53-4,57, (Jul. 16, 1986).

1773 Kraus, N. Professional liability risk management and incident management in obstetrics. J. Nurse Midwife, 30(5):p295-6, (Sept.-Oct. 1985).

1774 Latessa P.; Long G.; McCracken S.B. Risk management: incident data compiled and compared. Hospitals, 53(22):p54,56,58, (Nov. 16, 1979).

1775 Lockhart, P.B.; Feldbau, E.V.; Gabel, R.A.; Connolly, S.F.; Silversin, J.B. Dental complications during and after tracheal intubation. J. Am. Dent. Assoc., 112(4):p480-3, (Apr. 1986).

1776 Long, G.; Johnson, C. A pilot study for reducing medication errors. QRB, 7(4):p6-9, (Apr. 1981).

1777 McDonald, J.S.; Peterson, S.F.; Hansell, J. Operating room event analysis. Med. Instrum., 17(2):p107-8, (Mar.-Apr. 1983).

1778 Miller, O.D. Risk management. II. Interruption of operations. Top Health Care Financ., 9(4):p51-60, (Summer 1983).

1779 MMIE malpractice claim review. Orthopedic surgery. MMIE Risk Management Committee. Minn. Med., 68(2):p113-4, (Feb. 1985).

1780 MMIE malpractice claim review. Oncology. MMIE Risk Management
Committee. Minn. Med., 68(8):p631, (Aug. 1985).

1781 MMIE malpractice claim review, General surgery. MMIE Risk
Management Committee, Minn. Med., 69(2):p93, (Feb. 1986).

1782 Perr, I.N. Suicide litigation and risk management: a review of
32 cases. Bull. Am. Acad. Psychiatry Law, 13(3):
p209-19, (1985).

1783 Rainville, N.G. Effect of an implemented fall prevention
program on the frequency of patient falls. QRB,
10(9):p287-91, (Sept. 1984).

1784 Reilly, J.S.; Kenna, M.A.; Stool, S.E.; Bluestone, C.D. Nasal
surgery in children with cystic fibrosis: complications and
risk management. Laryngoscope, 95(12):p1491-3,
(Dec. 1985).

1785 Riggs, L., Jr. Medical-legal problems in the emergency
department related to hand injuries. Emerg. Med.
Clin. North Am., 3(2):p415-8, (May 1985).

1786 Rodricks, J.; Taylor, M.R. Application of risk assessment to
food safety decision making. Regul. Toxicol. Pharmacol.,
3(30):p275-307, (Sept. 1983).

1787 Sadowsky, D.; Kunzel, C. Clinician compliance and the
prevention of bacterial endocarditis. J. Am. Dent.
Assoc., 109(3):p425-8, (Sept. 1984).

1788 Salman, S.L. The impact of comparative negligence on
malpractice. Hospitals, 55(6):p46-9, (Mar. 16, 1981).

1789 Schaeffer, J.N.; Millen, H. Controlling risks in patient
transfers. Hospitals, 54(14):p46,50, (Jul. 16, 1980).

1790 Soler, J.M.; Montes, M.F.; Egol, A.B.; Nateman, H.R.; Donaldson,
E.A.; Greene, H.H. The ten-year malpractice experience of a
large urban EMS system. Ann. Emerg. Med., 14(10):0982-5,
(Oct. 1985).

1791 Spooner, R.B.; Kirby, R.R. Equipment-related anesthetic
incidents. Int. Anesthesiol Clin., 22(2):p133-47, (Summer
1984).

1792 Squire, R.A. Caracinogenicity testing and safety assessment.
Fundam. Appl. Toxicol., 4(3 Pt. 2):pS326-34, (Jun.
1984).

1793 Squire, R.A.; Cameron, L.L. An analysis of potential
caracinogenic risk from formaldehyde. Regul. Toxicol.
Pharmacol., 4(2):p107-29, (Jun. 1984).

1794 Stearns, G.; Fox, L.A. Assessing quality assurance and risk management activities: a profile analysis. QRB, 5(10):p26-9, (Oct. 1979).

1795 Stern, R.M. The management of risk for industrial metallic aerosols: in vitro assessment of delivered dose per unit exposure. Prog. Clin. Biol. Res., 208:p121-4, (1986).

1796 Stern, R.M. Analysis of the decision making process in chemical safety. Sci. Total Environ., 51:p27-62, (May 1986).

1797 Suzuki, K. [Rehabilitation of psychiatric nursing personnel: thoughts on the incident at Hotoku-kai Utsunomiya Hospital]. Kangogaku Zasshi, 48(9):p1030-4, (Sept. 1984).

1798 Swartzbeck, E.M.; Milligan, W.L. A comparative study of hospital incidents. Nurs. Manage., 13(1):p39-43, (Jan. 1982).

1799 Tannenbaum, S.R.; Skipper, P.L. Biological aspects to the evaluation of risk: dosimetry of caracinogens in man. Fundam. Appl. Toxicol., 4(3 Pt. 2):pS367-73, (Jun. 1984).

1800 Tatge, M. Risk management. Hospitals may take shot at paring infection rate to cut patient stays. Mod. Healthc., 14(5):p80-1, (Apr. 1984).

1801 Tilbury, M.S.; Ganley, S. The perioperative role: new avenue risk management. Todays OR Nurse, 4(4):p16-9, (Jun. 1982).

1802 Valaske, M.J. Loss control/risk management. A survey of the contribution of autopsy examination. Arch. Pathol. Lab. Med., 108(6):p462-8, (Jun. 1984).

1803 Valaske, M.J. Loss control/risk management. A survey of the contribution of autopsy examination. Arch. Pathol. Lab. Med., 108(6):p462-8, (Jun. 1984).

1804 Vogel, C.H.; Blom, M.F. A retrospective study of alcohol use by VA. psychiatric inpatients. Hosp. Community Psychiatry, 36(3):p287-90, (Mar. 1985).

1805 Wasiuta, V. Reporting incidents: how many is too many? Dimens. Health Serv., 59(9):p16-8, (Sept. 1982).

1806 Wilson, M.H. Childhood injury control. Pediatrician, 12(1):p20-7, (85-1983).

1807 Wilson, S.L. Risk management workshops in Georgia--an assessment of their impact. J. Med. Assoc. Ga., 72(7): p479-82, (Jul. 1983).

Management

1808 Adelman, D.N.; Donovan, M.J. Advisory panel improves
      communication, reduces risks. Hospitals, 55(2):p59-60, (Jan.
      16, 1981).

1809 Baxter, C.E. What every nurse manager should know about
      risk management. Health Serv. Manager, 13(8):p4-6, (Aug. 1980).

1810 Blinn, J.D.; Cole, M.J. Justifying a risk management
      information system's cost. Risk Manage, 29(7):p28-30,32-4,
      (Jul. 1982).

1811 Brazil, A. The role of UR coordinators in risk
      management. Tex. Hosp., 36(3):p9, (Aug. 1980).

1812 Carpenter, J.K. Directors' and officers' and fiduciary
      liability. Top Health Care Financ., 9(3):p47-58, (Spring 1983).

1813 Clements, G.W. Health care institutions need dedicated
      counsel for advice. Dimens Health Serv., 63(5):p14-5,
      (Jun. 1986).

1814 Collins, P. Hospital aims quality assurance risk
      management education at staff. Hospitals, 55(11):p93-5, (Jun.
      1, 1981).

1815 Cournoyer, C.P. Protecting yourself legally after a
      patient's injured. Nurs. Life, 5(2):p18-22, (Mar.-Apr. 1985).

1816 Coyne, J.S. Capital formation and allocation in MIOs.
      Top Health Care Financ., 11(2):p53-62, (Winter 1984).

1817 Craddick, J.W. Use existing motivations to involve
      physicians in risk management. Hospitals, 55(11):p63-4,85,
      (Jun. 1, 1981).

1818 Creighton, H. Incident reports subject to discovery?
      Nurs. Manage., 14(2):p55-7, (Feb. 1983).

1819 Cushing, M. The legal side: gaps in documentation.
      Am. J. Nurs., 82(12):p1899-900, (Dec. 1982).

1820 Donovan, R.J., Jr.; Bader, B.S. The systems approach
      to patient safety: role of the medical staff. QRB,
      5(4):p16-20, (Apr. 1979).

1821 Drury, S.J. Harvard offers hospital risk management
      course. Bus. Insur., 17(15):p10, (Apr. 11, 1983).

1822 Dudley, R.H. Risk management: The patient
      representative's role. QRB, 6(4):p4-5, (Apr. 1980).

1823 Groah, L.; Reed, E.A. Your responsibility in documenting
      care. AORN J., 37(6):p1174-88, (May 1983).

1825 Groves, J.; Korsak, A. Risk management: successful
      program needs support of hospital board of trustees. Hospitals,
      52(10):p40,44, (May 16, 1978).

1826 Haffner, A.N. Essential administrative ingredients of
      risk management as a preventive against malpractice.
      Public Health Rep., 92(5):p462-5, (Sep.-Oct. 1977).

1827 Harris, S. Fine-tuning risk management.
      J. Am. Health Care Assoc., 11(7):p51, (Nov. 1985).

1828 Hirsh, H.L. Risk management--the physician's role.
      Leg. Aspects Med. Pract., 7(1):p49-51, (Jan. 1979).

1829 Holder, A.R. The lawyer's role in risk management. QRB,
      5(4):p25-6, (Apr. 1979).

1830 Hollander, E.C. Risk management education: program
      development--Part two. Tex. Hosp., 35(10):p26-7, (Mar. 1980).

1831 Hollander, E.C. Risk management education: program
      development. Part three. Tex. Hosp., 35(11):p50-1, (Apr.
      1980).

1832 Hollander, E.C. Risk management educaiton program
      development. Tex. Hosp., 35(9):p22, (Feb. 1980).

1833 Julian, R.L. The role of the utilization reviewer in
      risk management. Tex. Hosp., 35(11):p46-7, (Apr. 1980).

1834 Kaddatz, M.M.; Huntington, R.R. Risk management
      consultants: call in problem-solving specialists.
      Healthc. Financ. Manage., 37(3):p36-9,42,47-50, (Mar. 1983).

1835 Kuntz, E. Educational programs reduce liability.
      Mod. Healthc., 9(12):p66-7, (Dec. 1979).

1836 Kuntz, E.F. Risk management: hospitals' premiums are
      beginning to rise again. Mod. Healthc., 11(10):p95-6,98, (Oct.
      1981).

1837 LaCava, F.W. The roles of legal counsel in hospital risk
      management. QRB, 11(1):p20-4, (Jan. 1985).

1838 Lambert, R.L. Medical staff is key in hospital risk
      management. Pa. Med., 81(11):p20-2, (Nov. 1978).

1839 LeRoux, M. Risk management, 'healthy' hospital-insurers
      grapple with commercial firms. Mod. Healthc., 12(9):p83-5,
      (Sep. 1982).

1840 McDonald, N. Patient rep can be viewed as fiscal asset.
      Hospitals, 54(9):p42,47, (May 1, 1980).

1841 McNulty, E.G. Direct patient settlements best for all
      parties. Hospitals, 54(9):p129-31, (May 1, 1980).

1842 Meyers, D.R. Risk management: beware of workshops'
      quick 'certification.' Mod. Healthc., 12(9):p86, (Sep. 1982).

1843 Nacman, M. Social worker can eliminate potential risks.
      Hospitals, 54(12):p189-92, (Jun. 16, 1980).

1844 O'Donnell, J. The role of the clinical pharmacist in
      risk management. Top Hosp. Pharm. Manage., 6(2):p37-45, (Aug.
      1986).

1845 Oppman, C.D. Practical risk management cosiderations.
      Todays OR Nurse, 1(10):p7-13, (Dec. 1979).

1846 Oppman, C.D. Staff training vital for risk management.
      Hospitals, 53(24):p95-6,98, (Dec. 16, 1979).

1847 Oppman, C.D. Training: the key to an effective risk
      management program. Health Care Newsl., p3p, (Nov.-Dec. 1980).

1848 Oppman, C.D. Staff training vital for risk management.
      Hospitals, 53(24):p95-6,98, (Dec. 16, 1979).

1849 Punch, L. Risk management: managers target broad
      quality assurance goal. Mod. Healthc., 12(9):p88-9, (Sep.
      1982).

1850 Punch, L. Risk management. More in-house attorneys
      hired to cut costs, improve access. Mod. Healthc.,
      14(5):p76,78, (Apr. 1984).

1851 Rabinow, J. Patient injury in the hospital: how to
      protect yourself legally. Nursinglife, 2(1):p44-48, (Jan.-Feb.
      1982).

1852 Raz, T.; Demlo, L.K. Efficient allocation of risk
      management efforts. QRB, 9(6):p183-4, (Jun. 1983).

1853 Roberts, C.J. Medical care as a risk-avoidance
      procedure: underwriting the cost of care in the UK.
      Br. Med. J. [Clin. Res.], 285(6343):p751,754-5, (Sep. 11, 1982).

1854 Salman, S.L. Committee is an important tool in risk
      management. Hospitals, 54(18):p45,48,50, (Sep. 16, 1980).

1855 Sax, A. AHA seminars encourage risk management program.
      Hospitals, 52(8):p38-39, (Apr. 16, 1978).

1856 Shahoda, T. Insurance & liability. Save time, save
      problems: use consultants. Hospitals, 60(2):p112-3, (Jan. 20,
      1986).

1857 Stearns, G.; Fox, L.A. Assessing quality assurance and
      risk management activities: a profile analysis. QRB,
      5(10):p26-9, (Oct. 1979).

1858 Touchstone, W.A. Fiscal accountability through effective
      risk management. Ther. Recreation J., 18(4):p20-6, (4th Quarter
      1984).

1859 Troyer, G.; Salman, S. Committees can help oversee
      hospital's QA activities. Hospitals, 55(11):p87-91, (Jun. 1,
      1981).

1860 Trustee development program: the board's role in risk
      management. Trustee, 32(9):p55-62, (Sep. 1979).

1861 Van Sluyter, C.K. Organizing for patient safety and
      liability control. QRB, 5(4):p21-4, (Apr. 1979).

1862 Van Sluyter, C.K.; Hays, P.G. Interdisciplinary task
      force designs risk management program. Hospitals,
      52(15):p87-8,90, (Aug. 1, 1978).

1863 Willenbrink, M. Use nursing medical knowledge for
      alternative careers [interview]. Nurs. Success Today,
      2(1):p12-5, (Jan. 1985).

1864 Willets, J.W. Risk management and the medical record
      professional. J. Am. Med. Rec. Assoc., 53(5):p68-70, (Oct.
      1982).

1865 Wilson, S.L. Risk management workshops in Georgia--an
      assessment of their impact. J. Med. Assoc. Ga., 72(7):p479-82,
      (Jul. 1983).

Overviews

1866 Abelson, P.H. Environmental risk management
      (editorial). Science, 226(4678):p1023, (Nov. 30, 1984).

1867 Affeldt, J.E. Coordination, communication: watchwords
      for risk management. Hosp. Med. Staff, 7(8):p8-10, (Aug. 1978).

1868 Alexander, M. The integration of QA and risk
      management. Tex. Hosp., 38(12):p30-1, (May 1983).

1869 Ansley, C.E.; Cleverley, W.O. Lease financing and risk
      in the hospital industry. Top. Health Care Financ.,
      9(4):p69-77, (Summer 1983).

1870 Archer, R.L. Professional liability risk management in
      Pennsylvania. Risk Manage., 25(11):p52-4, (Nov. 1978).

1871 Barracato, J.S. Risk management. Fires should spark
      hospital's suspicion of in-house arsonist. Mod. Healthc.,
      14(5):p82, 84, (Apr. 1984).

1872 Bartek, W. Combining risk management and quality
      assurance. Tex. Hosp., 40(8):p12, (Jan. 1985).

1873 Beardshaw, V. The whistle-blowers [interview by Cherrill
      Hicks]. Nurs. Times, 77(45):p1921, (Nov. 4-10, 1981).

1874 Berger, S. Risk management. Legal threats scare board
      recruits. Mod. Healthc., 14(5):p88, 90, (Apr. 1984).

1875 Bernstein, A.H. Why another hospital malpractice
      insurance crisis? Hospitals, 54(21):p50, 55-6, (Nov. 1, 1980).

1876 Bianco, E.A. It works--risk management and drug-induced
      disease. Internist, 25(2):p29-30, (Feb. 1984).

1877 Brown, B.L. Risk Management for Hospitals--A Practical
      Approach. Publ: Germantown, Md.: Aspen Systems, p186, (1979).

1878 Brown, B.L., Jr. Risk management. Am. J. Infect. Control,
      9(3):p82-6, (Aug. 1981).

1879 Burda, D. Early warning systems can reduce liability
      risk. Hospitals, 60(10):p33, 36, (May 20, 1986).

1880 Burnhill, M.S. Risk management in pregnancy termination.
      Clin. Obstet. Gynaecol., 13(1):p145-56, (Mar. 1986).

1881 Cain, C. Rogers cures hospital's risk management ills.
      Bus. Insur., 20(15):p131-3, (Apr. 14, 1986).

1882 Carlson, K. Presidential address (risk management).
      NITA, 9(4):p260-1, (Jul.-Aug. 1986).

153

1883 Carnesecchi, R. Risk management--a second chance. Biomed. Commun., 10(1):p16-7, 20, (Jan.-Feb. 1982).

1884 Chapman, G. Management. Incidents and accidents. Nurs. Mirror, 160(11):p38-9, (Mar. 13, 1985).

1885 Clarke, C. Can medical practice be free of risk? J. R. Soc. Med., 72(1):p35-8, (Jan. 1979).

1886 Cohn, S.D. The nurse midwife: malpractice and risk management. J. Nurse Midwife, 29(5):p316-21, (Sep.-Oct. 1984).

1887 Collins, E.M. Quality assurance and risk management: linking both benefits all. Group Pract., 29(4):p11-2, (Apr. 1980).

1888 Cunningham, R.M., Jr. Rise in malpractice claims forces look at previous scare. Hospitals, 55(6):p85-6, 88, 90, (Mar. 16, 1981).

1889 Curran, W.J. Law-medicine notes. A further solution to the malpractice problem: corporate liability and risk management in hospitals. N. Engl. J. Med., 310(11):p704-5, (Mar. 15, 1984).

1890 Curtin, L.L. Honesty, incident reports and risk management. Nurs. Manage., 12(10):p7-8, (Oct. 1981).

1891 Davis, D. Risk management: another OR puzzle to solve? AORN J., 38(5):p767-71, (Nov. 1983).

1892 deFerranti, D. Strategies for paying for health services in developing countries. World Health Stat. Q., 37(4):p428-50, (1984).

1893 Densmore, B. Risk management. Malpractice reform: NY's ready... Mod. Healthc., 13(4):p99-100, (Apr. 1983).

1894 DiPaolo, V. Risk management: spiraling premiums predicted. Mod. Healthc., 9(12):p56-8, (Dec. 1979).

1895 Doody, M.F. President's page: risk management program (editorial). OH, 21(9):p6, (Oct. 1977).

1896 Dooley, T.P. Risk management in the NHS. Health Serv. Manpower Rev., 6(4):p11-6, (Nov. 1980).

1897 Duran, G.S. On the scene: risk management in health care. Nurs. Adm. Q., 5(1):p19-36, (Fall 1980).

1898 Edelman, J.; Peloquin, R.J. Systematic risk management: take no chance with hospital liability. OH, 23(1):p14-8, (Jan. 1979).

1899　FAH manual outlines control programs on risk management for hospital use. Rev. Fed. Am. Hosp., 10(1):p13-4, 16-8, (Feb. 1977).

1900　Fifer, W.R.　Risk management and medical malpractice: an overview of the issues. QRB, 5(4):p9-13, (Apr. 1979).

1901　Fifer, W.R.　Risk management and quality assurance: integration for optimal effectiveness. QRB, 5(8):p15-9, (Aug. 1979).

1902　Flamm, W. G.　Risk assessment policy in the United States. Prog. Clin. Biol. Res., 208:p141-9, (1986).

1903　Florida law requires hospitals to have internal program on risk management. Rev. Fed. Am. Hosp., 10(1):p22-3, 26-8, (Feb. 1977).

1904　Freilich, H.; Farkas-Finkelstein, S.　Risk management fights back--the hospital's response to the malpractice explosion. Hosp. Top., 61(3):p2-4, (May-Jun. 1983).

1905　Geisel, J.　Risk management honor roll. Tax-exempt entity: Gene M. Marsh. Bus. Insur., 16(16):p100, 106-7, (Apr. 19, 1982).

1906　Glass, L.S.　The medical record: shield or sword of Damocles? Alaska Med., 26(2):p2 following 48, (Apr.-Jun. 1984).

1907　Goodman, T.　Risk management. Why it became necessary. AORN J., 39(7):p1256, 1258, 1260-1, (Jun. 1984).

1908　Gregory, D.R.　Does medicine need risk management? (editorial) Leg. Aspects Med. Pract., 7(1):p4, (Jan. 1979).

1909　Greve, P.A., Jr.　Hospital risk management: challenge of the '80s. Hosp. Admin. Curr., 29(3):p13-8, (1985).

1910　Grothaus, C.L.　Risk management and quality assurance-- so what? Healthc. Prot. Manage., 3(1):p8-9, (Oct.-Dec. 1982).

1911　Hardy, M.　Risk management: treating the causes vs. the symptoms. Mich. Hosp., 21(11)p27-8, (Nov. 1985).

1912　Hirsh, H.L.　Hospital law: the changing scene. Leg. Med. Annu., p325-59, (1978).

1913　Hirsh, H.L.; White, E.R.　Risk management: preventive medicine for malpractice. Hosp. Med. staff, 7(10):p1-7, (Oct. 1978).

1914 Holbrook, R.F. Legal aspects of risk management. Trustee, 34(6):p13-4, 17-8, (Jun. 1981).

1915 Holloway, S.T.; Sax, A.B. AHA urges, aids hospitals to adopt effective risk management plans. Hospitals, 51(10):p57-9, 66, (May 16, 1977).

1916 Holmberg, B. Occupational cancer risk management in Sweden. Ann. NY. Acad. Sci., 363:p255-60, (1981).

1917 Holroyd, B.R.; Knopp, R.; Kallsen, G. Medical control. Quality assurance in prehospital care. JAMA, 256(8):p1027-31, (Aug. 22-29, 1986).

1918 Howie, C. Accidents will happen ... Nurs. Times, 80(13):p19, (Mar. 28-Apr. 3, 1984).

1919 Jacoby, J.E. Risk management rounds: promoting quality care. QRB, 9(3):p85-6, (Mar. 1983).

1920 Jones, D.B. Risk management: one way to fight malpractice suits. Tex. Med., 81(6):p64-6, (Jun. 1985).

1921 Joseph, E. Patient rights--key to risk management in mental health settings. QRB, 6(11):p4-6, (Nov. 1980).

1922 Katz, P.S. Integrating quality assurance, utilization review, and risk management activities for the small hospital. QRB, 12(3):p114-5, (Mar. 1986).

1923 Kroll, J.; Mackenzie, T.B. When psychiatrists are liable: risk management and violent patients. Hops. Community Psychiatry, 34(1):p29-36, (Jan. 1983).

1924 Kumagai, J.; Matsuzawa, T.; Kuroda, Y.; Ogane, T. [Case conference about troubles in hospitals]. Kango Tenbo, 9(12):p1061-92, (Dec. 1984).

1925 Ladner, H.A., Jr. How to be sued less often and at less cost. J. Miss. State Med. Assoc., 23(10):p281-3, 287, (Oct. 1982).

1926 Langslow, A. Nurse and the law. What the nurse saw. Aust. Nurses J., 14(1):p48-9, 59, (Jul. 1984).

1927 Lanham, G.B.; Orlikoff, J.E. Full coverage of issues reflects importance of risk management. Hospitals, 55(7):p165-8, (Apr. 1, 1981).

1928 LaRocco, S.A. Patient abuse should be your concern. J. Nurs. Adm., 15(4):p27-31, (Apr. 1985).

1929 Lenhard, C.G. Hospital risk management coming into its own. South Hosp., 48(5):p6, 8, 13, (Sep.-Oct. 1980).

1930 Ludlam, J.E. States move toward legislated hospital risk management. Hospitals, 51(10):p63-6, (May 16, 1977).

1931 Ludlam, J.E. Payment systems, cost management, and malpractice. Hospitals, 58(21):p102-4, (Nov. 1, 1984).

1932 Mant, D. Energy conservation and the housing environment: the need for risk management. Community Med., 7(1):p30-6, (Feb. 1985).

1933 Marco, C.H. Why hospitals are getting tougher about your privileges. Leg. Aspects Med. Pract., 7(7):p18-22, (Jul. 1979).

1934 Martin, H. Hospital risk management: a Canadian perspective. Health Manage. Forum, 2(3):p23-34, (Autumn 1981).

1935 McCollum, W.E. Hospital system works to ensure risk management, quality of care. Hospitals, 52(19):p86-8, (Oct. 1, 1978).

1936 Medicare program; revision of explanation of Medicare benefit notice and review procedures for beneficiaries; supplementary medical insurance (Part B); court order--HCFA. Notice with comment period. Fed. Regist., 50(233):p49770-5, (Dec. 4, 1985).

1937 Miller, L.A. Risk management: preventive medicine for hospitals. Internist, 21(4):p17-8, (May 1980).

1938 Miller, S.A. Symposium on safety assessment: the interface between science, law and regulation. Introductory remarks to session on risk assessment and risk management. Fundam. Appl. Toxicol., 4(3 Pt. 2):pS380-2, (Jun. 1984).

1939 Moon, J.E. The great risk: ignoring risk management. Ala. J. Med. Sci., 17(3-4):p332-4, (Jul.-Oct. 1980).

1940 Mulholland, J.H.; Bittle, L. Quality assurance & risk management in Maryland hospitals in the 1980s. Md. State Med. J., 31(4):p60-2, (Apr. 1982).

1941 O'Connell, J.A. Risk management for hospitals. Hosp. Prog., 55(11):p40-2, (Nov. 1974).

1942 Oppman, C.D. Practical risk management considerations. Todays OR Nurse, 1(10):p7-13, (Dec. 1979).

1943 Orlikoff, J.E.; Lanham, G.B. Integrated approach improves quality assurance, risk management activities. Hospitals, 54(17):p59-61, (Sep. 1, 1980).

1944 Oulton, R. Reducing risk through compliance with
     accreditation standards. QRB, 6(5):p3-4, (May 1980).

1945 Parker, S. Risk management: many solutions proposed and
     successes noted. Hospitals, 52(7):p156-8, (Apr. 1, 1978).

1946 Pecorino, D.J. Risk management--loss prevention. W. Va.
     Med. J., 75(12):p360-2, (Dec. 1979).

1947 Perr, I.N. Suicide litigation and risk management: a
     review of 32 cases. Bull. Am. Acad. Psychiatry Law,
     13(3):p209-19, (1985).

1948 Pocchiari, F.; Silano, V.; Zapponi, G. The chemical
     risk management process in Italy. A case study: the Seveso
     accident. Sci. Total Environ., 51:p227-35, (May 1986).

1949 Pollack, B.R. Plan for the best, prepare for the worst.
     Trends Tech. Contemp. Dent. Lab., 1(5):p47-5, (Sep.-Oct. 1984).

1950 Posner, J.R. An update on current trends and problems:
     the financial manager's guide to risk management. Hosp.
     Finance. Manage., 36(4):p64-70, (Apr. 1982).

1951 Post, R.S. Risk management. Ohio State Med. J.,
     77(11):p645-7, (Nov. 1981).

1952 Poteet, G.W. Risk management and nursing. Nurs. Clin.
     North Am., 18(3):p457-65, (Sep. 1983).

1953 Press, F. Symposium on safety assessment: the interface
     between science, law and regulation. Keynote address.
     Fundam. Appl. Toxicol., 4(3 Pt. 2):pS257-60, (Jun. 1984).

1954 Rantanen, J. Risk assessment and the setting of
     priorities in occupational health and safety. Scand.
     J. Work Environ. Health, 7 Suppl 4:p84-90, (1981).

1955 Rasinski, D. Risk management in practice. Internist,
     23(4):p8 following 12, (May 1982).

1956 Reagan, B.M. Risk management: an evolving hospital
     tool. Times, 22(8):p2-3, 23, (Sep.-Oct. 1981).

1957 Revzan, H. Mergers and acquisitions: a how-to
     perspective on...2. Risk-management implications.
     Manage. Rev., 73(4):p19-25, (Apr. 1984).

1958 Rice, A.P. Risk management in chemical safety: some
     general observations relating to the state of the art.
     Sci. Total Environ., 51:p1-17, (May 1986).

1959 Richards, G. Malpractice losses are building--again. Hospitals, 58(18):p108-12, 115, (Sep. 16, 1984).

1960 Riger, S.; Gordon, M.T.; LeBailly, R.K. Coping with urban crime: women's use of precautionary behaviors. Am. J. Community Psychol., 10(4):p369-86, (Aug. 1982).

1961 Risk management held 'preventive' medicine. US Med., 14(23):p6, (Dec. 1, 1978).

1962 Risk management in chemical safety. Sci. Total Environ., 51:p1-263, (May 1986).

1963 Roberts, F. Accidents in hospital. Learning from past mishaps. Nurs. Times, 81(10):p24-6, (Mar. 6-12, 1985).

1964 Robinson, W.J. Governmental factors in establishment of risk assessment procedures in the United States. Sci. Total Environ., 51:p69-73, (May 1986).

1965 Rogers, W.E. Risk management checkup. Health care changes demand action. Bus. Insur., 18(43):p21-2, (Oct. 22, 1984).

1966 Rosenthal, T.; Rosenthal, S. Managing risks. Nurs. Manage., 14(4):p38-40, (Apr. 1983).

1967 Ross, T. Accidents in hospital. Why did it happen in my ward? Nurs. Times, 81(10):p27-8, (Mar. 6-12, 1985).

1968 Rozovsky, L.E.; Rozovsky, F.A. Protecting the hospital with risk management. Hosp. Trustee, 4(4):p9-10, (Jul.-Aug. 1980).

1969 Ryan, W. Risk management checkup. Hospitals still have a long way to go. Bus. Insur., 18(43):p21-2, (Oct. 22, 1984).

1970 Sax, A.B. Patient relations in risk management. QRB, 5(4):p14-5, (Apr. 1979).

1971 Schultz, F.W. Risk management. II. Catastrophe liability. Top Health Care Financ., 9(4):p25-35, (Summer 1983).

1972 Schultz, F.W. Risk management. II. Property coverages. Top Health Care Financ., 9(4):p37-50, (Summer 1983).

1973 Selikoff, I.J. Carcinogenic risk management in the United States. Ann. NY. Acad. Sci., 363:p283-93, (1981).

1974 Severson, L.C. Hospital risk management. Hosp. Admin. Curr., 23(5):p19-22, (Sep.-Oct. 1979).

1975   Shmock, C.L.   Quality patient care through risk
        management.   J. Leg. Med., 5(12):p27-8, (Dec. 1977).

1976   Sielicki, A.P., Jr.   Risk management philosophy and
        techniques--an overview.   Top Health Care Financ., 9(4):p1-4,
        (Summer 1983).

1977   Silver, A.P.   2000--the year of the "super CFO".   Top
        Health Care Financ., 7(1):p47-51, (Fall 1980).

1978   Skillicorn, S.A.   Improved quality controls in
        hospitals: a necessity.   J. Leg. Med., 2(4):p471-89, (Dec.
        1981).

1979   Skillicorn, S.A.   A conversation with Dr. Stanley A.
        Skillicorn: a leading proponent of integrated, problem-oriented
        quality assurance is interviewed by the QRB (by Cheryl
        Tabatabai).   QRB, 7(4):p20-3, (Apr. 1981).

1980   Sklar, C.   You and the law: negligence in the hospital
        labor room: a tragic lesson for all concerned.   Can. Nurse,
        78(1):p48-50, (Jan. 1982).

1981   Sklar, C.   You and the law: the incident report.   Can.
        Nurse, 77(10):p42-3, (Nov. 1981).

1982   Somers, E.   Environmental health risk management in
        Canada.   Regul. Toxicol. Pharmacol., 3(1):p75-81, (Mar. 1983).

1983   Sorrell, M.A., Jr.   Risk management.   II. Other liability
        considerations.   Top. Health Care Financ., 9(4):p19-23, (Summer
        1983).

1984   Steadman, J.   The risky professions.   Hosp. Community
        Psychiatry, 34(1):p5, (Jan. 1983).

1985   Stewart, K.P.   Risk management: no task for the timid.
        Trustee, 32(4):p10-2, 16, (Apr. 1979).

1986   Stock, R.   Risk management: minimizing errors and
        liability.   Dimens. Health Serv., 63(1):p22-3, (Feb. 1986).

1987   Stoltz, M.K.   Risk management is big operation to
        hospitals hit by malpractice costs.   Health Care Week, 2(17):p1,
        10, (Oct. 30, 1978).

1988   Strazewski, L.   Risk management....and Florida's working
        on a plan.   Mod. Healthc., 13(4):p99-102, (Apr. 1983).

1989   Tabatabai, C.   On the quality of anesthesia care: an
        introduction to the special section.   QRB, 7(3):p8-9, (Mar.
        1981).

160

1990 Tehan, J.; Colegrove, S.L. Risk management and home
health care: the time is now. QRB, 12(5):p179-86, (May 1986).

1991 The honeymoon is over: malpractice update. J. Indiana
State Med. Assoc., 75(2):p130, (Feb. 1982).

1992 The liability issue: protecting the profession. J. Am.
Dent. Assoc., 112(5):p607-17, (May 1986).

1993 Throdahl, M.C. Practical implications of risk management
in industry. Ann. NY. Acad. Sci., 363:p167-72, (1981).

1994 Todhunter, J.A. Risk management strategy under the Toxic
Substances Control Act and the Federal Insecticide, Fungicide,
and Rodenticide Act. Regul. Toxicol. Pharmacol., 3(2):p163-71,
(Jun. 1983).

1995 Trandel-Korenchuk, D.M. Legal forum. Malpractice and
preventive risk management. Nurs. Adm. Q., 7(3):p75-80, (Spring
1983).

1996 Trandel-Korenchuk, D.M.; Trandel-Korenchuk, K.M. Legal
forum. Malpractice and preventive risk management.
Nurs. Adm. Q., 7(3):p75-80, (Spring 1983).

1997 Tremblay, J. Drug-use review and risk management:
another view (letter). Am. J. Hosp. Pharm., 39(4):p578-80,
(Apr. 1982).

1998 Wallace, C. Risk management. Moore prescribes
'no-fault' bill to relieve pain of malpractice claims.
Mod. Healthc., 14(5):p65-6, 70-4, (Apr. 1984).

1999 Warren, R.W. Hospitals are saving more than lives--the
Texas voluntary effort. Risk management. Tex. Hosp.,
35(11):p43-5, (Apr. 1980).

2000 Yodaiken, R.E. Occupational disease. Problems of risk
management. Clin. Lab. Med., 4(3):p475-82, (Sep. 1984).

AUTHOR INDEX

CHAPTER 2:

QUALITY ASSURANCE REFERENCES

Theory and Concept

0001 Alaszewski, A.
0002 Alexander, L.L.; Lewis,
      N.
0003 Andrew, R.R.
0004 Bailit, H.L.
0005 Bartlett, D.P.;
      Intagliata, J.
0006 Beezley, D.; Tabel, C.;
      Kordick, M.
0007 Bergman, B.B.
0008 Blake, B.L.
0009 Blanton, W.B.
0010 Blum, H.L.
0011 Boehm, A.H.
0012 Bohnet, N.L.
0013 Bouchard, R.E.; Tufo,
      H.M.; Beaty, H.N.
0014 Brook, R.H.; Williams,
      K.N.
0015 Burakoff, R.P.; Demby,
      N.A.
0016 Burck, K.
0017 Burkhart, R.L.
0018 Butler, R.J.
0019 Chism, S.
0020 Christoffel, T.
0021 Cicatiello, J.; Zimmer,
      M.J.; Christman, L.
0022 Cohn, S.S.
0023 Crawford, J.B.
0024 De La Haye, W.
0025 de Verdier, C-H;
      Haabrekke, O.; Leskinen,
      E.; Uldall, A.
0026 Decker, C.M.
0027 Dennis, B.W.; Pierpaoli,
      P.G.
0028 Dennis, D.A.
0029 Diamond, I.
0030 DiAngelis, A.J.
0031 Dieter Haussmann, R.K.;
      Hegyvary, S.T.; Newman,
      J.F.; Bishop, A.C.

0032 Dodosh, M.N.
0034 Donabedian, A.
0035 Doughty, E.O.
0036 Duncan, A.
0037 Eddy, D.M.
0040 Egdahl, R.H.; Taft, C.H.
0041 Eisenberg, J.M.; Sussman,
      E.J.
0043 Farrington, J.F.; Felch,
      W.C.; Hare, R.L.
0044 Ferguson, J.W.
0045 Fifer, W.R.
0046 Fifer, W.R.; Aldrich, S.Y.
0047 Filiatrault, L.J.; Larsen,
      P.J.
0048 Flint, L.S.; Hammett,
      W.H.; Martens, K.
0049 Funkhouser, G.R.
0050 Gatere, G.
0051 Gibson, R.W.
0052 Gilbert, B.
0053 Goldberg, B.A.
0054 Greeley, H.
0055 Greenspan, J.
0056 Gregg, T.E.; Hahn, J.A.
0057 Griffith, J.R.
0058 Grogan, J.
0059 Gurevich, I.
0060 Gustafson, C.I.; Walden,
      R.T.
0061 Hadley, R.D.
0062 Harbo, J.N.; Heaney, K.M.
0063 Honovich, D.
0065 Howell, J.N.
0066 Hughes, S.L.
0067 Hurwitz, L.S.; Kohler, E.
0068 Hutton, B.F.; Smart, R.C.
0069 Hyden, J.P.
0071 Jarvis, B.M.
0072 Jessee, W.F.
0073 Kane, R.A.
0074 Katz, P.S.
0075 Kearns, P.M.

162

0076	Kerr, I.L.	0120	Purinton, L.W.
0077	Kiikuni, K.	0124	Ransdell, L.A.
0078	Kohles, M.T.	0126	Restuccia, J.D.; Holloway, D.C.
0079	Kresky, B.; Cohen, A.		
0080	Krinsky, L.W.; Carone, P.A.	0127	Rinaldi, L.A.
		0128	Roberts, R.F.
0081	Laessig, R.H.; Ehrmeyer, S.S.; Hassemer, D.J.	0129	Rosen, P.
		0130	Rudd, T.N.
0082	Larson, E.	0131	Runnells, G.
0083	Lawson, N.S.; Haven, G.T.; Ross, J.W.	0132	Ryan, P.J.
		0133	Ryder, R.
0084	Leach, J.; Nagy, S.; Cercone, R.	0134	Sanazaro, P.J.
		0135	Sandlow, L.J.
0085	Lee, B.A.; Lee, W.A.	0136	Schron, S.R.
0086	Legge, D.	0137	Shaffer, K.L.; Lindenstein, J.; Jennings, T.A.
0087	Legge, D.G.; Hutton, P.A.		
0088	Lewis, C.E.		
0089	Linn, M.W.; Gurel, L.; Linn, B.S.	0138	Shanahan, M.
		0139	Skillicorn, S.A.
0090	Linn, M.W.; Linn, B.S.	0140	Skillicorn, S.A.
0091	Liptzin, B.	0141	Slack, P.
0092	Longest, B.B., Jr.	0142	Small, E.W.
0093	Lynch, T.	0143	Smart, G.A.
0094	Markus, A.C.	0144	Smith, D.
0095	Mass, D.; Galen, R.S.	0145	Sniff, D.
0096	Matoth, Y.	0146	Spivak, H.R.; Levy, J.C.; Bonanno, R.A.; Cracknell, M.
0097	McIntyre, K.J.		
0098	McKillop, W.		
0099	McClure, M.L.	0147	Spotts, S.J.
0100	McMahon, J.A.	0148	Stern, S.K.
0101	McSherry, C.K.	0149	Stolar, M.H.
0102	Migliozzi, A.A.	0151	Sushkevich, G.N.; Rakovianu, N.
0103	Mikeal, R.L.; Brown, T.R.; Lazarus, H.L.; Vinson, M.C.		
		0152	Swanson, A.L.
		0155	Thompson, R.
0104	Miller, T.W.; Jay, L.L.	0156	Thompson, R.E.
0105	Mills, D.H.	0157	Thompson, R.E.
0106	Moeller, D.	0158	Tupa, B.M.
0107	Monagle, J.F.	0159	Vanagunas, A.; Egelston, E.M.; Hopkins, J.; Walczak, R.M.
0108	Moore, B.		
0109	Mulholland, J.H.; Bittle, L.		
		0160	Vogel, D.P.; Gurwich, E.; Hutchinson, R.A.
0110	Nafziger, J.		
0111	Nelson, A.R.	0162	Wendorf, B.
0112	Orlikoff, J.E.; Lanham, G.B.	0163	Westerman, J.H.; Spano, R.M.; Keyes, M.A.
0113	Orth-Gomer, K.; Britton, M.; Rehnqvist, N.	0165	Williamson, J.W.
		0166	Wilson, L.L.
0114	Ostrow, P.C.	0167	Yoder, D.L.
0115	Peele, R.; Palmer, R.R.	0168	Youell, L.
0116	Pelley, G.	0169	Zintel, H.A.
0117	Porterfield, J.D.		
0118	Porterfield, J.D.		
0119	Price, S.B.		

Techniques Programs Procedures

0171 Ackerman, D.; Vicha, D.
0172 Ackerman, V.P.; Pritchard, R.C.
0173 Adamow, C.L.
0174 Adams, H.G.; Campbell, A.F.
0175 Affeldt, J.E.
0176 Affeldt, J.E.
0177 Ahuja, S.D.
0178 Akhter, M.N.
0179 Allison, S.; Kinloch, K.
0180 Anderson, K.; Mattsson, O.
0181 Anderson, R.E.; Hill, R.B.
0182 Anderson, T.B.; Forquer, S.L.
0183 Anderson T.P.; Baldridge, M.; Ettinger, M.G.
0185 Armenian, H.K.
0186 Aydelotte, M.K.
0187 Bailit, H.L.
0188 Baker, B.M.
0189 Bailit, H.L.
0190 Barney, M.
0191 Barr, D.M.; Woolstadt, L.J.; Goodrich, L.L.; Pittman, J.G.; Booher, C.E.; Evans, R.L.
0192 Barr, W.T.; Williams, F.D.
0193 Bartilotta, K.; Rzasa, C.B.
0194 Bartlett, D.P.; Intagliata, J.
0195 Bartlett, R.C.; Tetreault, J.; Evers, J.; Officer, J.; Derench, J.
0196 Bates, B.A.; Alexander, S.A.; Gale, C.; Roberts, R.F.; Pearson, I.Y.
0197 Batsakis, J.G.; Lawson, N.S.; Gilbert, R.K.
0198 Beautyman, W.; Rawnsley, H.M.
0199 Beck, B.; Hardwick, K.
0200 Beck, B.; Hardwick, K.
0201 Benson, D.; Wilder, B.; Gartner, C.
0202 Berg, J.K.; Kelly, J.T.
0203 Berkman, B.; Rehr, H.
0204 Berkman, B.; Rehr, H.
0205 Black, A.; Emerton, E.
0206 Blalock, W.R.

0207 Bradham, R.R.; Buxton, J.T.; Clark, J.S.
0208 Brashear, J.
0209 Broekemeier, R.L.; Brewer, P.E.; Johnson, M.K.
0210 Brown, D.E.; Levy, J.D.; Sarmiento, M.
0211 Brown, D.E.; Levy, J.D.; Sarmiento, M.
0212 Brown, E.M.
0213 Bruce, G.L.; Hinds, P.; Hudak, J.; Mucha, A.; Taylor, M.C.; Thompson, C.R.
0214 Buddi, J.
0215 Bullen, M.A.; Bye, R.T.
0216 Bulman, T.
0217 Burger, M.C.
0218 Burkle, W.S.
0219 Bush, R.S.
0220 Bush, R.S.
0221 Buske, S.M.
0222 Byalin, K.; Jed, J.; Bender, P.
0223 Cada, R.L.; West, D.K.
0224 Caldwell, G.B.
0225 Cameron, J.C.
0226 Cardellino, H.
0227 Carey, D.L.
0228 Carlton, R.
0229 Carver, A.M.
0230 Catlin, D.
0231 Celeste, S.M.; Folick, M.A.; Dumas, K.M.
0232 Chae, Y.M.
0233 Chaffey, J.T.
0234 Chernesky, R.H.; Lurie, A.
0235 Cimprich, B.
0236 Clark, M.R.; MacIntyre, K.A.
0237 Clemence, E.
0238 Cohen, A.G.; Tucker, E.
0239 Colchamiro, E.K.; Herbst, E.; Carr, N.; Kourre, N.
0240 Cole, L.; Cayten, C.G.; Staroscik, R.
0241 Coulthard, S.W.
0243 Cradduck, T.D.; Busemann-Sokole, E.
0244 Crandell, C.E.
0245 Crane, V.S.; Louviere, M.L.
0246 Crawford, N.; Smith, S,; Myer, N.

164

0247 Cunningham, J.R.
0248 Curtis, D.J.; Jones, R.L.
0249 Danielson, N.E.
0250 Darnell, R.E.; Fitch, D.H.
0251 Darnell, R.E.; Fitch, D.H.
0252 Davis, A.; Nagelhout,
     M.J.; Hoban, M.; Barnard,
     B.
0253 Davis, S.; Bryant, J.
0254 Davitt, P.A.
0255 De Armond, M.M.
0256 Debski-Himberger, A.
0257 Dehn, T.G.
0258 Deiker, T.; Osborn, S.M.;
     Distefano, M.K., Jr.;
     Payer, N.W.
0259 Delaney, M.C.;
     Trachtenberg, J.
0260 Demby, N.A.; Rosenthal,
     M.; Angello, M.; Calhoun,
     W.F.
0261 DeVries, R.A.
0262 Dinel, B.
0263 Distel, L.
0264 Donahue, J.J.
0265 Donald, K.J.; Collie, J.P.
0266 Doss, H.L.; James, J.D.;
     Killough, D.M.; Snodgrass,
     G.L.
0267 Doust, K.M.
0268 Drew, R.J.
0269 Drexler, L.; Caliendo,
     M.A.
0270 Drogege, R.T.
0271 Duckett, S.J.;
     Kristofferson, S.M.
0272 Dyer, E.D.; Monson, M.A.;
     Cope, M.J.
0273 Edmunds, L.
0274 el-Guebaly, N.; Papineau,
     D.
0275 Ellingham, C.T.;
     Fleischaker, K.
0276 Esser, P.D.; Fawwaz, R.A.
0277 Eusana, P.L.
0278 Felber, W.
0279 Felton, G.; Frevert, E.;
     Galligan, K.; Neill, M.K.;
     Williams, L.
0280 Ferguson, K.; Bowden, L.;
     Halman, M.; Huff, A.;
     Langlie, J.; Morgan, G.

0281 Ferguson, K.; Bowden,
     M.L.; Lachiniet, D.;
     Malcolm, A.; Morgan, G.
0282 Fifer, W.R.
0283 Finkle, B.S.
0284 Finley-Cottone, D.; Link,
     M.K.
0285 Finnegan, R.
0286 Fleisher, D.S.; Brown,
     C.R., Jr.; Zeleznik, C.;
     Escovitz, G.H.; Omdal, C.
0287 Forquer, S.L.; Anderson,
     T.B.
0288 Fredenburg, A.M.
0289 Freeberg, M.L.
0290 Fries, R.C.; Heide, P.W.
0291 Gallina, J.N.
0292 Ganti, A.R.; Piper, N.J.;
     Nagy, E.J.
0293 Gardner, K.
0294 Gardner, R.M.; Clausen,
     J.L.; Crapo, R.O.; Epler,
     G.R.; Hankinson, J.L.;
     Johnson, J.L, Jr.;
     Plummer, A.L.
0295 Garrell, M.
0296 Gaskill, A., Jr.; Jayanty,
     R.K.
0297 George, A.J.
0298 Georgopoulos, B.S.
0299 Geyman, J.P.
0300 Giddings, J.C.
0301 Glaze, S.; Schneiders, N.;
     Archer, B.; Bushong, S.
0302 Glendinning, M.
0303 Glicksman, A.S.;
     Reinstein, L.E.; Brotman,
     R.; McShan, D.
0304 Glicksman, A.S.;
     Reinstein, L.E.; McShan,
     D.; Laurie, F.
0305 Glor, B.A.; Barko, W.F.
0306 Goldson, A.L.;
     Nibhanupudy, J.R.
0307 Gonzalez, R.O.
0308 Gonnella, J.S.; Goran,
     M.J.
0309 Gonnella, J.S.; Louis,
     D.Z.; McCord, J.J.
0310 Goplerud, E.N.; Finger, J.
0311 Goran, M.J.
0312 Gothlin, J.H.; Alders, B.
0313 Gotowka, T.; Bailit, H.L.

0314 Gotowka, T.D.; Bailit,
     H.L.; Ellis, C.D.
0315 Gottlieb, T.W.
0316 Gould, E.J.
0317 Grant, A.K.
0318 Grant, R.L.
0319 Greenfield, S.; Cretin,
     S.; Worthman, L.G.; Dorey,
     F.J.; Soloman, N.E.,
     Goldberg, G.A.
0320 Griffith, N.L.; Megel,
     M.E.
0321 Gurwich, E.L.; Hanold, L.;
     Schaeffer, P.
0322 Guy, M.E.; Moore, L.S.
0323 Hamilton, J.C.
0324 Hanks, G.E.
0325 Hansen, P.J.
0326 Hansen, P.J.
0327 Harris, R.L.
0328 Hart, G.C.; Davis, K.M.
0329 Harty, M.K.
0330 Hattner, J.A.; Wood, P.
0331 Haussmann, R.K.; Hegyvary,
     S.T.
0332 Hayami, A.
0333 Hegedus, K.S.; Bourdon,
     S.M.
0334 Heggie, J.C.; Petty, R.J.
0335 Heggie, J.C.; Petty, R.J.
0336 Heintz, D.H.
0337 Henry R.L.; Johnson, C.R.
0338 Hill, B.S.
0339 Hill, R.K.
0340 Hines, J.
0341 Hoffman, R.P.; Ellerbrock,
     M.C.; Lovett, J.E.
0342 Hoffmann, R.P.; Ravin, R.;
     Colaluca, D.M.; Gifford,
     R.;Grimes, D.; Grzegorczyk,
     R.; Keown, F.; Kuhr, F.;
     McKay, R.; Peyser, J.;
     Ryan, R.; Zalewski, C.
0343 Hogan, N.S.
0344 Holmes, T.W.; McCullough,
     E.C.
0345 Hoory, S.; Levy, L.M.;
     Schiff, R.; Moskowitz, G.;
     Bandyopadhyay, D.
0346 Horowitz, K.N.; Lamnin M.
0347 Horwitz, W.; Kamps, L.R.;
     Boyer, K.W.
0348 Hunt, R.S.; Redmond, J.M.

0349 Hunter, S.A.; Dunlop, C.R.
0350 Jackson, J.M.; Hughes, W.
0351 Jackson, M.M.; Lynch, P.
0352 Jeffrey, L.P.; Temkin,
     L.A.; Krugman, M.E.
0353 Jerge, C.R.; Orlowski,
     R.M.
0354 Jessee, W.F.
0355 Johnson, L.; MacLellan,
     L.; Richardson, E.;
     Sandel, J.
0356 Joseph, E.
0357 Kaistha, K.K.; Tadrus, R.
0358 Kammerer, J.
0359 Kasprisin, C.A.;
     Kasprisin, D.O.; Marks,
     D.; Yogore, M.G;
     Williams, H.L.
0360 Kaufman, M.; Vermeersch,
     J.A.
0361 Kearns, P.M.
0362 Keblusek, J.
0363 Kekki, P.
0364 Keys, P.W.; Narduzzi, J.V.
0365 King, B.
0366 Kirkpatrick, D.L.;
     Shotwell, A.J.
0367 Kirkpatrick, K.W.; Flasck,
     E.D.
0368 Klerman, L.V.
0369 Klopfer, A.H.
0370 Knickerbocker, G.G.
0371 Knittig, M.J.
0372 Kokuyama, T.
0373 Kordick, M.F.
0374 Korsak, A.J.
0375 Krejci, C.B.
0376 Kuehl, D.W.; Butterworth,
     B.C.; Johnson, K.L.
0377 Kunin, C.M.; Sabatino,
     F.G.
0378 Ladwig, J.P.
0379 Laing, M; Nish, M.
0380 Land, M.J.; Gaska, J.;
     Shull, J.C.; Jones, D.R.
0381 Langenfeld, M.L.; Rzasa,
     C.B.
0382 LaViolette, S.
0383 Lawson, L.A.; Blouin,
     R.A.; Parker, P.F.
0384 Lebow, J.
0385 Lillensand, K.M.; Koroff,
     S.

0386	Lindstrom, R.
0387	Lindy, C.N.
0388	Lohff, M.R.
0389	Lomando, K.; Faulconer, D.R.
0390	Longabaugh, R.; Fowler, D.R.; Hostetler, M.; McMahon, L.; Sullivan, C.
0391	Longest, B.B., Jr.
0392	Looney, D.H.; Gibson, C.
0393	Luff, C.A.; Walker, P.C., 2nd.
0394	Lurie, A.
0395	Lurie, A.
0396	Macaluso, D.; Stein, B.; Polster, L.R.
0397	Macartney, J.C.; Henson, D.E.; Codling, B.W.
0398	Mackie, L.C.; Welch, J.W.
0399	Mackie, R.J.; Peddie, R.; Pendleton, R.
0401	Mansfield, M.
0402	Manson-Hing, L.R.; Bloxom, R.M.
0403	Mapa, J.; Turner, G.
0404	Marcin, J.; Forrest, J.L.
0405	Marsh, L.A.
0406	Martin, R.D.
0407	McAninch, M.
0408	McAuliffe, W.E.
0409	McColl, M.A.; Quinn, B.
0410	McCollum, W.E.
0411	McGowan, P.
0412	McInerny, K.F.; Archer, S.E.
0413	McKeever, D.A.
0414	McKenzie, R.; Hines, J.
0415	McManus, C.D.; Smalley, D.L.; Sanders, D.E.
0416	McMartin, C.
0417	McNamara, J.J.; Gourji, A.; Green, M.
0419	Mehnert, T.
0420	Meisel, S.
0421	Menzel, F.S.; Teegarden, K.
0422	Meudt, R.; Buser, C.; Bosch, A.
0423	Miler, R.; Drake, M.
0424	Miller, S.I.
0425	Miller, S.I.; Schlachter, R.H.

0426	Mills, W.
0427	Minniear, W.A.
0428	Moore, L.; Damewood, D.M.; Floyd, C.; Jewell, K.
0429	Morgenstein, S.; Simpkins, S.; Maring, J.
0430	Morris, C.R.
0431	Morrison, B.J.; Rehr, H.; Rosenberg, G.; Davis, S.
0432	Moyer, R.F.
0433	Mulholland, J.H.; Bittle, L.
0434	Murthy, M.S.; Derman, H.
0435	Mushlin, A.I.; Appel, F.A.
0436	Nadolny, M.D.
0438	Needham, L.L.; Burse, V.W.; Korver, M.P.; Lapeza, C.R.; Liddle, J.A.: Bayse, D.D.; Price, H.A.
0439	Newman, F.L.
0440	Nichols, A.C.; Wirginis, M.B.
0441	Nobles, C.
0442	Noel, P.R.
0443	Novick. L.F.; Dickinson, K.; Asnes, R.; Lan, S.M.; Lowenstein, R.
0444	Nusslin, F.
0445	Oberfell, M.S.; Ometer, J.L.
0446	Oller, W.L.; Gough, B.; Littlefield, N.A.
0447	Ometer, J.L.
0448	Ometer, J.L.; Oberfell, M.S.
0449	Orlikoff, J.E.; Lanham, G.B.
0450	Oulton, R.
0451	Padilla, G.V.; Grant, M.M.
0452	Palmer, R.H.; Strain, R.; Maurer, J.V.; Rothrock, J.K.; Thompson, M.S.
0453	Paras, P.
0454	Park, B.A.; Benderev, K.P.
0456	Patterson, D.
0457	Peter, M.A.
0458	Pien, F.D.; Bruce, A.
0459	Pilat, J.M.
0460	Pinkerton, P.H.; Wood, D.E.
0461	Ponce, A.Z.; Ponce, M.L.

0462 Posey, L.M.
0463 Pray, S.
0464 Price, M.
0479 Reichert, K.
0480 Reinhoff, O.; Machleidt, W.
0481 Reinstein, L.E.; McShan, D.; Glicksman, A.S.
0482 Richman, A.
0483 Rifkin, M.; Lynne, C.; Williams, R.; Hilsenbeck, C.
0484 Robertson, S.C.; Martin, E.D., Jr.
0485 Rodger, C.
0486 Roedler, H.D.
0487 Roemer, M.I.; Hopkins, C.E.
0488 Rotwein, S.
0489 Rouse, S.; Cowen, A.R.
0490 Rozenfeld, M.; Jette, D.
0491 Ruark, T.
0492 Rubenstein, L.; Mates, S.; Sidel, V.W.
0493 Russell, Z.
0494 Rutstein, D.D.; Berenberg, W.; Chalmers, T.C.; Child, C.G, 3rd; Fishman, A.P.; Perrin, E.B.
0495 Sadin, R.R.
0496 Saladino, A.J.
0497 Satzger, R.D.; Bonnin, E.; Fricke, F.L.
0498 Savander, G.R.
0499 Schenck, J.M.
0500 Schiller, R.; Behm, V.
0501 Shimeld, A.
0502 Schneiders, N.J.; Bushong, S.C.
0503 Schroeder, P.S.; Maibusch, R.M.; Anderson C.A.; Formella, N.M.
0504 Scott, W.R.; Flood, A.B.; Ewy, W.
0505 Seijo, C.A.
0506 Selbmann, H.K.
0507 Self, P.C.; Gebhart, K.A.
0508 Shamansky, S.L.; Young, K.L.
0509 Shannon, M.
0510 Shaughnessy, P.W.; Kurowski, B.

0511 Shaw, C.D.
0512 Shaw, M.A.; Russell, W.L.; Bradham, D.D.
0513 Shephard, M.D.; Penberthy, L.A.; Fraser, C.G.
0514 Shephard, M.D.; Penberthy, L.A.; Fraser, C.G.
0515 Sherber, J.
0516 Sherman, P.S.; Gomez, M.
0517 Shimeld, A.
0518 Skillicorn, S.A.
0519 Skreenock, J.J.
0520 Small, E.W.
0521 Smeltzer, C.H.; Feltman, B.; Rajki, K.
0522 Smith, N.G.
0523 Souhami, L.
0524 Spano, R.M.; Lund, S.H.
0525 Stearns, G.; Fox, L.A.
0526 Stender, H.S.
0527 Stephany, T.M.
0528 Stevens, J.E.
0529 Stewart, R.D.; Burgman, J.; Cannon, G.M.; Paris, P.M.
0530 Stieve, F.E.
0531 Stolar, M.H.
0532 Stolar, M.H.
0533 Suntharalingam, N.
0534 Svensson, G.K.
0535 Svensson, H.
0536 Sveska, K.J.; Roffe, B.D.; Solomon, D.K.
0537 Swamidoss, P.
0538 Swope, M.B.
0540 Taylor, H.
0541 Thompson, A.B.; Wilson, A.M.
0542 Thompson, J.S.
0543 Thompson, R.E.
0544 Thompson, R.E.; Rodrick, A.B.
0545 Thur, M.P.
0546 Tucker, F., II.
0547 Tucker, J.
0548 Turco, S.J.
0549 Ungethum, M.
0550 Ungethum, M.
0551 Valachovic, R.W.; Reiskin, A.B.; Kirchhof, S.T.
0552 Valentine, J.
0553 Van Herten, J.H.
0554 Vanzetti, G.
0555 Vermeersch, J.A.; Kaufman, M.

0556 Vogel, D.P.
0557 Vogel, D.P.; Gurwich, E.;
     Campagna, K.; Sula, J.;
     Eck, T.A.; Hutchinson,
     R.A.
0558 Walczak, R.M.
0559 Walkley, P.H., Jr.
0561 Walts, L.; Blair, F.
0562 Wambersie, A.
0563 Wascom, K.R.; Keiser, M.F.
0564 Watkinson, S.; Moores,
     B.M.; Hill, S.J.
0565 Watkinson, S.; Shaw, M.;
     Moores, B.M.; Eddleston,
     E.
0566 Webster, H.J.
0567 Weiner, J.P.; Gibson, G.;
     Munster, A.M.
0568 Wenz, B.; Dugan, E.P.
0569 West, J.G.
0570 West, W.G.; Freudenstein,
     C.S.
0571 Westfall, U.E.
0572 Wheeler, P.S.
0573 Whitcomb, J.E.; Stueven,
     H.; Tonsfeldt, D.;
     Kastenson, G.
0574 White, S.J.; Godwin, H.N.
0575 Williamson, J.W.;
     Greenfield, S.; Van Andel,
     H.; Torr, S.
0576 Willis, R.
0577 Wolfe, P.C.; Haveliwala,
     Y.
0578 Wolter, J.M.
0579 Wong, W.T.
0580 Yaffe, R.
0581 Zalar, R.W.;
     Houston-Screnzel, D.
0582 Zambito, R.F.
0583 Zelonis, A.; Fleischer,
     N.; Walling, R.
0584 Zimble, J.A.
0585 Zimmer, J.G.

Research: Studies and Data

0586 Alaszewski, A.
0587 Aldhizer, T.G.; Solle,
     M.M.; Bohrer, R.O.
0588 Allanach, E.J.; Allanach,
     B.C.

0589 Anderson, D.; Legator, M.S.
0590 Armenian, H.K.; Dajani,
     A.W.; Fakhro, A.M.
0591 Bailey, P.E.
0592 Bailit, H.L.
0593 Baughman, B.B.; Knutson,
     C.O.; Ahmad, W.; Jones,
     C.E.; Polk, H.C., Jr.
0594 Bays, C.W.
0595 Becker-Gaab, C.; Borcke,
     E.; Bunde, E.; Hagemann,
     G.; Kutterer, G.; Lang,
     G.R.; Schofer, H.;
     Stender, H.S.; Stieve,
     I..E.; von Volkmann,
     T.; et al.
0596 Beghi, E.; Sasanelli, F.;
     Spagnoli, A.; Tognoni, G.
0597 Berbatis, C.G.; Eckert,
     G.M.; Neale, F.G.;
     Rothwell, J.P.
0598 Bernard-Stevens, J.; Gust,
     W.F.; Moore, G.; Zetterman,
     R.
0599 Blumberg, M.S.; Gentry, D.W.
0600 Brazil, A.
0601 Brenner, L.H.; Jessee, W.F.
0602 Brook, R.H.; Williams, K.N.;
     Rolph, J.E.
0603 Brunner, M.A.
0604 Buchner, H.
0605 Burkle, W.S.; Matzke, G.R.;
     Lucarotti, R.L.
0606 Chambers, L.W.;
     Bruce-Lockhart, P.; Black,
     D.P.; Sampson, E.; Burke,
     M.
0607 Chase, R.S.; Burg, F.D.
0608 Chassin, M.R.; McCue, S.M.
0609 Cohen, M.R.
0611 Compton, P.J.; Stuart, M.C.;
     Lazarus, L.
0612 de Almeida, C.E.; Cecatti,
     E.R.
0613 Detmer, D.E.; Moylan, J.A.;
     Rose, J.; Schulz, R.;
     Wallace, R.; Daly, R.
0614 Didonato, K.
0615 DiSilvio, T.V.; Lawson, N.S.;
     Haven, G.T.; Gilmore, B.F.
0616 Distel, L.
0617 Donofrio, N.M., Jr.; Hanson,
     J.A.; Hirsch, J.H.; Moore,
     W.E.

0618	Doss, H.L.; James, J.D.; Killough, D.M.; Snodgrass, G.L.	0648	Herrmann, F.; Heuerburg-Heusler, D.; Nissen, P.
0619	Duff, R.S.; Cook, C.D.; Margolis, C.Z.; Lattanzi, W.E.; Landwirth, J.	0649	Heuwer, K.: Laurinat, H.
		0650	Hokanson, J.A.; Guernsey, B.G.; Bryant, S.G.; Doutre, W.H.; Ingrim, N.B.; Grant, J.A.; Galvan, E.
0620	Dwyer, J.; Fitch, F.R.; Doolan, P.T.; Dwyer, V.M.; Halls, N.A.; Tallentire, A.		
		0651	Horder, M.
0621	Eastaugh, S.R.	0652	Horn, S.D.; Pozen, M.W.
0622	Eckelman, W.C.; Herrara, N.E.; Hauser, W.	0653	Howanitz, P.J.; McBride, J.H.; Kliewer, K.E.; Rodgerson, D.O.
0623	Eder, H.; Schofer, H.	0654	Inui, T.S.; Hill, T.A.; Leiby, G.M.
0624	Eichhorn, M.L.; Frevert, E.I.		
		0655	Julien, J.Y.; Barbeau, G.
0625	Escovitz, G.H.; Burkett, G.L.; Kuhn, J.C.; Zeleznik, C.; Gonnella, J.S.	0656	Keywood, D.
		0657	Kirchman, M.M.
		0658	Kirkegaard, L.H.; Fout, R.E.
0626	Farman, A.G.; Hines, V.G.	0659	Knowles, R.C.; Gilmore, B.
0627	Feigenson, J.S.: Feigenson, W.D.; Gitlow, H.S.; McCarthy, M.L.; Greenberg, S.D.	0660	Knowles, R.C.; Gilmore, B.F.
		0661	Knowles, R.C.; Moore, T.D.
		0662	Koepke, J.A.; Protextor, T.J.
		0663	Kresky, B.; Mangano, L.
0628	Feller, I.; Tholen, D.; Cornell, R.G.	0664	Landsberg, G.
		0665	Lasky, L.C.; Lin, A.; Kahn, R.A.; McCullough, J.
0629	Fernow, L.C.; Mackie, C.; McColl, I.; Rendall, M.		
		0666	Lawson, N.S.; Haven, G.T.; DiSilvio, T.V.; Gilmore, B.F.
0630	Fernow, L.C.; McColl, I.; Thurlow, S.C.		
		0667	Lawson, N.S.; Haven, G.T.; DiSilvio, T.V.; Gilmore, B.F.
0631	Finkelstein, S.M.; Budd, J.R.; Ewing, L.B.; Wielinski, C.L.; Warwick, W.J.; Kujawa, S.J.		
		0668	Levy, R.; Goldstein, B.; Trott, A.
0632	Forehand, J.M.	0669	Lindsay, M.I., Jr.; Nobrega, F.T.; Offord, K.P.; Carter, E.T.; Rutherford, B.D.; Kennel, A.J.; Mankin, H.T.
0633	Garb, J.L.; Brown, R.B.; Garb, J.R.; Tuthill, R.W.		
0634	Garrell, M.; Jekel, J.F.		
0635	Gerstein, J.	0670	Linn, B.S.
0636	Glaser, S.M.; Dehn, T.G.	0671	Littbrand, B.
0637	Glicksman, A.S.; Reinstein, L.E.; Laurie, F.	0672	Locker, D.; Dunt, D.
		0673	Lohr, K.N.; Brook, R.H.
0638	Greenstein, M.	0674	Longest, B.B., Jr.
0639	Grundmann, R.; Salamon, C.; Weber, F.	0675	Lutz, W.R.; Maddox, B.J.; Kase, K.R.
0640	Hagemann, G.	0676	Lyons, T.F.; Payne, B.C.
0641	Hanks, G.E.; Kramer, S.	0677	Mannisto, M.
0642	Hardy, M.E.	0678	Marks, S.D.; Greenlick, M.R.; Hurtado, A.V.; Johnson, J.D.; Henderson, J.
0643	Hart, G.C.		
0644	Hassenstein, E.; Nusslin, F.	0679	Marriner, J.
0645	Hayes, D.M.	0680	Martini, C.J.; Allan, G.H.; Davison, J.; Backett, E.M.
0646	Hegedus, K.S.; Bourdon, S.M.		
0647	Hein, M.A.	0681	McAuliffe, W.E.
		0682	McMillin, B.A.; Jasmund, J.M.

0683 Miller, M.B.; Elliott, D.F.
0684 Miller, P.L.; Berry, T.J.
0685 Miller, T.W.; Lee, L.T.
0686 Molzahn-Yanitski, A.E.
0687 Moore, K.
0688 Mossel, D.A.; Bonants-Van Laarhoven, T.M.; Ligtenberg-Merkus, A.M.; Werdler, M.E.
0689 Munyworki, S.; Shimoni, M.; Hyndman, G.
0690 Nakamura, R.M.; Rippey, J.H.
0691 Nelson-Wernick, E.; Currey, H.S.; Taylor, P.W.; Woodbury, M.; Cantor, A.
0692 Nelson, E.C.; Kirk, J.W.; Bise, B.W.; Chapman, R.J.; Hale, F.A.; Stamps, P.L.; Wasson, J.H.
0693 Nowotny, R.; Rechtberger, W.
0694 Oakley, R.S.; Bradham, D.D.
0695 Olin, P.; Bolme, P.; Ewert, G.; Lagerkvist, B.; Sterky, G.; Tengvald, K.; Zetterstrom, R.
0696 Orden, S.R.; Collette, P.; Souchek, J.; Masover, L.; Stamler, J.
0697 Ostrow, P.C.; Kuntavanish, A.A.
0698 Oxley, D.K.
0699 Palmer, R.H.; Louis, T.A.; Hsu, L.N.; Peterson, H.F.; Rothrock, J.K.; Strain, R.; Thompson, M.S.; Wright, E.A.
0700 Palmer, R.H.; Reilly, M.C.
0701 Parente, R.; Anderson-Parente, J.
0702 Pascoe, D.W.; Wilson, A.; Worsfold, J.B.
0703 Perez, C.A.; Gardner, P.; Glasgow, G.P.
0704 Ponto, J.A.; Ponto, L.L.
0705 Potsaid, M.S.; Rhea, J.T.; Llewellyn, H.J.; Pfister, R.C.; Newhouse, J.H; Yoder, I.C.
0706 Presly, A.S.; Ballinger, B.R.; Fraser, D.; Lindsay, B.
0708 Racoveanu, N.T.

0709 Raff, U.; Spitzer, V.M.; Hendee, W.R.
0710 Raynes, N.V.; Pratt, M.W.; Roses, S.
0711 Reiners, C.; Moll, E.
0712 Rhee, S.O.
0713 Rhee, S.O.
0714 Rhee, S.O.
0715 Rhee, S.O.; Lyons, T.; Payne, B.
0716 Rhee, S.O.; Lyons, T.F.; Payne, B.C.
0717 Rifkin, M.; Lynne, C.; Williams, R.; Hilsenbeck, C.
0718 Roake, J.A.; Morton, J.
0719 Rosenberg, thw.
0720 Roy, A.; Looney, G.L.; Anderson, G.V.
0721 Sanazaro, P.J.; Worth, R.M.
0722 Schmall, B.; Conti, P.S.; Bigler, R.E.; Zanzonico, P.B.; Dahl, J.R.; Sundoro-Wu, B.M.; Jacobsen, J.K.; Lee, R.
0723 Schwing, C.
0724 Segovia, J.
0725 Selbmann, H.B.; Warncke, W.; Eissner, H.J.
0726 Shaughnessy, P.W.; Breed, L.D.; Landes, D.P.
0727 Shortell, S.M.; LoGerfo, J.P.
0728 Sinclair, C.; Frankel, M.
0729 Smith, M.K.; Fullen, D.
0730 Soroker, E.P.
0731 Spector, R.; McGrath, P.; Alpert, J.; Cohen, P.; Aikins, H.
0732 Spivak, H.R.; Levy, J.C.; Bonanno, R.A.; Cracknell, M.
0733 Stewart, J.E.
0734 Strain, R.; Palmer, R.H.; Maurer, J.V.; Lyons, L.A.; Thompson, M.S.
0735 Thomas, T.
0736 Tracy, R.P.; Currie, R.M.; Young, D.S.
0740 Truscott, B.L.; Kretschmann, C.M.; Toole, J.F.; Pajak, T.F.
0742 van der Voorde, F.; van der Snoek, J.A.; Reerink, E.
0743 Vanloh, S.W.; Stanges, M.T.; Cohen, R.
0744 Vasey, E.K.
0745 Vik, A.G.; MacKay, R.C.

0746 Votava, K.M.; Cleveland, T.; Hiltunen, K.
0747 Wagner, P.L.; Stapleton, J.A.; Stein, R.; Wadina, C.
0748 Wasserman, B.S.
0749 Watkinson, L.R.; Fraser, C.G.
0750 Welker, K.
0751 Wendorf, B.
0752 Werman, D.S.; Agle, D.; McDaniel, E.; Schoof, K.G.
0753 Westermeyer, J.; Doheny, S.; Stone, B.
0754 Whitehead, M.E.; Fitzwater, J.E.; Lindley, S.K.; Kern, S.B.; Ulirsch, R.C.; Winecoff, W.F. III.
0755 Whitehead, M.E.; Grieve, J.H.; Payne, M.J.; Ross, M.S.
0756 Williamson, J.W.; Braswell, H.R.; Horn, S.D.
0757 Williamson, J.W.; Greenfield, S.; van Andel, H.; Torr, S.
0758 Willis, R.W.
0759 Wilner, S.; Schoenbaum, S.C.; Monson, R.R.; Winickoff, R.N.
0760 Wilson, J.F.; Marshall, R.W.; Williams, J.; Richens, A.
0761 Windsor, R.A.
0762 Winialski, N.
0763 Wolinsky, H.
0764 Zimmer, J.G.
0765 Zoebelein, E.; Levy, M.; Greenwald, R.A.

Management

0767 Aduddell, P.A.; Weeks, L.C.
0768 Archambault, G.F.
0769 Austin, C.J.; Carter, H.S.
0770 Baird, J.
0771 Banner, M.T.
0772 Birkett, D.P.
0773 Black, J.R.
0774 Blaes, S.M.
0775 Borden, L.P.
0776 Bradford, L.W.
0777 Brazil, A.

0778 Brazil, A.
0779 Brook, R.H.; Davies-Avery, A.
0780 Brown, D.E.
0781 Chase, T.B.
0782 Chayet, N.L.; Reardon, T.M.
0783 Clemenhagen, C.
0784 Clemenhagen, C.J.
0785 Collins, P.
0787 Couch, J.B.
0788 Cunningham, R.M., Jr.
0789 del Bueno, D.
0790 Demby, N.A.
0791 Der Yuen, D.
0792 Dietz, J.W.; Phillips, J.L.
0793 Donabedian, A.
0794 Donovan, R.J., Jr.; Bader, B.S.
0796 Edwardson, S.R: Anderson, D.I.
0797 Elder, M.Q.
0798 Evenson, B.O.
0799 Ferguson, C.G.
0800 Ferguson, C.G.
0801 Fine, R.B.
0802 Flensborg, P.
0803 Foglesong, D.H.
0804 Fox, L.A.
0805 Frank, R.E.
0806 Friend, G.
0807 Friend, G.
0808 Gardner, C.
0809 Gardner, L.P.
0810 Garrell, M.
0811 Gaston, S.R.
0812 Gerber, R.L.
0813 Goldberg, B.A.
0814 Goldberg, G.A.
0815 Goodspeed, S.W.
0816 Gothlin, J.H.
0817 Harmon, C.A.
0818 Harris, L.J.
0819 Heimanson, R.
0820 Hendrix, K.K.; Baltz, A.
0821 Hetherington, R.W.
0822 Hicks, A.M.
0823 Holbrook, R.F.; Dunn, L.J., Jr.
0824 Honovich, D.
0826 Hovind, O.B.
0827 Howie, H.
0828 Huckabay, L.M.
0829 Hunter, S.A.; Dunlop, C.R.

0830 Isaac, D.N.	0874 Nelson, S.
0831 Johnson, D.E.	0875 Nodolny, M.D.
0832 Jones, M.	0876 Orlikoff, J.E.
0833 Judkins, S.B.	0877 Penkhus, M.L.; Schear,
0834 Kaderbhai, F.A.	W.A.
0835 Kagan, R.M.	0878 Peterson, S.
0836 Kahn, J.	0879 Pfeffer-Kloss, L.L.
0837 Kaluzny, A.D.	0881 Porter, K.W.
0838 Kane, R.L.	0882 Post, R.S.
0839 Kelly, P.	0883 Prybil, L.D.
0840 Kinsella, C.R.	0884 Purgatorio-Howard, K.
0841 Kirchner, E.	0886 Reerink, E.
0842 Klapp, D.	0887 Reeves, D.M.; Underly, N.
0843 Klopfer, A.H.	0888 Restuccia, J.D.; Holloway,
0844 Knowlton, H.C.	D.C.
0845 Kresky, B.; Henry, M.C.	0889 Rifkin, M.; Lynne, C.;
0846 Kress, G.C., Jr.;	Williams, R.; Hilsenbeck, C.
Silversin, J.B.	0890 Rifkin, M.; Lynne, C.;
0847 Kuehnert, P.	Williams, R.; Hilsenbeck, C.
0848 Kuramoto, A.M.; Sandahl,	0891 Rinaldi, L.
B.B.	0892 Rodin, A.E.; Calhoun, K.P.;
0849 Lamnin, M.	Bledsoe, S.D.
0850 Lane, G.H.; Cronin, K.M.;	0893 Rosen, H.M.; Feigin, W., Sr.
Peirce, A.G.	0894 Rovinsky, J.J.
0851 Lang, D.A.	0895 Saternus, K.S.; Staak, M.
0852 Laurie-Shaw, B.; Stove, V.	0896 Schor, E.L.
0853 LaViolette, S.	0897 Shannon, M.; McIver, B.;
0854 Lazes, P.M.; Wasilewski,	MacLeod, S.
Y.; Redd, J.D.	0898 Shimeld, A.
0855 Leach, J.; Nagy, S.;	0899 Sibley, H.
Cercone, R.	0900 Sniff, D.
0856 Lindstrom, R.	0901 Sommers, L.S.; Sholtz, R.;
0857 Lippitt, G.L.	Shepherd, R.M.; Starkweather,
0858 Luke, R.D.; Boss, R.W.	D.B.
0859 Maciorowski, L.F.; Larson,	0902 Southwick, A.F.; Slee, D.A.
E.; Keane, A.	0903 Spaeth, R.G.
0860 Marcus, M.	0904 Spencer, D.S.
0861 Marshik-Gustafson, J.;	0905 Stearns, G.; Fox, L.A.
Kopher, S.; Terze, M.	0906 Stearns, G.; Fox, L.A.
0862 Martin, N.S.	0907 Stoelwinder, J.U.; Clayton,
0863 McConkey, R.	P.S.
0864 McGee, P.A.	0908 Stromberg, R.E.
0865 McSherry, C.K.	0910 Thompson, R.E.
0866 Metzger, N.	0911 Tilson, J.Q.
0867 Milgrom, P.; Chapko, M.;	0912 Tolpin, B.B.
Milgrom, L.; Weinstein, P.	0913 Troyer, G.; Salman, S.
0868 Miller, J.R.; Lewis, F.M.	0914 Turner, G.P.; Mapa, J.
0869 Mitchell, M.	0916 Van Sluyter, C.K.
0870 Moore, R.D.; Klein, W.F.	0917 Van Vorst, C.B.
0871 Morse, E.V.; Gordon, G.;	0918 Vogel, D.P.; Gurwich, E.;
Moch, M.	Compagna, K.; Sula, J.; Eck,
0872 Mulroy, T.R.	T.A.; Hutchinson, R.A.
0873 Nelson, R.E.; Barnes,	0919 Wallace, R.F.; Donnelly, M.
G.T.; Witten, D.M.	0921 Warner, A.M.

1025	Legge, D.
1026	Legge, D.G.; Hutton, P.A.
1027	Lempenau, M.C.
1028	Lentchner, E.
1029	Litt, I.F.; Cohen, M.I.
1030	Looney, D.H.; Gibson, C.
1031	Maestrini, V.; Riley, M.A.
1033	Manjoro, J.W.
1034	Margan, I.
1035	Marram, G.
1036	Martin, A.E.; Mann, J.L.
1037	Martin, P.J.
1038	Martin, R.J.
1039	Mass, D.
1040	Matoth, Y.
1041	Mattson, M.R.
1042	McGrail, W.
1043	McGuill, G.
1044	McSherry, C.K.
1046	Meisenheimer, C.G.
1047	Merlino, J.; London, E.; Turner, S.
1048	Miccio, B.L.
1049	Miller, J.N.
1050	Miringoff, M.L.
1051	Moaninch, M.; Weedman, R.D.; Jones, R.E.
1052	Morris, A.L.; Bentley, J.M.; Bomba, M.R.
1057	Newmark, G.L.
1058	Nuallain, C.O.
1059	Ostrow, P.C.
1060	Paine, L.H.
1061	Palmer, H.; Hillestad, B.
1062	Phelps, C.E.
1063	Pimlott, J.F.; Chambers, L.W.; Feller, S.J.; Scherer, F.K.
1064	Posatko, R.C.
1065	Pratt, R.
1066	Quaethoven, P.
1070	Reed, E.A.
1071	Reerink, E.
1072	Regan, W.A.
1073	Regan, W.A.
1074	Reichaman, S.
1076	Rhodes, D.
1077	Rinaldi, L.A.
1078	Roberts, J.S.; Walczak, R.M.
1079	Rose, V.
1080	Rubsamen, D.S.
1081	Runnells, G.

1082	Salmore, R.
1083	Samuels, T.M.
1084	Sanazaro, P.J.
1085	Sanazaro, P.J.
1087	Saypol, G.M.
1088	Scarf, C.G.; Weaver, C.J.; Duckett, S.J.; Schmiede, A.M.
1089	Schade, C.P.; Garland, M.F.; Seggar, J.K., Jr.
1090	Schega, W.
1091	Schmidt, P.R.
1092	Schmincke, W.
1093	Schoen, M.H.
1094	Schriner, F.; Martin, P.; Bigge, R.
1095	Schumacher, D.N.
1096	Schurmeier, L.J.
1097	Schwartz, H.
1098	Scibetta, L.P.
1099	Shanahan, M.
1100	Shanahan, M.
1101	Sigal, S.N.
1102	Simola, H.
1103	Slaven, T.M.
1104	Smits, H.L.; McMahon, L.P.
1105	Soares, D.P.
1106	Sommers, S.C.; Carter, M.; Palmer, E.
1107	Spasoff, R.A.; Lane, P.; Steele, R.
1108	Spellberg, M.A.
1110	Steggles, W.A.
1111	Stehbens, W.E.
1112	Stern, S.K.
1113	Stern, S.K.
1114	Stolte, J.B.
1115	Sweeney, S.B.
1116	Szucs, G.F.
1117	Tabatabai, C.
1118	Tan, I.K.; Jacob, E.
1119	Terkla, L.G.; Ueno, H.
1123	Thompson, R.
1124	Tibbitts, S.B.
1125	Tobin, E.
1126	Tucker, J.H.; Rogers, J.
1128	Umbdenstock, R.J.; Mohr, B.J.
1130	Vail, J.D.; Jacobs, M.E.
1131	Vaisrub, S.
1132	van Maanen, H.M.
1133	Vetere, C.
1134	Walczak, R.
1135	Wallace, J.L.
1136	Watkin, B.

```
1137   Weissburg, A.A.
1138   West, D.
1139   Wheelock, R.D.
1140   Wiley, L.
1141   Williams, K.N.; Brook, R.H.
1142   Wilson, L.L.
1143   Wiseman, J.
1144   Wittrock, J.W.
1145   Wolkstein, I.
1146   Young, M.G.
1147   Zambito, R.F.
1148   Zaremski, M.J.
```

CHAPTER 3:

UTILIZATION REVIEW REFERENCES

Theory and Concept

Programs, Techniques & Procedures

1216	Block, W.E.
1217	Budkin, A.; Jacobs, W.A.; Smith, C.D.; Daily, J.D.; Button, J.H.; Berman, R.L.
1218	Butler, R.J.
1219	Chase, C.R.; Merz, B.A.; Mazuzan, J.E.
1220	Dancey, J.W.
1221	DesHarnais, S.; Kibe, N.M.; Barbus, S.
1222	Dexter, C.
1223	Dodds, J.J.
1224	Dollard, V.M.
1225	Dunn, R.T.
1226	Echols, R.M.; Kowalsky, S.F.
1227	Edwards, A.B.
1228	Fielding, J.E.
1229	Garg, M.L.; Kleinberg, W.M.; Schmitt, B.; Barzansky, B.M.
1230	Gertman, P.M.; Restuccia, J.D.
1231	Goldberg, G.A.; Holloway, D.C.
1232	Goldensohn, S.S.
1233	Goldstein, J.; Miller, L.V.
1234	Groves, R.E.
1235	Guest, K.; McLean, A.J.; Wellington, C.V.
1237	Hall, J.
1238	Heineman, H.S.; Watt, V.S.
1239	Hekster, Y.A.; Friesen, W.T.; Boerema, J.B.
1240	Helling, D.K.; Hepler, C.D.; Herman, R.A.
1241	Hermansen, M.C.; Blodgett, F.M.
1242	Hirt, F.D.; Solomon, J.R.
1243	Hlynka, J.N.; Smith, W.E., Jr.; Brodie, D.C.
1244	Hoffmann, R.P.
1245	Hoffmann, R.P.
1246	Hollmann, M.
1247	Homer, C.G.
1248	Huber, S.L.; Patry, R.A.
1249	Hunter, S.A.
1250	Ingman, S.R.; Claus, L.M.
1251	John, G.W.
1252	John, G.W.; Spieler, J.L., Jr.

1253	Kabat, H.F.; Kidder, S.W.; Marttila, J.K.; Stewart, J.E.
1254	Kabat, H.F.; Marttila, J.; Stewart, J.
1255	Kane, R.L.; Olsen, D.M.; Thetford, C.; Byrnes, N.
1256	Kane, R.L.; Rubenstein, L.Z.; Brook, R.H.; VanRyzin, J.; Masthay, P.; Schoenrich, E.; Harrell, B.
1257	Kilarski, D.J.; Schneider, P.J.; Teil, S.M.; Lemay, A.P.
1258	Kincaid, W.H.
1259	Kleffel, D.
1260	Kleffel, D.; Wilson, E.
1261	Knapp, D.A.
1262	Komaroff, A.L.; Sherman, H.; Ervin, C.T.; Pass, T.M.
1263	Kramer, P.M.; Martin, B.A.
1264	Krischer, J.P.; Cheung, A.; Bush, P.; Sleight, S.M.
1265	Kuhnmuench, P.; Hill, C.
1266	Lamin, M.
1267	Legge, D.
1268	Leist, E.R.
1269	Manion, C.V.; Hassanein, K.
1270	Martin, R.D.
1271	Mashford, M.L.; Robertson, M.B.
1272	McConnell, T.S.; Berger, P.R.; Dayton, H.H.; Umland, B.E.; Skipper, B.E.
1273	McCormick, R.A.; Ramirez, L.F.
1274	McManus, C.D.; Smalley, D.L.; Sanders, D.E.
1275	Mehl, B.
1276	Mitchell, N.L.
1277	Morgan, J.P.
1278	Moss, J.; Wyatt, G.; Christopherson, D.; Routh, S.
1279	Mott, P.D.
1280	Mullin, R.L.
1281	Mushlin, A.I.
1282	O'Donnell, L.

1283 Opit, L.J.; Selwood, T.S.
1284 Pelletier, L.L., Jr.
1285 Perler, J.M.
1286 Reed, D.M.; Hepler, C.D.; Helling, D.K.
1287 Reisine, S.T.; Bailit, H.L.
1288 Rishpon, S.; Lubacsh, S.; Epstein, L.M.
1289 Salsberry, P.; Glynn K.
1290 Scarafile, P.D.; Campbell, B.D.; Kilroy, J.E.; Mathewson, H.O.
1291 Schwartz, J.I.; Kennedy, T.J.
1292 Schwarz, F.
1293 Shannon, R.C.; DeMuth, J.E.
1294 Spencer, J.H., Jr.; Mattson, M.R.
1296 Stephany, T.M.
1297 Stewart, J.E.
1298 Studnicki, J.; Honemann, D.
1299 Sussman, E.J.; Eisenberg, J.M.; Williams, S.V.
1300 Thompson, R.E.
1301 Tobin, R.G.
1302 Tremblay, J.
1303 Vaughan, W.P.; Waalkes, T.P.; Lenhard, R.E., Jr.; Watkins, S.P.; Sadler, W.P.; Stout, D.A.; Carney, S.P.; DelCarmen, B.V.; Herring, D.F.
1304 Walter, R.S.
1305 Weaver, P.G.
1306 West, S.K.; Brandon, B.M.; Stevens, A.M.; Zauber, A.; Chase, G.; Stolley, P.D.; Rumrill, R.E.
1307 Withersty, D.J.; Spradlin, W.W.
1308 Witte, K.W.; Leeds, N.H.; Pathak, D.S.; Campagna, K.D.; West, D.P.; Spunt, A.L.
1309 Wright, G.; Goldberg, M.; Mark, H.; Petrillo, M.K.; Wiesel, B.
1310 Yaffe, R.

1311 Zegans, L.S.; Geller, J.; Flynn, H.; Swartzburg, M.; Schowalter, J.
1312 Zeleznik, C.; Gonnella, J.S.
1313 Zilz, D.
1314 Zimmerman, M.H.; Schlein, P.; Fuller, N.A.; Carrier, E.

Research: Studies and Data

1316 Adler, N.E.; Milstein, A.
1317 Akhter, M.N.
1318 Ambrosioni, E.; Costa, F.V.; Marata, A.M.
1319 Anderson, H.R.; Bailey, P.; West, S.
1320 Aycock, E.K.
1321 Bailit, H.L.; Balzer, J.A.; Clive, J.
1322 Barnes, B.A.; O'Brien E.; Comstock, C.; D'Arpa, D.G.; Donahue, C.L.
1323 Barriere, S.L.; Conte, J.E., Jr.
1324 Benedict, S.
1325 Bernstein, L.R.; Barriere, S.L.; Conte, J.E., Jr.
1326 Boone, C.R.; Coulton, C.J.; Keller, S.M.
1327 Calogero, M.A.; Hill, D.B.
1328 Casewell, M.
1329 Charlwood, R.; Gibbons, K.
1330 Chinn, F.J.
1331 Cleary, P.D.; Jette, A.M.
1332 Clemans, S.; Hamlin, R.H.
1333 Clendenning, M.K.; Wolfe, H.; Shuman, L.J.; Huber, G.A.
1334 Cohen, E.; Bernier, D.; Tam S.; Schimel, D.; Postel, A.H.; Scheidt, S.; Stamm, J.B.
1335 Connell, F.A.; Blide, L.A.; Hanken, M.A.
1336 Counahan, R.
1337 Covell, B.; Angus, M.M.

179

1338 Crane, V.S.
1339 Cummins, R.O.; LoGerfo,
     J.P.; Inui, T.S.; Weiss,
     N.S.
1340 Curry, C.E., Jr.; Antal,
     E.G.; Keys, P.W.; Duffy,
     M.G.
1341 Detmer, D.E.; Nevers,
     L.E.; Sikes, E.D., Jr.
1342 Dexter, C.
1343 Dini, M.; Fua, C.; Renga,
     G.
1344 Durkin, J.W., Jr.;
     Bennett, J.B.
1345 Eastaugh, S.R.
1346 Echols, R.M.; Kowalsky,
     S.F.
1347 Eisenberg, J.M.; Williams,
     S.V.
1348 Eiser, C.; Eiser, J.R.
1349 Elliott, R.V.; Kahn, K.A.;
     Kaye, R.
1350 Evans, J.G.; Wandless, I.;
     Prudham, D.
1351 Evens, R.G.; Jost, R.G.;
     Evens, R.G., Jr.
1352 Faden, F.B.; Goldman, H.H.
1353 Farina, M.L.; Levati, A.;
     Tognoni, G.
1354 FitzGerald, G.A.; Beggan,
     M.; Drury, M.I.
1355 Fitzpatrick, C.
1356 Fowkes, F.G.; Davies,
     E.R.; Evans, K.T.; Green,
     G.; Hartley, G.;
     Hugh, A.E.; Nolan, D.J.;
     Power, A.L.; Roberts,
     C.J.; Roylance, J.
1357 Gardner, L.P.
1358 Gaskins, R.R.; Davis,
     F.A.; Greer, J.G.
1359 Gertman, P.M.; Egdahl,
     R.E.
1360 Gertman, P.M.; Monheit,
     A.C.; Anderson, J.J.;
     Eagle, J.B.;
     Levenson, D.K.
1361 Goldfarb, M.G.; Hornbrook,
     M.C.; Higgins, C.S.
1362 Goldstein, R.S.;
     Contreras, M.; Craig,
     G.A.; Cheung, O.T.

1363 Greene, V.L.; Monahan,
     D.J.
1364 Greer, J.G.; Bodin, L.O.;
     Robeson, F.E.;
     Pfaffenberger, R.
1365 Guernsey, B.G.; Hokanson,
     J.A.; Ingrim, N.B.; Fuchs,
     J.E.; Sanders, A.G.;
     Doutre, W.H.; Bryant,
     S.G.
1366 Guernsey, B.G.; Ingrim,
     N.B.; Hokanson, J.A.;
     Fuchs, J.E., Jr.;
     Prohaska, C.; Doutre,
     W.H.; Bryant, S.G.;
     Sigler, K.A.
1367 Helling, D.K.; Norwood,
     G.J.; Donner, J.D.
1368 Hladik, W.B. III; Dujovne,
     C.A.
1369 Holt, R.J.; Gaskins, J.D.
1370 Horgan, C.M.
1371 Horn, S.D.; Roveti, G.C.;
     Kreitzer, S.L.
1372 Horn, S.D.; Schumacher,
     D.N.
1373 Huber, G.A.
1374 Huckleberry, S.D.
1375 Huebler, L.A.; Christian,
     J.A.; Marcella, L.W.
1376 Hull, J.H.; Brown, H.S.,
     Jr.; Yarborough, F.F.;
     Murray, W.J.
1377 Ireland, A.W.; Harris, J.;
     Scarf, C.G.
1378 Ives, T.J.; Parry, J.L.;
     Gwyther, R.E.
1379 Kiesler, C.A.; Sibulkin,
     A.E.
1380 Kimelblatt, B.J.; Lerro,
     R.C.; Franchak, N.;
     Potter, S.K.;
     Greasley, D.M.;
     Silverman, H.M.; Simon,
     G.I.
1381 King, R.W.; Suthers, M.B.
1382 Kirstein, L.; Weissman,
     M.M.
1383 Kirstein, L.; Weissman,
     M.M.; Rrusoff, B.

1384 Klapp, D.; Harrison, W.L.
1385 Knapp, D.E.; Knapp, D.A.; Speedie, M.K.; Yaeger, D.M.; Baker, C.L.
1386 Knoben, J.E.
1387 Leopold, D.A.; Lagoe, R.J.
1388 Levin, J.M.
1389 Martinez, D.R.; Reitz, J.A.; Miller, W.A.; Nolly, R.J.
1390 McCaughan, B.C.; May, J.
1391 Morse, M.L.; Leroy, A.A.; Gaylord, T.A.; Kellenberger, T.
1392 Moskowitz, M.A.
1393 Muno, F.J., Jr.; Chen, G.T.
1394 Murphy, W.A.; Totty, W.G.; Gado, M.; Levitt, R.G.; Lee, J.K.; Evens, R.G.
1395 Myers, R.A.; Britten, J.S.; Grassi, R.T.; Kietur, L.M.; Weitzel, C.J.
1396 Newble, D.I.; Wangel, A.G.; Nelson, A.W.
1397 Nishimura, M.; Egawa, H.; Suzuki, H.; Kobayashi, T.; Baba, K.; Matsui, K.; Yoshimura, T.
1398 Parker, W.A.; Reid, L.W.
1399 Phillips, L.A.
1400 Phillips, L.A.
1401 Rederscheid, P.
1402 Redmond, F.C.
1403 Restuccia, J.D.
1404 Restuccia, J.D.; Gertman, P.
1405 Rihn, T.L.; DeBalko, J.N.; Keys, P.W.
1406 Sabath, L.D.; Notto, D.A.
1407 Sandrick, K.M.
1408 Sargenti, C.; Zelman, L.; Beauclair, T.; Garrard, E.; Boehm, R.
1409 Satoh, Y.; Ichiwata, T.; Tsukui, J.; Yashiro, J.; Ryu, S.; Kasai, S.; Ishigami, K.; Ibonai, T.; Nakamura, A.; Ohki, K.

1410 Seifert, R.; Jamieson, J.; Gardner, R., Jr.
1411 Seshadri, R.S.; Odell, W.R.; Roxby, D.; Morley, A.A.
1412 Shackford, S.R.; Hollingworth-Fridlund, P.; Cooper, G.F.; Eastman, A.B.
1413 Shapiro, M.; Rosner, B.; Townsend, T.R.; Kass, E.H.
1414 Shapiro, S.
1415 Shapiro, S.; West, S.K.; Brandon, B.M.; Chase, G.A.; Stolley, P.D.
1416 Sheridan, E.P.; Teplin, L.A.
1417 Shock, J.A.; Jones, W.N.; Bootman, J.L.; Goldman, S.
1418 Sloane, P.D.
1419 Studnicki, J.; Honemann, D.
1420 Thibault, G.E.; Mulley, A.G.; Barnett, G.O.; Goldstein, R.L.; Reder, V.A.; Sherman, E.L.; Skinner, E.R.
1421 Tolentino, P.
1422 Walton, J.R.; Shapiro, B.A.
1423 Wareham, D.V.; Deliganis, S.G.
1424 Wareham, D.V.; Deliganis, S.G.
1425 Weaver, P.G.
1426 Wells, K.B.; Manning, W.G., Jr.; Duan, N.; Newhouse, J.P.; Ware, J.E., Jr.; Benjamin, B.
1427 Westphal, M.; Frazier E.; Miller, M.C.
1428 Witte, K.W.; Nelson, A.A., Jr.; Hutchinson, R.A.
1429 Young, W.W.; Swinkola, R.B.; Hutton, M.A.

Management

1432 Ankrum, A.D.
1433 Bailit, H.L.; Balzer,
     J.A.; Clive, J.
1434 Bender, F.H.; DeMatteo,
     C.S.
1435 Black, F.O.; Johnson, J.;
     Myers, E.N.; Perkun, O.
1436 Boyle, D.A.
1437 Bruhn, P.S.; Howes, D.H.
1438 Conneen, T.F.
1439 Craddick, J.W.
1441 Douglas, R.M.; Catchlove,
     E.; Reid, D.P.; Young,
     J.F.
1442 Ferguson, J.S.
1443 German, T.L.
1444 Given, C.W.; Morrill,
     C.E.; Lachance, R.;
     Gifford, W.;
     Bedell, A.; Kowaleski,
     E.; Haddock, D.
1445 Goldberg, G.A.; Hein,
     L.M.; Rosales, S.M.;
     Alexander, J.F.
1446 Hall, J.
1447 Hancock, C.
1449 Henderson, W.J.; Ichinose,
     C.; Goto, U.; Tom, B.;
     Stewart, J.; Sage,
     W.; Judd, C.;
     Gresham, S.; Thompson,
     H.; McDonald, B.A.; Kim,
     M.
1450 Hirt, F.D.; Solomon, J.R.
1451 Hoffmann, R.P.
1452 Holbrook, F.K.
1453 Hoyt, J.P.
1454 Huber, G.A.; Wolfe, H.;
     Hardwick, C.P.
1455 Hutchinson, S.; Malamud,
     J.; Stearns, N.S.;
     Moulton, B.
1456 Jacoby, J.E.
1457 Jones, B.
1458 Kidder, S.W.
1459 Lange, M.
1460 LeBrun, P.
1461 Lipp, C.S.
1462 Little, J.C.; Austing,
     R.H.

1463 McGowan, J.E., Jr.
1464 McSherry, C.K.
1465 Meyers, V.W.; Hober, F.
1466 Micheletti, J.A.; Shlala,
     T.J.
1467 Monroe, R.D.; Grant, E.A.
1468 Moody-Williams, J.D.
1469 Newmark, G.L.
1470 O'Brien, J.R.
1472 Pattee, J.J.
1473 Pattee, J.J.
1475 Raymond, D.
1476 Restuccia, J.D.
1477 Ryckman, D.; Sourapas,
     J.K.
1479 Schaeffer, P.M.
1480 Schmitz, H.H.; Schoenhard,
     W.C., Jr.
1481 Schumacher, D.N.; Chan, C.
1482 Sherber, J.
1483 Sieverts, S.
1484 Snider, M.E.
1485 Spencer, J.H., Jr.;
     Mattson, M.R.
1486 Studnicki, J.; Honemann,
     D.
1487 Sway, E.M.
1489 Thompson, K.S.; Cheng,
     E.H.
1490 Tom, B.C.; Gresham, S.C.;
     Goto, U.; Henderson, W.J.;
     Judd, C.S.,
     Jr.; McDonald, B.A.
1491 Tremblay, J.
1492 Turley, R.M.; Edwardson,
     S.R.
1496 Walkley, P.H., Jr.
1497 Wilson, L.L.
1498 Zeleznik, C.; Gonnella,
     J.S.
1499 Zoebelein, E.

Overviews

1500 Anderson, J.
1502 Ashby, J.L., Jr.
1503 Baltaxe, H.A.
1504 Bice, T.W.
1505 Breeden, B.
1506 Carpenter, R.A.

1507 Corder, M.P.; Lachenbruch, P.A.; Lindle, S.G.; Sisson, J.H.; Johnson, P.S.; Kosier, J.T.
1508 Curran, W.J.
1509 Diblase, D.
1510 Dittman, D.A.; Magee, R.P.
1511 Edelston, J.M.; Valentine, S.T.; Ginoza, D.
1512 Eisenberg, J.M.
1513 Faulkner, P.L.; Nevick, R.; Williams, S.V.; Pascale, L.A.; Poyss, L.; Eisenberg, J.M.
1515 Fetter, R.B.; Shin, Y.; Freeman, J.L.; Averill, R.F.; Thompson, J.D.
1516 Fielding, J.E.
1517 Frey, R.J.
1519 Friedman, D.; Schwartzbard, A.; Velcek, F.T.; Klotz, D.H.; Kottmeier, P.K.
1520 Froh, R.
1521 Gardner, S.F.; Kyzr-Sheeley, B.J.; Sabatino, F.
1522 Goldstein, R.L.; Stanton, B.; Burwell, L.
1523 Hansen, A.S.
1525 Himler, G.
1526 Hoyt, J.D.; Davies, J.M.
1527 Huff, J.W.
1528 Jackson-Beeck, M.
1529 Kaiser, J.; Townsend, E.J.
1530 Katz, P.S.
1531 Kaufmann, J.S.
1532 Kittrell, A.
1533 Korcok, M.
1534 Krinsky, L.W.; Carone, P.A.
1535 Krischer, J.P.; Cheung, A.; Bush, P.; Sleight, S.M.
1536 Legge, D.
1537 Lewis, S.
1538 Ludlam, J.E.
1539 Mandsager, R.L.

1540 Margolis, J.A.; McDermott, J.F., Jr.; Vaughan, W.T., Jr.
1541 McGarvey, M.R.
1542 Moorefield, J.L.
1543 Murchison, G.C.
1545 Ness, C.O.
1546 Nyberg, J.; Wolff, N.
1547 Osifo, N.G.; Ogbuebele, H.U.
1548 Palmer, D.B.
1549 Paradisi, F.; Cioffi, R.; Cristiano, P.; Caruso, G.; Caiazza, M.; Corona G.
1550 Pearson, D.A.; Abernethy, D.S.
1551 Powills, S.
1552 Rice, T.; De Lissovoy, G.; Gabel, J.; Ermann, D.
1553 Richards, G.
1554 Rosen, H.M.; Feigin, W., Sr.
1555 Rothberg, D.L.; Gertman, P.M.
1556 Rucker, T.D.; Visconti, J.A.
1557 Rzasa, C.B.
1558 Sack, R.A.
1559 Schlicke, C.P.
1560 Schroer, K.A.; Taylor, E.
1561 Shah, N.M.; Turner, G.P.
1562 Shahoda, T.
1563 Shaw, J.
1564 Spies, J.J.
1565 Stone, DA.
1566 Thompson, R.W.
1569 Vladeck, B.C.
1570 Vraciu, R.A.
1571 Wilcox, D.P.
1572 Wills, C.
1573 Wirtschafter, D.
1574 Yeater, D.C.
1575 Zuidema, G.D.

CHAPTER 4:

RISK MANAGEMENT REFERENCES

Theory and Concept

Programs, Techniques & Procedures

1648	Flamm, W.G.; Winbush, J.S.	1700	Pena, J.J.; Schmelter,
1649	Freilich, H.		W.R.; Ramseur, J.E.
1650	Freilich, H.; Farkas, S.	1701	Pierce, M.E.
1651	Gardner, C.	1702	Pollack, B.R.
1652	Garrison, H.; Griggs, T.	1704	Pollack, B.R.; Waldman,
1653	Goetz, A.; Bernstein, J.		H.B.
1654	Grose, V.L.	1705	Punch, L.
1655	Halpert, A.; Connors, J.P.	1706	Raz, T.; Baretich, M.F.
1656	Hart, M.A.; Sliefert, M.K.	1707	Raz, T.; Baretich, M.F.
1657	Hayes, A.H., Jr.	1708	Rendell-Baker, L.
1658	Hepplewhite, D.W.	1709	Richards, G.
1659	Hibbert, J.; Craven, R.;	1711	Rodger, C.Z.
	Balinski, J.	1712	Salman, S.; Click, N.
1660	Hodgin, L.	1713	Sandrick, K.M.
1661	Holmberg, B.	1714	Schrenzel, S.N.
1662	Huber, G.A.; Wolford, J.A.	1715	Schultz, F.W.
1663	Hyman, W.A.	1716	Schultz, F.W.
1665	Innes, E.M.	1717	Shotwell, H.P.
1666	Jackson, M.M.; Lynch, P.	1718	Sielicki, A.P., Jr.
1667	Jacoby, J.E.	1719	Siler, E.
1668	Johnson, F.E.	1720	Smith, N.G.
1669	Jones, M.; Dodge, D.	1721	Sorrell, M.A., Jr.
1670	Joseph, V.D.; Jones, S.K.	1722	Sorrell, M.A., Jr.
1671	Kapp, M.B.	1723	Spaulding, J.A.
1672	Kennedy, J.R.	1724	Stock, R.
1674	Keys, P.W.	1725	Stofberg, J.; Kirschman,
1675	Kinloch, K.		J.C.
1676	Korsak, A.	1726	Stolar, M.H.; Gabriel T.;
1677	Korsak, A.		Grant, K.L.; Koeller, J.;
1678	Kraus, N.		Letendre, D.E.
1679	Kroll, J.; Mackenzie, T.B.	1727	Stollard, P.
1680	Kucera, W.R.; Ator, N.	1728	Swartzbeck, E.M.
1681	Langdon, A.; Windle, L.	1729	Talboom, S.J.; Elder, H.A.
1682	Larkin, M.	1730	Tehan, J.; Colegrove, S.L.
1683	LaViolette, S.	1731	Tideiksaar, R.
1684	Lee, P.S.; Pash, B.J.	1732	Tilbury, M.S.; Ganley, S.
1685	Lenckus, D.	1733	Webster, C.L.
1686	Lohman, J.	1734	Williams, C.W.
1687	MacHattie, L.	1735	Wrenn, A.J.
1688	Massanari, R.M.;	1736	Wright, R.E.; Gaudiosi,
	Hierholzer, W.J., Jr.		T.S.
1689	McCollum, W.E.	1737	Yanish, D.L.
1690	McLain, N.B.	1738	Young, R.L.; Du Vall, E.M.
1691	McLain, N.B.		
1692	McNulty, E.G.		
1693	Merryman, P.		
1694	Miller, O.D.		
1695	Miller, S.A.; Skinner, K.		
1696	Murphy, M.J.		
1697	Newbower, R.S.; Cooper,		
	J.B.; Long, C.D.		
1698	Oppman, C.D.		
1699	Oulton, R.		

1739 Abramson, N.S.; Wald,
     K.S.; Grenvik, A.N.;
     Robinson, D.; Snyder,
     J.V.
1740 Barbieri, E.B.
1741 Beck, B.; Hardwick, K.;
     Ingram, B.; Taylor, A.
1742 Beezley, D.; Tabel, C.;
     Kordick, M.
1743 Braff, J.; Way, B.B.;
     Steadman, H.J.
1744 Brantley, G.C.
1745 Brown, B.
1746 Brown, G.C.
1747 Brown, S.L.
1749 Cook, P.F.; Massie, D.
1750 Dandoy, S; Kirkman-Liff,
     B.; Krakowski, F.
1751 Der Yuen, D.
1752 Der, Yuen D.
1753 Devoe, L.D.; Sholl, J.S.
1754 Dodge, D.D.; Dodson, B.,
     Jr.; Helms, T.S.
1755 Dossing, M.; Andreasen,
     P.B.
1756 Elnicki, R.A.; Schmitt,
     J.P.
1757 Gibbs, J.
1758 Gleicher, N.
1759 Guernsey, B.G.; Ingrim,
     N.B.; Hokanson, J.A.;
     Doutre, W.H.;
     Bryant, S.G.; Blair,
     C.W.; Galvan, E.
1760 Guernsey, B.G.; Ingrim,
     N.B.; Hokanson, J.A.;
     Doutre, W.H.;
     Bryant, S.G.; Blair,
     C.W.; Galvan, E.
1761 Hamory, B.H.
1762 Hampton, R.L.; Newberger,
     E.H.
1763 Heizer, D.E.; Hsieh, H.
1764 Holsomback, T.C.
1765 Innes, E.M.; Turman, W.G.
1766 Jackson, M.M.; Dechairo,
     D.C.; Gardner, D.F.
1767 Jackson, M.M.; Lynch, P.
1768 Johnson, F.E.
1769 Jones, I.H.

1770 Jones, M.K.
1771 Karki, M.; Mayer, C.
1772 Korsak, A.J.
1773 Kraus, N.
1774 Latessa P.; Long G.;
     McCracken S.B.
1775 Lockhart, P.B.; Feldbau,
     E.V.; Gabel, R.A.;
     Connolly, S.F.;
     Silversin, J.B.
1776 Long, G.; Johnson, C.
1777 McDonald, J.S.; Peterson,
     S.F.; Hansell, J.
1778 Miller, O.D.
1782 Perr, I.N.
1783 Rainville, N.G.
1784 Reilly, J.S.; Kenna, M.A.;
     Stool, S.E.; Bluestone,
     C.D.
1785 Riggs, L., Jr.
1786 Rodricks, J.; Taylor, M.R.
1787 Sadowsky, D.; Kunzel, C.
1788 Salman, S.L.
1789 Schaeffer, J.N.; Millen,
     H.
1790 Soler, J.M.; Montes, M.F.;
     Egol, A.B.; Nateman, H.R.;
     Donaldson, E.A.;
     Greene, H.H.
1791 Spooner, R.B.; Kirby, R.R.
1792 Squire, R.A.
1793 Squire, R.A.; Cameron,
     L.L.
1794 Stearns, G.; Fox, L.A.
1795 Stern, R.M.
1796 Stern, R.M.
1797 Suzuki, K.
1798 Swartzbeck, E.M.;
     Milligan, W.L.
1799 Tannenbaum, S.R.; Skipper,
     P.L.
1800 Tatge, M.
1801 Tilbury, M.S.; Ganley, S.
1802 Valaske, M.J.
1803 Valaske, M.J.
1804 Vogel, C.H.; Blom, M.F.
1805 Wasiuta, V.
1806 Wilson, M.H.
1807 Wilson, S.L.

Management

1808	Adelman, D.N.; Donovan, M.J.
1809	Baxter, C.E.
1810	Blinn, J.D.; Cole, M.J.
1811	Brazil, A.
1812	Carpenter, J.K.
1813	Clements, G.W.
1814	Collins, P.
1815	Cournoyer, C.P.
1816	Coyne, J.S.
1817	Craddick, J.W.
1818	Creighton, H.
1819	Cushing, M.
1820	Donovan, R.J., Jr.; Bader, B.S.
1821	Drury, S.J.
1822	Dudley, R.H.
1823	Groah, L.; Reed, E.A.
1824	Groves, J.; Korsak, A.
1825	Groves, J.; Korsak, A.
1826	Haffner, A.N.
1827	Harris, S.
1828	Hirsh, H.L.
1829	Holder, A.R.
1830	Hollander, E.C.
1831	Hollander, E.C.
1832	Hollander, E.C.
1833	Julian, R.L.
1834	Kaddatz, M.M.; Huntington, R.R.
1835	Kuntz, E.
1836	Kuntz, E.F.
1837	LaCava, F.W.
1838	Lambert, R.L.
1839	LeRoux, M.
1840	McDonald, N.
1841	McNulty, E.G.
1842	Meyers, D.R.
1843	Nacman, M.
1844	O'Donnell, J.
1845	Oppman, C.D.
1846	Oppman, C.D.
1847	Oppman, C.D.
1848	Oppman, C.D.
1849	Punch, L.
1850	Punch, L.
1851	Rabinow, J.
1852	Raz, T.; Demlo, L.K.

1853	Roberts, C.J.
1854	Salman, S.L.
1855	Sax, A.
1856	Shahoda, T.
1857	Stearns, G.; Fox, L.A.
1858	Touchstone, W.A.
1859	Troyer, G.; Salman, S.
1861	Van Sluyter, C.K.
1862	Van Sluyter, C.K.; Hays, P.G.
1863	Willenbrink, M.
1864	Willets, J.W.
1865	Wilson, S.L.

Overviews

1866	Abelson, P.H.
1867	Affeldt, J.E.
1868	Alexander, M.
1869	Ansley, C.E.; Cleverley, W.O.
1870	Archer, R.L.
1871	Barracato, J.S.
1872	Bartek, W.
1873	Beardshaw, V.
1874	Berger, S.
1875	Bernstein, A.H.
1876	Bianco, E.A.
1877	Brown, B.L.
1878	Brown, B.L., Jr.
1879	Burda, D.
1880	Burnhill, M.S.
1881	Cain, C.
1882	Carlson, K.
1883	Carnesecchi, R.
1884	Chapman, G.
1885	Clarke, C.
1886	Cohn, S.D.
1887	Collins, E.M.
1888	Cunningham, R.M., Jr.
1889	Curran, W.J.
1890	Curtin, L.L.
1891	Davis, D.
1892	deFerranti, D.
1893	Densmore, B.
1894	DiPaolo, V.
1895	Doody, M.F.
1896	Dooley, T.P.
1897	Duran, G.S.

1898	Edelman, J.; Peloquin, R.J.	1948	Pocchiari, F.; Silano, V.; Zapponi, G.
1900	Fifer, W.R.	1949	Pollack, B.R.
1901	Fifer, W.R.	1950	Posner, J.R.
1902	Flamm, W.G.	1951	Post, R.S.
1904	Freilich, H.; Farkas-Finkelstein, S.	1952	Poteet, G.W.
		1953	Press, F.
1905	Geisel, J.	1954	Rantanen, J.
1906	Glass, L.S.	1955	Rasinski, D.
1907	Goodman, T.	1956	Reagan, B.M.
1908	Gregory, D.R.	1957	Revzan, H.
1909	Greve, P.A., Jr.	1958	Rice, A.P.
1910	Grothaus, C.L.	1959	Richards, G.
1911	Hardy, M.	1960	Riger, S.; Gordon, M.T.; LeBailly, R.K.
1912	Hirsh, H.L.		
1913	Hirsh, H.L.; White, E.R.	1963	Roberts, F.
1914	Holbrook, R.F.	1964	Robinson, W.J.
1915	Holloway, S.T.; Sax, A.B.	1965	Rogers, W.E.
1916	Holmberg, B.	1966	Rosenthal, T.; Rosenthal, S.
1917	Holroyd, B.R.; Knopp, R.; Kallsen, G.		
		1967	Ross, T.
1918	Howie, C.	1968	Rozovsky, L.E.; Rozovsky, F.A.
1919	Jacoby, J.E.		
1920	Jones, D.B.	1969	Ryan, W.
1921	Joseph, E.	1970	Sax, A.B.
1922	Katz, P.S.	1971	Schultz, F.W.
1923	Kroll, J.; Mackenzie, T.B.	1972	Schultz, F.W.
1924	Kumagai, J.; Matsuzawa, T.; Kuroda, Y.; Ogane, T.	1973	Selikoff, I.J.
		1974	Severson, L.C.
1925	Ladner, H.A., Jr.	1975	Shmock, C.L.
1926	Langslow, A.	1976	Sielicki, A.P., Jr.
1927	Lanham, G.B.; Orlikoff, J.E.	1977	Silver, A.P.
		1978	Skillicorn, S.A.
1928	LaRocco, S.A.	1979	Skillicorn, S.A.
1929	Lenhard, C.G.	1980	Sklar, C.
1930	Ludlam, J.E.	1981	Sklar, C.
1931	Ludlam, J.E.	1982	Somers, E.
1932	Mant, D.	1983	Sorrell, M.A., Jr.
1933	Marco, C.H.	1984	Steadman, J.
1934	Martin, H.	1985	Stewart, K.P.
1935	McCollum, W.E.	1986	Stock, R.
1937	Miller, L.A.	1987	Stoltz, M.K.
1938	Miller, S.A.	1988	Strazewski, L.
1939	Moon, J.E.	1989	Tabatabai, C.
1940	Mulholland, J.H.; Bittle, L.	1990	Tehan, J.; Colegrove, S.L.
		1993	Throdahl, M.C.
1941	O'Connell, J.A.	1994	Todhunter, J.A.
1942	Oppman, C.D.	1995	Trandel-Korenchuk, D.M.
1943	Orlikoff, J.E.; Lanham, G.B.	1996	Trandel-Korenchuk, D.M.; Trandel-Korenchuk, K.M.
1944	Oulton, R.	1997	Tremblay, J.
1945	Parker, S.	1998	Wallace, C.
1946	Pecorino, D.J.	1999	Warren, R.W.
1947	Perr, I.N.	2000	Yodaiken, R.E.

CHAPTER 2

QUALITY ASSURANCE INDEX

Accountability: 120,163,279,524,552,735,883,1039,1074,1097,1143.

Accreditation: 52,127,258,795,915,931,934-6,1071, 1144.

Administration: 17,540,586,629,641-2,692,745,771-2,790,793,804-5,
                       822,828,866,872,874,920,930,1032,1096.

Advisory Board: 877,914,917,955,1011,1106.

Ambulatory Care: 135,216,221,309,360,371,443,555,581,678,696,734,779,
                       814,838,

Appropriateness,   2,35,84,205,491.
  Defined:

Assessment: 1,10,20,34,40,43,79,80,88,98,111,117,134,173,181,183,
                       236,242,261,275,309,319,327,348,375,417,419,434,442-3,
                       469-70,480,492,526,596,599,601,640-1,645,655,657,669,
                       677,696,726,730,753,905,986.

Audit: 11,22,55,85,118,199,200,203-4,209,212,226,240,269,
                       317,326,340-1,364,398,401,436,447,587,625,687,705,
                       729,748,762,803,987,991.

  Departmental: 500,579,809,844,865,891,894,1127.

Authority: 1005-7,1028,1093,1104.

Behaviours: 5,92,194,391.

Capital Costs: 908,911.

Centralized
Quality Assurance:

  Programs: 125,131-2,176,229,249,342,474,485,522,525,646,688,
                       816,830,855-6,873,886,1065,1072,1076.

  Certification: 52,54,607,812,1116.

Change: 9,36,65,119,308,513,664,705,835,849,853,907,933-5,
                       938,965,977-8,980,982,985,1000,1008,1016,1035,1041,
                       1055,1078,1120,1128,1134.

Committees: 125,471,791-2,823,891,894,913.

Communication: 778,786,880.

QUALITY ASSURANCE INDEX

QUALITY ASSURANCE INDEX

CHAPTER 2 (Continued)

QUALITY ASSURANCE INDEX

Information system: 454,464,498,506,507,546,692,766,769,879-80,
                                    926.

Interpretation: 7,27,38-9,63-4,70,72,94,96,110,121,139,144,148,
                                    268,288,462,475,479,673,700,997.

Interviews   9,54,58,131,455,547,960,963,970,988,1042,1067,
                                    1081.

Joint Commission for the Accreditation

    Of Hospitals (JCAH):   42,118,127,137,238,558,795,915,935,937-8,
                                    970,977-8,980,982,1042,1046,1051,1053-4,
                                    1056,1059,1070,1077-8,1082,1125-6,1128,
                                    1134.

Knowledge Deficiencies: 611,620,652,841,1002.

Lawsuits: 997,1103.

Legality: 8,157,799,800,827,937,1042,1080,1103.

Malpractice Claims: 336,374,810,823,1054,1087.

Measurement Validity: 547,586,648,682,686,693,709,750,760.

Methodologies: 126,165,170,174,182,201,208,213,257,282,
                                    296,299,321,325,396,403,409,443-4,476,
                                    496,503,539-40,544,569,720,737-41,758,
                                    784,820,868,875,882,888-9,898,906,918.

Monitoring: 26,31,93,119,158,289,895,331,388,415,
                                    588-9,598,607,631,675,890.

Needs Analysis: 234,580,724.

Negligence: 768,966.

Nursing Quality Assurance
    Committee: 887.

Nursing Quality Assurance

    Director: 99,925.

192

QUALITY ASSURANCE INDEX

Nursing Quality Assurance:	31,39,49,82,99,121,133,147,238,256,263, 331,340,365,372,385,387,398-9,400,414,423, 426,428,440,451,457,464,503,508,521,571, 606,616,624,632,731,803,817-8,840,848,852, 960,991,1010,1024,1031-2,1043,1073,1094, 1132.
Hospice Care:	12,66,89,102,214,235,316,407,527.
Objectives:	2,373,531.
Organizational Structure:	106,132,151-2,179,198,217,228,246,404,504, 594,717,727,745,759,773-4,801,807,821, 835,839,871,879,907,1003,1050,1115.
Outcome Approach:	309,319,408,435,439,492,498,610,627,669, 707,744,746.
Patients:	19,22,53,76,79,113,138,141,146,167-8, 210-11,258,286,295,308,343,390,416.
Patients Questionnaires:	384.
Peer Review:	122,394,552,567,575,590,602,757,1004.
Physicians:	11,13,18,76,518,676,696,712-5,901,1015, 1080.
Planning:	116,185,188,218,222,229,259,277,349,355, 362,368,525,815,824,829-30,861,892,906.
Preadmission Review:	845,1001.
Problem:	
Assessment Of:	580,599,601,617,621,640,683,698.
Causes Of:	610,635,643,783,858.
Defined:	553,928,1002.
Identification Of:	617,640,654,683,890.
Prioritizing Of:	196,756.
Resolution Of:	84,245,515,599,618,621,698,780.
Process Approach:	408,492,521,625,707,744.

QUALITY ASSURANCE INDEX

Risk Management: 44-4,74,107,109,112,156,351,410,433,449-50,
                    522,572,629-30,723,785,791,808,905,1016.

Safety: 626,794,916.

Selection: 3,84,651.

Staff: 53,160,413,417,541,685,710,727,756,770,774,782,785,
                    794,813,817,833,847,862,868,879,897-8.

Standards: 4,42,46,57,68,104,115,118,127,137,154,231,243,305-6,
                    334-5,392,400,423,445,473,543,589,605,623,640,656,
                    681,688,709,887,903,915,963,965,977,982,991,1030,
                    1042,1046,1051,1053-6,1059,1078,1103,1105,1125-6,
                    1128,1134.

Structure: 92,106,152,198,217,253-4,260,270,285,313,323,329,
                    346,379-81,389,421,430,437-8,448,473,493.

Support Service
  Evaluation: 6,743,751.

Surveys: 150,224,431,591,596,599,613,708,752,994.

Teaching: 13,206,265,281,299,483,588,634.

Technology: 177,180,192,195,215,219,268,270,305,324,328,334-5,
                    344,357,376,422,432,453,486,489,497,595,612,620,
                    621,643,650,722,985,1050,1145.

Utilization Of
  Data: 374,450,580,615,659,666,929.

Utilization Review: 2,74-5,111,310,361,418,515,580,809,865.

Values: 8,95,597.

CHAPTER 3

UTILIZATION REVIEW INDEX

UTILIZATION REVIEW INDEX

Nursing:	1466,1484.
Nursing Facilities:	1253,1254,1255,1256,1293,1297,1308,1324,1363, 1410,1418,1508.
Patients Characteristics:	1337,1429.
Peer Review:	1150,1185,1201,1316,1317,1536,1540,1548,1552.
PRSO:	1183,1186,1217,1300,1314,1475,1510,1522,1525, 1541.
Pretreatment Review:	1188.
Procedures:	1216.
Programs:	1206,1282,1284,1430,1436,1453,1457.
Prospective Reimbursement:	1164,1169,1170,1465,1486,1530.
Physicians:	1258,1346,1443,1455,1456,1476,1490.
PPO:	1285.
Quality Control And Assurance:	1150,1171,1176,1177,1182,1218,1357,1386,1542, 1554,1561.
Radiographic Studies:	1233,1315,1356,1399,1400.
Referral:	1339,1354.
Regional:	1341,1412.
Regulation:	1202,1471,1478,1493,1494,1502,1504,1516,1519.
Reliability:	1288,1334.
Risk Management:	1176,1178.
Second Opinions:	1166.
Standards:	1160,1173,1248,1559.
Surgery:	1322,1345,1349,1387,1411.

CHAPTER 4

Risk Management Index

CHAPTER 4 (Continued)

Risk Management Index

Education:	(See Also Training) 1835.
Environment:	1747,1866,1932,1982,1994.
Equipment:	1663,1708,1791.
Evaluation:	1742,1744,1755,1783,1794,1799,1807.
Finances:	1718,1858,1869,1950.
Fire:	1727,1871.
Future:	1578.
Government:	(See Regulation)
Incident Reports:	1636,1641,1650,1652,1656,1658,1660,1670,1675, 1693,1698,1699,1700,1701,1727,1731,1734,1735, 1735,1737,1743,1774,1805,1884,1890,1981.
Injury:	1761,1762,1806,1851.
Insurance:	1676,1680,1685,1715,1721,1733,1812,1836,1839, 1853,1856,1875,1881,1894.
Law:	1620,1818,1912,1926,1930,1964,1994,1998.
Legal Litigation:	1782,1785,1813,1815,1818,1819,1829,1837,1841, 1850,1851,1914,1925,1947.
Liability:	1608,1638,1678,1679,1705,1716,1719,1722,1724, 1773,1812,1870,1879,1898,1971,1983,1984,1986, 1992.
Loss:	
Programs:	1580,1622,1648,1754,1802,1946.
Malpractice:	1590,1615,1654,1671,1772,1779,1780,1781,1788, 1790,1886,1888,1889,1893,1900,1904,1913,1920, 1931,1959,1987,1991,1995,1996.
Medical Staff:	1766,1820,1838.
Medication:	(See Drugs and Pharmacy)

Methods (Risk
  Management):   1628,1629,1632,1635,1648,1666,1677,1688,1696,
                           1697,1741,1767,1800.

Negligence: 1980,1981.

Nurses: 1675,1766,1809,1926,1952.

Patients:

    Problems: 1679,1728,1740,1748,1749,1765,1770.

    Relations: 1613,1970.

Patients Right: 1921.

Pharmacy: 1726,1759,1760,1764,1795.

Physicians: 1587,1612,1619,1630,1667,1736,1748,1787,1817,
                           1820,1828,1838,1923,1933.

Planning: 1949,1988.

Plant: (See Property) 1972.

Problems:
  (e.g.'s if approp.)   1589,1623,1626,1633,1637,1645,1646,1651,1655,
                           1659,1664,1697,1702,1703,1704,1728,1729,1732,
                           1739,1775,1880,1960,1973,2000.

Professional Liability: 1602.

    Programs:
    (Risk Management) 1576,1599,1604,1607,1618,1624,1627,1631,1640,
                           1642,1643,1647,1657,1661,1662,1665,1667,1681,
                           1689,1705,1720,1723,1827,1903,1940,1941,1942,
                           1955,1957,1974.

    Property: 1972.

Quality Assurance: 1600,1608,1682,1849,1917,1919,1922,1935,1943,
                           1975,1978,1979,1989.

Records: 1639,1644,1711,1906.

Regulation: 1696,1953,1964,1994.

Research: 1756,1757,1758,1763,1774,1793,1798,1804,1948.

Rights: 1584,1591.

Risk Management:

    Defined: 1588,1593,1594,1595,1611,1614.

    Benefits: 1598,1887,1934,1990.

    Concept: 1585,1586,1593,1597,1605,1606,1616,1617,1730,
                                 1733,1849,1868,1872,1956,1966,1968,1969,1976,
                                 1993.

    Cost: 1810.

    Personnel: 1592,1811.

    Purposes: 1579,1596,1609,1610,1877,1878,1901,1927,1937,
                                 1961,1985.

    Problem
      Identification
      Reduction Of
      Risk: 1683,1684,1789,1939.

Safety: 1625,1686,1687,1695,1717,1725,1792,1796,1861,
                                 1928,1938,1953,1958,1962.

Society: 1603,1621.

Staff: 1843.

Standards: 1944.

Surgery: 1694,1777,1778,1779,1781,1784,1801,1891.

Training: 1669,1807,1814,1821,1830,1831,1832,1842,1846,
                                 1855,1865.

Utilization Review: 1833.

Volunteers: 1999.

Workers Compensation: 1581,1634.

About The Editor

James T. Ziegenfuss, Jr. holds the Ph.D. degree in Social Systems
Sciences from the Wharton School, University of Pennsylvania; the M.P.A.
in Public Administration from Penn State University; the M.A. in
Psychology from Temple University; and the B.A. in English from the
University of Maryland. He has worked full-time for ten years in
organization analysis, planning and development. Professional memberships
include the Academy of Management, the American Society of Public
Administration, the American Society of Law and Medicine and the
American Public Health Association.

Since 1983, Dr. Ziegenfuss has been a professor of health care
management at The Pennsylvania State University at Harrisburg in the
graduate program in public administration. He teaches courses in health
systems, management policy and strategic planning and he is an
organization and management consultant and researcher. His work
experience involves consulting, research and development, and planning
including: organizational evaluations; organization planning at the
single and multi-organizational levels; organizational development and
research and development of health care systems. He has written
extensive technical reports along with more than 50 papers for
national/international conferences and journals and eight books.

His current work and research interests are in the field of
organizational development, especially consumer/employee feedback
systems. Dr. Ziegenfuss' dissertation, Patients' Rights & Organizational
Models was published in book form by University Press of America (1983).
He has written Patients' Rights and Professional Practice published
(1983) by Van Nostrand Reinhold; Patient - Client - Employee Complaint
Programs: An Organizational Systems Model published (1985) by Charles
C. Thomas Publishers; Law, Medicine & Health Care: A Bibliography (Facts
on File, 1984); Health Information Systems: A Bibliography (Plenum,
1984); Behavioral Scientists in Courts and Corrections (Van Nostrand
Reinhold, 1985); Therapeutic Communities for Addictions (Ed.) Charles
C. Thomas, 1986). Dr. Ziegenfuss has also written DRG's and Hospital
Impact: An Organizational Systems Analysis (McGraw-Hill, May 1985).